BK   624.17   A544
INTRODUCTION TO STRUCTURAL MECHANI

1960   .00 FV

3000 007015 30015
St. Louis Community College

ST. LOUIS, MO.

WITHDRAWN

624.17 A544   EV
ANDERSEN
INTRODUCTION TO STRUCTURAL
MECHANICS
                              9.50

Junior College District of St. Louis
Library
4386 Lindell Boulevard
St. Louis 8, Missouri

PRINTED IN U.S.A.

INTRODUCTION TO

STRUCTURAL MECHANICS

PAUL ANDERSEN

Professor of Structural Engineering
University of Minnesota

and

GENE M. NORDBY

Professor and Head, Department of Civil Engineering
University of Arizona

THE RONALD PRESS COMPANY • NEW YORK

Copyright © 1960 by

THE RONALD PRESS COMPANY

All Rights Reserved

No part of this book may be reproduced
in any form without permission in writing from
the publisher.

2

Library of Congress Catalog Card Number: 60–13150

PRINTED IN THE UNITED STATES OF AMERICA

PREFACE

This book is intended for use by civil engineering students taking a first course in structural analysis. In recent years there has been a trend toward the more scientific aspects of engineering. This trend has been followed here to a certain extent. Many of the problems now encountered are much more complex and intricate, and electronic computers which make their solution possible have come into use. While "Yankee ingenuity" is given proper emphasis as a major factor in American engineering, many problems must be solved by more scientific methods. The view that the "art" of engineering is based upon a firm scientific foundation has been taken throughout this text.

Consequently, the material in the book has been broken into two types of chapters. The general theory has been treated in chapters separate from the traditional applications of theory. Thus, Chapters 1, 2, 3, 4, 5, 7, 8, and 12 treat stress analysis in a general way and are applicable to aircraft structures and machine design as well as the more traditional civil engineering structures. Chapters 6, 9, 10, 11, and 13 apply the theory to the usual structures, such as roof trusses, railway bridges, and highway bridges. Any of the latter chapters may be left out without interrupting the continuity of the book.

Chapters 1 and 2, on reactions and shear and moment diagrams, are intended only as a review, but they are thorough enough for a first treatment also. Chapters 3 and 4 introduce graphic statics. Although the student was probably exposed to graphic statics in his regular mechanics course, these chapters extend the subject to the solution of more complicated problems. This is done with the idea that the graphical "picture" of the problem will aid in understanding the algebraic treatment in later chapters. Chapter 5, on trusses, is unique in that it treats the theoretical concept of a truss from a philosophical viewpoint before progressing into applications. Emphasis is placed upon understanding the stability of a truss. Methods of analysis are presented for simple, compound, and complex trusses. The usual specialized methods of approach to the various types and forms of simple trusses are avoided in favor of methods which are applicable to all types so long as basic concepts are understood.

The effects of moving loads on structures are discussed in Chapters 7 through 10. The student is first introduced to the concept of the influence line—its essential character and its applications. This is followed by a discussion of the general principles of moving loads. Finally, these principles are applied to the analysis of railway and highway bridges. Conventional structures as well as unique, original ones are analyzed. The rhomboid truss and the Wickert truss confront the student with unusual situations and wider horizons.

Three-hinged arches are part of the domain of statically determinate structures and are covered in Chapter 11 prior to the extension of these frames into three dimensions.

Chapter 12 contains probably the most complete treatment of space truss structures in American technical literature. It is the result of extensive research into the work of early German and French writers. Chapters 5 and 12 are correlated so that parallel treatment is given to simple, compound, and complex trusses in both chapters. Chapter 13 has been added so that students may become acquainted with the usual approximate methods of statically indeterminate structural analysis.

The authors are indebted to Professor W. J. Eney and Professor E. C. Sword of Lehigh University for constructive criticism of the manuscript.

PAUL ANDERSEN
GENE M. NORDBY

August, 1960

CONTENTS

INTRODUCTION TO

STRUCTURAL MECHANICS

CHAPTER 1

REACTIONS

1–1. Definitions. Certain terms are used to explain the theory of structures throughout this book. Some of these terms almost defy definition because they deal with phenomena that are extremely elementary. Such a term is *force*, which is something of human experience and not of mathematical definition. To aid in clarifying subsequent discussions, the following definitions are given.

Rigid bodies are shaped materials which essentially retain their geometry during application and removal of load. Common building materials are furnished in or acquire rigid shapes. This does not mean that there is *no* deformation but rather that the deformations are very small with respect to original size and hence do not appreciably affect the geometry of the body.

Structures consist of one or more rigid bodies so assembled that the group of bodies becomes rigid in the same sense as its components; i.e., there is no appreciable geometric change during loading and unloading.

Forces are those phenomena which tend to make bodies change their state of motion. All forces have three characteristics: magnitude, direction, and point of application. Forces whose lines of action do not pass through a given point tend to produce rotation of the rigid body about that point, known as the *moment center,* and the tendency to rotate is known as the *moment of force.* The moment of force is the product of magnitude of force and the perpendicular distance from the moment center to the line of action of the force.

Force systems are groups of two or more forces acting on a rigid body. Such systems, if acting in a single plane, are known as *coplanar force systems;* if in more than one plane, as *noncoplanar force systems.* If all the forces in the system meet in a point, it is a *concurrent force system;* if not, a *nonconcurrent force system.*

Single forces which will duplicate the effects of force systems are known as *resultants.* One or more forces which produce a given resultant force are called *components* of that force.

1–2. Selection of Loads. The stresses which are calculated throughout this book are dependent upon the loads to be imposed upon the structures.

Therefore the loads must be selected with care, since the entire design of the structure is dependent upon them. Faulty selection may mean that an uneconomical structure will be designed or, even worse, an unsafe structure will result. Loads are the result of human actions or of nature's phenomena. Both are difficult to predict.

When the engineer designs a building, he must forecast for years ahead the purposes for which the structure can be used, how many people will be in the building, and what they will want to place in the building. If it is an office building, the tenants may want to put office furniture, heavy safes, or rows of heavy files in various rooms. The use of the building by various tenants over several years may subject the building to a multitude or variety of loads, depending upon the nature of the activity. The engineer must select hypothetical loads to use in his design which will meet all these conditions.

When one considers the change in motor vehicle traffic on our highways over the past few years, the scope and difficulty of this type of load selection and forecasting is apparent. Here the engineer must design for the largest trucks and also have some concept of the frequency of these loads, to guard against fatigue of the bridge. Certainly the engineer must have a knowledge of the trend of social and humanistic sciences in order to forecast these human actions and use developments, since in structural engineering what we build today will be used tomorrow, and therefore we must design our structures with vision toward the future.

The forces of nature are no less difficult to predict. Wind forces and earthquake forces, for example, are almost impossible to predict exactly as to time of occurrence or intensity; yet they provide loads of large magnitudes which often are the most critical loads a structure will be required to resist. Both require detailed studies of the physical sciences, but this is impossible for the average engineer if he is to assimilate and apply the myriad details necessary to the design of a structure. For these reasons the use of "codes" is necessary.

A building code is a set of regulations adopted by a political or professional body to govern the construction within its jurisdiction. It combines the knowledge of many engineers and scientists into general rules which can be used by the designer. Thus a code may specify the floor loading to be used in certain types of buildings or the wind pressures that can be expected to be applied to the sides of buildings in the locale of the code. The inexperienced engineer should never fall into the trap, however, of accepting these codes as *laws*, either of nature or of his profession. He should keep his mind open for improvements and new methods. Remember that a building code is both a boon and a curse to the engineer. Since the codes are often incorporated into political law, they are sometimes difficult to change, and, worse, they often provide a shield for incompetence for an engineer who inadequately studies a design problem assigned to him.

1–3. Types of Loads. Loads are usually divided into two categories— dead loads and live loads. The dead loads are those which are contributed by the structure itself. For a given structure, they are rather easy to compute and are completely predictable. They are solely dependent upon the construction materials used, and once the unit weights are known, the dead loads (DL) can be computed almost exactly.

Live loads (LL), on the other hand, are more difficult. These are the human loads, the vehicle loads, and the multitude of human-caused loadings. In addition, wind, snow, ice, and earthquakes are also live loads. In the analysis of stresses in structures, both human-caused and nature-caused loads are often combined in various ways to provide the most critical condition in the structure or in individual parts of the structure. These live loads may be further divided into ordinary live loads caused by slowly moving vehicles and objects and live loads which cause shock or impacts, like an earthquake or a rapidly moving, but braking, locomotive on a bridge. Hence live load can be considered as the actual weight plus the dynamic effect, or impact load. Each of these live-load cases will be treated in detail in the chapters that follow.

1–4. Resultants and Resolution of Forces. One of the axioms of mechanics is the parallelogram rule, which states that the resultant of two forces is the diagonal of the parallelogram erected on the forces. In Fig. 1–1, since sides AB and DC are equal, it follows that the triangle ADC also serves to define the resultant of the original forces, and that AD and DC or AB are components of AC. Similarly, any force P as in Fig. 1–2 may be resolved into components P_p and P_q along axes pp' and qq', or into components P_r and P_s along axes rr' and ss', or into any two components along any two axes.

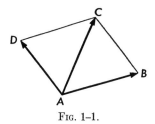

Fig. 1–1.

By further resolving P_r into components P_{r1} and P_{r2} and continuing as in Fig. 1–1, it will be seen that any force can be resolved into any desired number of components along any axis as long as the original force P is the resultant of all the components. Magnitude and direction characteristics are satisfied when forces are resolved into components. The remaining characteristic of a force—point of application—is such that components must be applied at the same point as was the original force.

1–5. Equilibrium of Forces. Forces have been defined as phenomena which tend to produce motion. Under such tendencies, there are two possible results: (1) there will be a change in the state of motion;

(2) there will be no change in the state of motion relative to adjacent
rigid bodies. By far the greater part of structural analysis is concerned
with the second condition, and that is the one which will be considered here.

Newton's first law of motion states that a body at rest or a body in
motion continues to move at constant velocity in a straight line unless
the body, in either case, is acted upon by an unbalanced force. Con-

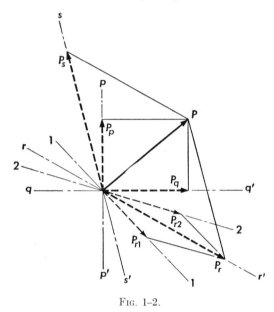

Fig. 1–2.

versely, in accordance with Newton's second law of motion, if the body
remains at rest or in constant motion, there can be no unbalanced force
acting on it; i.e., the resultant of all forces acting on the body must be
zero. Such a physical condition is known as a *state of static equilibrium*.

If a structure is in static equilibrium, a force system with which the
structure is loaded must be resisted by another force system to prevent a
change in the state of motion. If the resultant of the system of loads is
represented by P and the resultant of the system of resistances by R,
then P and R must be equal and opposite in order that their resultant
will be zero.

Since P and R may each be the resultant of several components, the
components of R must resist the components of P. For convenience it is
customary to resolve P and R into components at right angles, usually
(but not necessarily) horizontal and vertical. On a rigid body in static
equilibrium the sum of all the horizontal components must equal zero
and the sum of all the vertical components must equal zero.

Since most of these force systems are coplanar, i.e., all forces lie in the same plane, it will be convenient to summarize the algebra of the coplanar, concurrent force system and the coplanar, nonconcurrent force system and the special case of equilibrium before proceeding.

In Fig. 1–3 are several forces, P_1, P_2, $P_3 \cdots P_n$, which are concurrent. If two rectangular axes xx' and yy' are taken through the point of concurrency O, the component in the xx' direction is

$$X = P_1 \cos \theta_1 + P_2 \cos \theta_2 + P_3 \cos \theta_3 + \cdots + P_n \cos \theta_n$$
$$= \Sigma (P \cos \theta) \tag{1–1}$$

where each force makes the angle θ with xx'. The total vertical component in the direction yy' is

$$Y = P_1 \sin \theta_1 + P_2 \sin \theta_2 + P_3 \sin \theta_3 + \cdots + P_n \sin \theta_n \tag{1–2}$$

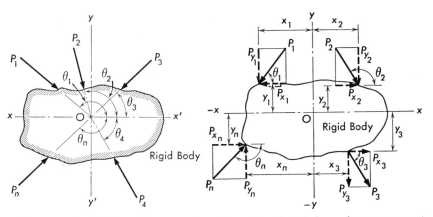

FIG. 1–3. Equilibrium of concurrent force system.

FIG. 1–4. Equilibrium of nonconcurrent force system.

The condition of equilibrium is that state obtained when the resultant of the force system is equal to zero; thus, for a concurrent force system, $X = Y = 0$ or

$$\Sigma F_x = \Sigma (P \cos \theta) = 0$$
$$\Sigma F_y = \Sigma (P \sin \theta) = 0 \tag{1–3}$$

where F_x and F_y are the various components in the xx and yy directions. If the system is not in equilibrium, the resultant is given by

$$R = \sqrt{(\Sigma F_x)^2 + (\Sigma F_y)^2} \tag{1–4}$$

and its direction is specified by $\tan \theta = \Sigma F_y / \Sigma F_x$. The resultant of the concurrent force system is the force R.

Fig. 1–4 illustrates the nonconcurrent force system in which all the forces do not intersect at a common point. In this case it is obvious that the resultant must provide a moment also. Moments of force also fulfill the definition of forces in that they tend to produce angular acceleration in rigid bodies. Three conditions must be fulfilled for this case, but only two of these conditions are specified by Eqs. 1–3, since the concurrent force system is only a special case of the noncurrent force system. In addition the moment about an arbitrary origin O must be specified, so that

$$M = \Sigma(y \cdot P_x \cos\theta - x \cdot P_y \sin\theta) = \Sigma M_O \qquad (1\text{–}5)$$

The distances x_1, x_2, x_3, $\cdots$ x_n represent the distances perpendicular to the components P_y, while the distances y_1, y_2, y_3, $\cdots$ y_n represent the distances perpendicular to the components P_x. In the case of equilibrium the resultant must be zero; therefore this condition is specified by the three equations

$$\Sigma F_x = 0$$

$$\Sigma F_y = 0 \qquad (1\text{–}6)$$

$$\Sigma M_O = 0$$

It may also be shown that the equilibrium conditions are satisfied if three equations of the type of Eq. 1–5, using three different origins, can be written for the force system; thus:

$$\Sigma M_{O1} = 0$$

$$\Sigma M_{O2} = 0 \qquad (1\text{–}7)$$

$$\Sigma M_{O3} = 0$$

Likewise, any combination of Eqs. 1–6 and 1–7, as long as they are independent, will specify equilibrium.

1–6. Free-Body Diagrams. Within the earth's gravitational field all rigid bodies must be supported in order to be in static equilibrium. Regardless of whether this support comes from fluids, from other rigid bodies, or from the earth itself, it is usually convenient to isolate the body being investigated, representing reactions from supporting bodies as forces. A sketch of such an isolated body, together with forces representing loads and reactions, is known as a *free-body diagram* (FBD).

Steps in drawing a free-body diagram are as follows:

1. Draw the body to be isolated.
2. Represent loads on the free body as forces.
3. Represent the reaction of each body which has been removed by a force or its components.
4. Represent any reactions of the original structure which act on the free body by forces or their components.

Magnitudes, directions, and points of application of all loads, reactions, and forces replacing missing parts must be shown, using symbols for unknown magnitudes and resolving the forces of unknown direction into convenient components. Fig. 1–5 illustrates the meaning of a free body. The rigid body (a pulley) in Fig. 1–5a is removed, and at each point of support the force provided by the support is substituted, as shown in Fig. 1–5b.

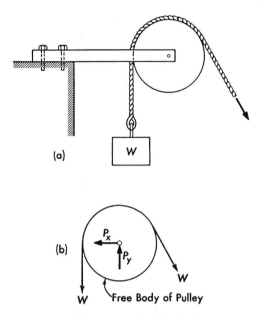

FIG. 1–5. Examples of free-body diagram.

1–7. Designations of Reactions. The first step in estimating the internal stresses on the structural components (beams, columns, etc.) of a structure is to compute the external forces on the structure other than the applied loads. These external restraints which maintain a state of equilibrium when external loads are applied to structures are known as *reactions*. They represent forces exerted on the structure by whatever body is supporting it. In computing these reactions, it is necessary to consider the equilibrium of the structure as a rigid body. The use of free-body diagrams is especially useful in these calculations.

Before proceeding with these calculations, certain symbols which are used to designate reactions must be described. Fig. 1–6 shows various types of supports which may be used. Fig. 1–6a shows the symbol representing a *roller support*. The roller indicates that the support mechanism used is such that only reactions perpendicular to the supporting surface can be resisted. The roller is assumed to be made in such a way that reactions in both directions can be taken but that the structure cannot lift free. This may, in practice, be a double roller running on both sides of a track, but in many instances it may be a loosely fitting bolt in a slotted hole in the supporting base plate.

The *pinned* (or *hinged*) *support,* Fig. 1–6b, indicates that a force in any direction can be taken, and that the direction which the force may take may be unknown by observation. The force can be represented in calculations by two unknown forces placed at right angles to each other as shown. In practice, the pin may actually be used, but usually a riveted joint or welded connection is assumed to be pinned, to simplify the calculations. In the majority of cases this results in negligible error.

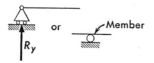 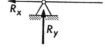

(a) Roller Support
May displace laterally.
May rotate.
One reaction component.

(b) Pinned Support
No displacement.
May rotate.
Two reaction components.

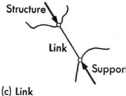

(c) Link
May displace perpendicular
   to link.
Reaction collinear with link.

(d) Fixed Support
No displacement.
No rotation.
Three reaction components.

Fig. 1–6. Symbols for types of support.

The *link,* Fig. 1–6c, has pins on both ends, but in action it closely duplicates the action of the roller. Due to its lateral flexibility, it can take only forces collinear with it. Thus a link defines the direction of the reaction it resists.

The *fixed support,* Fig. 1–6d, will not be encountered extensively in this book but may be used on a few important occasions. It adds moment resistance to the support and thus is one step beyond the pinned support in rigidity. In analysis it may be represented by two forces at right angles to one another and a moment, as shown applied to the embedded end of the member.

1–8. Calculation of Reactions. Fig. 1–7 illustrates a beam which has a roller at A and a pin at B. The first step in the analysis of the reactions is to substitute forces for these supporting devices: the pin, by two forces at right angles (B_x and B_y); and the roller, by a perpendicular force A_y.

The resulting sketch is called the free-body diagram because it represents the beam separated from its physical surroundings, with only the loads, whether known or unknown, imposed on it. In such a state the reactions of the beam can be found by analyzing the diagram with the aid of the equations of statics.

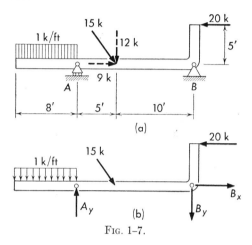

Fig. 1-7.

Moments may be taken about either support for the first equation. Support B is selected. In writing an equation of moments, a sign convention must be used. In this case all clockwise moments are taken as plus and all counterclockwise moments as minus. Since the direction of the reactions may not be known (although many times observation will show it), a direction may be assumed. If the direction is wrong, the answer will come out negative. If negative, the assumed direction of the reaction is reversed on the free body, and the calculations proceed without repetition.

$$\Sigma M_B = 15A_y - (8 \times 19) - \left(\frac{4}{5} \times 15 \times 10\right) - (20 \times 5) = 0 \tag{1-8}$$
$$A_y = 24.8 \text{ k } * \uparrow$$

The other reactions can be found by summing the forces vertically and horizontally. The directions of the resultant may be assumed, as before, allowing the resulting minus sign of the equations to show if the choice was in error.

$$\Sigma F_x = \frac{3}{5} \times (15) - 20 + B_x = 0$$
$$B_x = 11 \text{ k } \rightarrow \tag{1-9}$$
$$\Sigma F_y = -8 - \left(\frac{4}{5} \times 15\right) + 24.8 - B_y = 0$$
$$B_y = 4.8 \text{ k } \uparrow$$

* Kilopound is frequently abbreviated as "kip," but the American Standards Association has designated "k" as both singular and plural abbreviation.

As a further example, consider the truss shown in Fig. 1–8. The truss is subjected to two concentrated loads and is supported by a pinned support at A and a roller at B. There are two methods of approach. The obvious approach would be to take moments about A to find the reaction at B, which acts perpendicular to the supporting surface. It is seen, however, that the lever arm distance l may be somewhat difficult to compute.

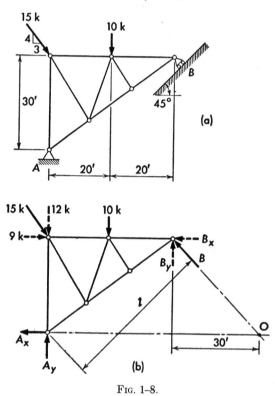

FIG. 1–8.

In general it is almost always easier to treat the vertical and horizontal components of the force rather than the oblique force itself. This is done by resolving B as shown.

$$\Sigma M_A = -(0.707B \times 40) - (0.707B \times 30) + (10 \times 20) + (9 \times 30) = 0$$

$$B = 9.50 \text{ k} \nwarrow$$

$$(1–10)$$

An alternate entry into the problem may be approached by projecting the line of action of A_x and B to the point O, which is used as an origin for moments; thus,

$$\Sigma M_O = 70A_y - (12 \times 70) + (9 \times 30) - (10 \times 50) = 0$$

$$A_y = 15.3 \text{ k} \uparrow \qquad (1\text{--}11)$$

The solution can be continued by summing forces in the vertical and horizontal direction. Solving for B and A_x yields

$$\Sigma F_y = 15.3 + 0.707B - 12 - 10 = 0$$

$$B = 9.50 \text{ k} \qquad (Check!)$$

$$\Sigma F_x = 0.707 \times 9.50 + A_x - 9 = 0 \qquad (1\text{--}12)$$

$$A_x = 2.30 \text{ k} \leftarrow$$

The use of the link in a structure is illustrated in another example shown in Fig. 1–9. At first glance it may seem that the structure is statically indeterminate, since there are two unknown components of reaction

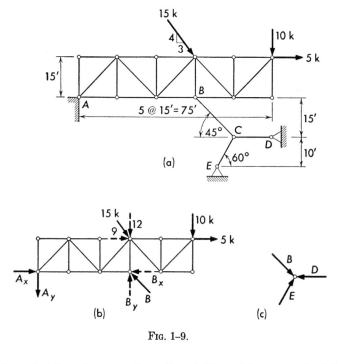

Fig. 1–9.

at A (A_x and A_y) and one each at E and D, making a total of four. If one separates the structure into two free-body diagrams, as shown in Fig. 1–9b and c, each part has only three unknowns, and three independent equations of statics can be written for each part. Application of the equations to Fig. 1–9b yields

$$\Sigma M_A = (12 \times 45) + (9 \times 15) + (10 \times 75) + (5 \times 15)$$
$$- (0.707B \times 45) = 0$$
$$B = 47.2 \text{ k} \quad \nwarrow$$

$$\Sigma F_x = 0.707B - A_x - 9 - 5 = 0 \qquad (1\text{--}13)$$
$$A_x = 19.33 \text{ k} \quad \rightarrow$$

$$\Sigma F_y = 0.707B - 12 - 10 - A_y = 0$$
$$A_y = 11.33 \text{ k} \quad \downarrow$$

As a check, another moment equation is written:

$$\Sigma M_B = 9 \times 15 + 10 \times 30 + 5 \times 15 - 45A_y = 0$$
$$A_y = 11.33 \text{ k} \qquad (1\text{--}14)$$

At Joint C

$$\Sigma F_y = 0.707\,(47.2) - 0.866E = 0$$
$$E = 38.5 \text{ k}$$
$$\Sigma F_x = 0.707\,(47.2) + (0.5 \times 38.5) - D = 0 \qquad (1\text{--}15)$$
$$D = 52.6 \text{ k}$$

1–9. Stability. When one considers the design of a structure, careful consideration must be given to the placement of the reactions. The direction of the reactions can be controlled by links, rollers, and similar devices. A danger sometimes arises when careless use of these devices leads to instability in a structure. Consider the rigid body in Fig. 1–10a, which is to be constrained by reactions. Total restraint is obtained when the structure cannot move in any direction. The rigid body may be a beam, a truss, or other object. It is obvious by trial that the body in Fig. 1–10a cannot move vertically or horizontally, nor can it rotate. Such restraint may be had by placing the forces in many different combinations and configurations. In every case only three forces are needed to constrain the body. The body in Fig. 1–10b has an entirely different set of links and forces and is totally restrained, for example. There are many cases which obviously are not stable, even though three forces are applied; for example, the object in Fig. 1–10c can be moved sideways even though it has three vertical reactions. The structure in Fig. 1–10d illustrates a less obvious instability, in which the lines of action of the reactions intersect at a point O and form a concurrent force system. Since a force P placed in any location other than one collinear with the reactions would cause a moment about the point O, the reaction system may be classed as unstable because a concurrent system cannot resist moments. Structures that have sufficient reactions but which are incorrectly placed for stability are called *geometrically unstable.* The condition in Fig. 1–10d can be corrected by

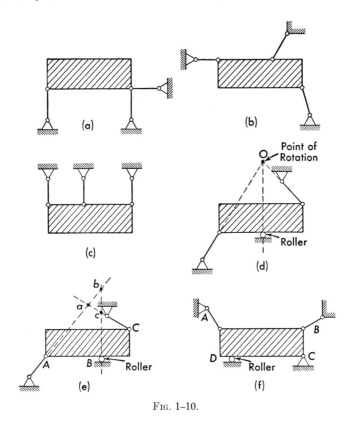

Fig. 1–10.

adjusting the intersection of the lines of action so that a definite triangle abc is formed, as shown in Fig. 1–10e. The larger this triangle is made, the more stability is assured. Again in Fig. 1–10d, if the body is allowed to rotate, collapse will be avoided by the links gradually assuming new positions, thus causing formation of a small triangle abc. However, this large movement may be undesirable.

1–10. Statically Indeterminate Structures. It has already been shown in Fig. 1–10a and b that three reactions, properly placed, are necessary to rigidly restrain a structure. Consider the beam of Fig. 1–11a, in which there are five components of the reaction—four vertical and one horizontal. It can readily be seen that removal of any two of the vertical reactions still leaves the beam stable (removal of the horizontal reaction at A, of course, gives instability). There are three independent equations of statics which can be solved simultaneously to give solutions to any three reactions, but only if two of the present reactions are removed. There are not enough independent equations of statics to solve for the fourth and fifth reactions if they are left on the structure. Such a structure is called *statically indeterminate*. In this case the structure is statically indeterminate to the second degree. The degree is increased by

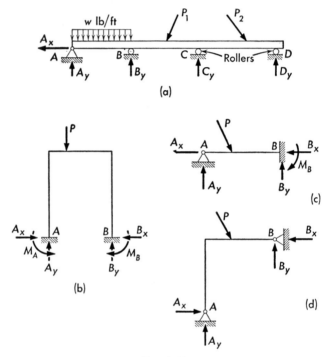

Fig. 1–11.

"one" for each extra reaction. Fig. 1–10f illustrates another statically indeterminate structure. In this case there are two reaction components at C and one at each of the other supports, making five components. This structure is statically indeterminate to the $5 - 3 = 2$d degree also. Fig. 1–11b illustrates a frame which involves two fixed supports; if the moments M are considered as components, the frame has six reaction components. This structure is statically indeterminate to the $6 - 3 = 3$d degree. Other statically indeterminate structures are shown in Fig. 1–11c and Fig. 1–11d. Can you tell why these are indeterminate? The extra reactions are sometimes called "redundant" reactions because they are not needed to insure the stability of the structure. The statically indeterminate structure is solvable only by introducing other independent conditions which are based upon the properties of the material and its deformation characteristics. The exact methods of solution for statically indeterminate structures are not covered in this text; however, certain approximate methods are treated in Chapter 13.

It may be noted that certain combinations of the reaction types shown in Fig. 1–6 will give stability and also give a statically determinate structure. These are (1) one fixed support, (2) one pin and one roller, (3) three rollers, and (4) three links. In the last two cases care must be taken to avoid special arrangements which could give instability.

1–11. Solutions Dependent upon Conditions of Construction. In general the three available equations of statics limit the class of statically determinate structures to those structures which have no more than three restraining components. There are, however, a number of cases in which some condition of construction allows partial solution by means of free-body diagrams. These partial solutions may in some cases be combined

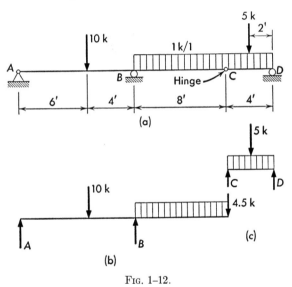

Fig. 1–12.

to find reactions of the complete structure. For example, upon casual observation of the structure illustrated in Fig. 1–12, one may observe a pin at A, rollers at B and D, and an internal hinge at C and may assume the structure to be statically indeterminate to the second degree. Upon closer analysis, one finds that the structure can be separated into two parts, as illustrated in Fig. 1–12b and Fig. 1–12c; it is a compound beam. In Fig. 1–12c is shown a simple beam CD, which is supported by a pin at D and a hinge at C. Solution for the reactions can be made by symmetry to find that both pin D and hinge C have 4.5 k vertical reactions. The hinge reaction is reversed and applied to C in Fig. 1–12b, and the calculations proceed as follows:

$$\Sigma M_A = (10 \times 6) - 10B + (8 \times 14) + (4.5 \times 18) = 0$$

$$B = 25.3 \text{ k}$$

$$\Sigma F_y = -10 - 8 - 4.5 + 25.3 + A = 0$$

$$A = -2.8 \text{ k}$$

(1–16)

The reaction A was assumed in the wrong direction and should be reversed on the free-body diagram as indicated by the sign of the answer.

PROBLEMS

The problems listed at the end of Chapters 2, 3, 4, and 5 may also be used for exercises in calculating reactions.

1–1 to 1–10. Examine the accompanying illustrations and calculate the reactions.

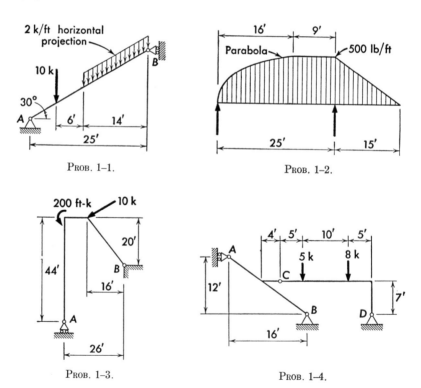

PROB. 1–1.

PROB. 1–2.

PROB. 1–3.

PROB. 1–4.

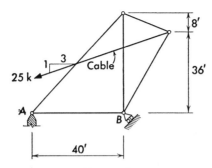

PROB. 1–5.

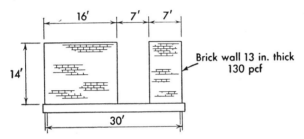

PROB. 1–6.

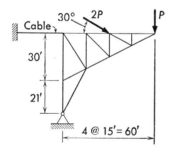

PROB. 1–7.

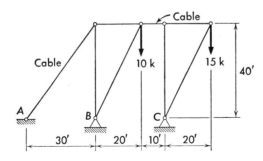

PROB. 1–8.

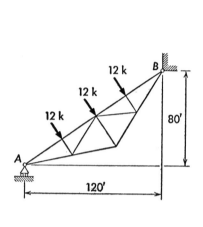

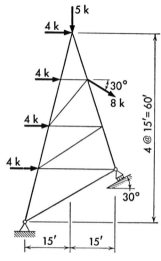

PROB. 1–9.   PROB. 1–10.

CHAPTER 2

SHEAR, MOMENT, AND THRUST DIAGRAMS

The object of the analysis of structures is to find the forces which act on the components, so that we may select materials and properly size the components for safety in service. All structural components are acted upon by either thrust (compression or tension), moments (flexure), or shears (transverse forces), or combinations of the three. In this chapter both graphic diagrams and algebraic expressions are used to analyze both beams and frames and to show the results.

2–1. Definition of Shear, Moment, and Thrust. Fig. 2–1 illustrates a beam with an arbitrary loading. A section is made at C, and the left half

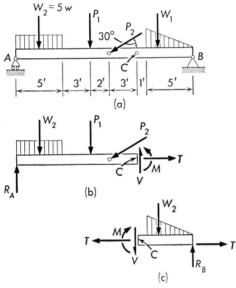

FIG. 2–1.

is considered as a free body. The section is in a state of equilibrium, and hence the three equations of statics in a plane must apply. Summation of forces in the vertical direction yields

$$R_A - 5w - P_1 - \frac{P_2}{2} + V = 0$$

$$V = 5w + P_1 + \frac{P_2}{2} - R_A$$

(2–1)

21

The force V at the cut section, needed to maintain equilibrium on the free body, is called the *shear*. It is designated positive if the resultant of all the vertical external force components to the left of the section are upward. As a consequence the shear must be downward on the cut section in order to balance this resultant. The sign convention is easy to recall if the diagram of Fig. 2–2 is remembered. If at a section the left portion of the beam tends to slip vertically upward, the shear is positive; if it tends to slip downward, the shear is negative.

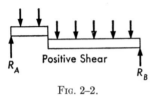

Positive Shear

R_A R_B

FIG. 2–2.

Returning to Fig. 2–1, the summation of forces in the horizontal direction on (c) yields

$$0.886P_2 = T \tag{2–2}$$

The force T at the cut section, needed to balance the horizontal summation of forces, is called the *thrust*. It is designated positive if it subjects the beam to tension; negative, if it subjects the beam to compression.

The final equation of statics can be written by summing moments about the neutral axis of the beam at the section in Fig. 2–1b.

$$M = 13R_A - 5w(13 - 2.5) - 5P_1 - 0.5P_2 \times 3 \tag{2–3}$$

The moment that must be applied at the end of the cut section in order to satisfy the equation is known as the *bending moment*. Numerous methods are used to designate the sign of the moment, but in this text the

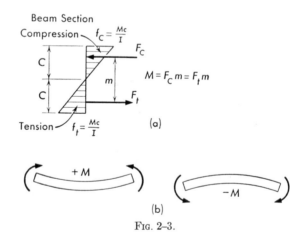

Beam Section

Compression $f_c = \frac{Mc}{I}$

F_c

C

m $M = F_c m = F_t m$

C

F_t

Tension $f_t = \frac{Mc}{I}$ (a)

$+ M$

$- M$

(b)

FIG. 2–3.

beam convention is used. By this system the moment is considered positive if it causes compression in the top of the beam; negative, if it causes tension in the top of the beam. The internal resisting moment of the beam is provided by the normal flexural action of the beam, as shown in Fig. 2–3a. Its bending action causes longitudinal stresses described by the familiar flexure equation $f = Mc/I$. The total compression in the top is denoted by the resultant F_c and the total tension by the resultant F_t. Since $F_t = F_c$ for the case of pure flexure, the two forces form a couple which is the resisting moment of the beam, denoted as M in Fig. 2–3a.

In the sign convention described, the fact that the moment is clockwise or counterclockwise is not directly related to the sign. Note that at a cut section the moment on the left section may be counterclockwise as illustrated, and therefore the moment on the right section must naturally oppose the moment on the left section. Both represent a positive moment, however. The sign may be conveniently remembered by the diagrams of Fig. 2–3b. If the beam is concave upward (holds water), the moment is positive; if the beam is convex upward (water runs off), the moment is negative.

2–2. Shear and Moment Diagrams. Since both shear and moment vary with the section from the beam which is analyzed, a graph of these quantities plotted along the length of the beam is a convenience to the designer. These graphs are known as *shear* and *moment diagrams*. They

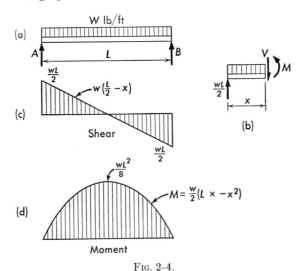

Fɪɢ. 2–4.

immediately tell the designer the state of shear and moment at any section he may wish to design. In addition, these diagrams, which are simple to construct, are a great aid in finding deflections and solving statically indeterminate structures in the more advanced structural analysis work.

The construction of the diagram is best illustrated by a series of examples. First consider the uniformly loaded beam of Fig. 2–4 on simple supports. The reaction at each end is $wL/2$. An arbitrary section of length x from the left is cut from the beam as shown in Fig. 2–4b. Summation of the vertical forces on the section yields

$$V = \frac{wL}{2} - wx = w\left(\frac{L}{2} - x\right) \tag{2–4}$$

This equation represents a straight line, and its plot in Fig. 2–4c, directly below the beam, is the shear diagram of the beam.

By taking moment about the end of the free body in Fig. 2–4b, the equation for moment may be found to be

$$M = \frac{wLx}{2} - \frac{wx^2}{2} = \frac{w}{2}(Lx - x^2) \tag{2–5}$$

The equation represents a parabola with its apex at the center of the beam, as shown in Fig. 2–4d, with the maximum value of $wL^2/8$.

A more complicated example is shown in Fig. 2–5. In this case a continuous equation cannot be written from one end of the beam to the other, as in the preceding example, because of discontinuities in the curve due to the concentrated loads. The loads represent a typical arrangement of wheel loads which may be passing over a bridge. The reactions have already been found, as shown in Fig. 2–5a.

One may begin by plotting the shears. Sections can be taken, starting at the left as shown in Fig. 2–5d. Since the reaction is 41 k in the first 12 ft of beam, it must be opposed by a shear of 41 k, as plotted in Fig. 2–5b. A new section can be taken for the interval CD. The shear changes in this interval because another force enters into the calculations. From the free body in Fig. 2–5e the following equation is written:

$$V_{CD} = 41 - 16 = 25 \text{ k} \tag{2–6}$$

Again, no other force changes this relationship, and therefore the shear remains the same throughout the interval CD. The shear in the other intervals can be found in a similar fashion.

$$V_{DE} = 41 - 16 - 32 = -7 \text{ k}$$

$$V_{EF} = 41 - 16 - 32 - 32 = -39 \text{ k}$$

$$V_{FG} = 41 - 16 - 32 - 32 - 8 = -47 \text{ k} \tag{2–7}$$

$$V_{GB} = 41 - 16 - 32 - 32 - 8 - 8 = -55 \text{ k}$$

The last equation checks the reaction at B; i.e., the reaction closes the shear diagram.

The sign of the moment is not always apparent by observation, and therefore a system is needed to determine it throughout the calculations. The system usually used assumes the moment to be in such a direction at

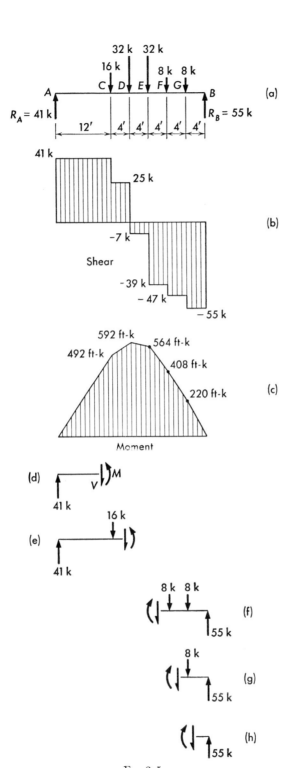

32 k   32 k

16 k   8 k 8 k

A   C D E F G   B   (a)

R_A = 41 k R_B = 55 k

12'   4' 4' 4' 4' 4'

41 k

25 k

(b)

−7 k

Shear

− 39 k
− 47 k
− 55 k

592 ft-k
492 ft-k   564 ft-k
408 ft-k
220 ft-k   (c)

Moment

(d) V M
41 k

16 k
(e)
41 k

8 k 8 k
(f)
55 k

8 k
(g)
55 k

(h)
55 k

Fig. 2–5.

25

the section that compression is caused in the top of the beam (positive moment), as previously described. All forces having moments in a direction causing compression in the top are also designated as positive in the equation of moments, whereas those causing tension in the top are designated as negative moments. If the result of the equation is positive, the assumption of positive moment was correct. If the resultant is negative, the moment is also negative.*

The moments can be computed by using the same free-body diagrams. Thus, for the first interval, the equation for moment is

$$M_{AC} = 41x$$
$$M_{(x=12)} = 41 \times 12 = 492 \text{ ft-k}$$

(2-8)

Similarly for the interval CD, the equation for moment (using the same origin as before) is

$$M_{CD} = 41x - 16(x - 12)$$
$$M_{(x=16)} = (41 \times 16) - (16 \times 4) = 592 \text{ ft-k}$$

(2-9)

Both these equations are of the straight-line type; consequently, when concentrated loads are involved, it is simpler to compute the moments at each load only and connect these moments by straight lines in the diagram. Thus:

$$M_E = (41 \times 20) - (16 \times 8) - (32 \times 4) = 564 \text{ ft-k}$$
$$M_F = (41 \times 24) - (16 \times 16) - (32 \times 8) - (32 \times 4) = 408 \text{ ft-k} \quad (2\text{-}10)$$
$$M_G = (41 \times 28) - (16 \times 20) - (32 \times 12) - (32 \times 8) - (8 \times 4) = 220 \text{ ft-k}$$

Although the moment can be computed by progressing from one end of the beam to the other by taking progressive sections, this is not considered good practice because sections from the other end may be used. For example, using the sections in Figs. 2–5f, g, and h, the moments at E, F, and G of Fig. 2–5c may be computed again as follows:

$$M_G = 55 \times 4 = 220 \text{ ft-k}$$
$$M_F = (55 \times 8) - (8 \times 4) = 408 \text{ ft-k} \quad (2\text{-}11)$$
$$M_E = (55 \times 12) - (8 \times 8) - (8 \times 4) = 564 \text{ ft-k}$$

After some practice the student will be able to visualize the simpler free-body diagrams, and then the elaborate computation shown for such

* The alternate system is to assume a moment direction (clockwise or counterclockwise) by visual examination. Most engineers become quite experienced at this and can pick the direction almost without fail. The moments are summed about the section. If the resultant is negative, the moment is in the direction opposite of that assumed. If the latter is the case, no recalculation is necessary; the direction is reversed, plotted on the diagram, and calculations continued at the next point.

a simple case will not be necessary. The student should not become over-confident of his skill, however, and should continue to draw complete free-body diagrams for a long time.

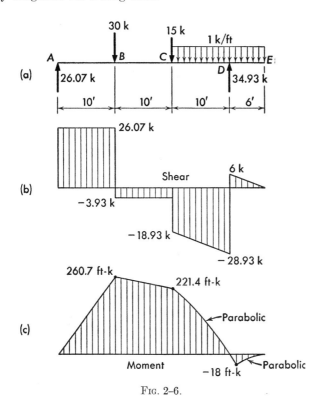

Fig. 2–6.

The combination of distributed and concentrated loads on the same beam is not an uncommon problem. The simple beam with the cantilever end in Fig. 2–6 will serve to illustrate the case. The calculations will be somewhat abbreviated.

SHEARS:

$$V_{AB} = 26.07 \text{ k}$$

$$V_{BC} = 26.07 - 30.0 = -3.93 \text{ k}$$

$$V_{(C+\Delta x)} = -3.93 - 15.0 = -18.93 \text{ k}$$

$$V_{(D-\Delta x)} = -18.93 - (1 \times 10) = -28.93 \text{ k}$$

$$V_{(D+\Delta x)} = -28.93 + 34.93 = +6.0 \text{ k}$$

$$V_E = 6.0 - 1 \times 6 = 0 \quad (Check!)$$

(2–12)

MOMENTS:

$$M_B = 26.07 \times 10 = 260.7 \text{ ft-k}$$

$$M_C = (26.07 \times 20) - (30 \times 10) = 221.4 \text{ ft-k} \qquad (2\text{--}13)$$

$$M_D = 6 \times 1 \times 3 = 18.0 \text{ ft-k}$$

The moment curve in the interval CD and DE must be curved because of the distributed load. The equations are

$$M_{DE} = -1 \times \frac{x^2}{2} \qquad \text{(Origin at } E\text{)}$$

$$(2\text{--}14)$$

$$M_{CD} = 34.93\,(x - 6) - \frac{x^2}{2} \qquad \text{(Origin at } E\text{)}$$

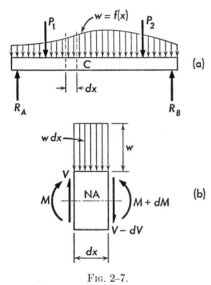

FIG. 2–7.

2–3. Relation Between Shear, Moment, and Loads. Fig. 2–7 illustrates a simple beam with an arbitrary loading, including both concentrated and distributed loads. The distributed load has an intensity w at any point. At a point x from the left, a segment of the beam dx is removed as a free body. The free body of the element as it approaches zero is shown in Fig. 2–7b. The forces acting include the segment of load cut by the sections and the shear and moment on each side. From previous discussion it is evident that the forces and moments act in the directions shown. The equations of statics will establish the relationships between these forces. Taking moments about the right force at the neutral axis (NA) of the beam, one finds

$$M + V\,dx - \frac{w}{2}\,\overline{dx^2} - (M + dM) = 0 \qquad (2\text{--}15)$$

Since products of differentials may be neglected, the equation reduces to the following:

$$V\,dx = dM \qquad \text{or} \qquad V = \frac{dM}{dx} \qquad (2\text{--}16)$$

i.e., the rate of change of moment is equal to the shear at a particular point.

The relationship between the shears on the two sections can be found from a summation of forces in the vertical direction; thus:

$$(V - dV) - V + w\,dx = 0$$

$$\frac{dV}{dx} = w \tag{2-17}$$

and since $dM/dx = V$ and $dV/dx = d^2M/dx^2$, then

$$\frac{d^2M}{dx^2} = \frac{dV}{dx} = w \tag{2-18}$$

A number of important conclusions may be drawn from Eqs. 2–15, 2–16, 2–17, and 2–18.

1. When the shear is positive, the rate of change of moment is positive, and the moment is *increasing* with x. Conversely, when the shear is negative, the moment is *decreasing* with x.
2. At the point in the beam where the shear changes from positive to negative (shear is equal to zero), the moment is neither increasing nor decreasing, and a maximum (or minimum) moment must exist. This is in accordance with the principles of calculus whereby the derivative of a curve is used to find maxima or minima by its zeros. (This is not always true, since important cases exist in which maximum moment occurs at maximum shear; cantilever beams, for example.*)
3. When $w = 0$, the shear has a constant value.†
4. An interesting and useful relationship may be found by integrating Eq. 2–16 thus:

$$\int_{M_1}^{M_2} dM = \int_1^2 V\,dx$$

$$M_2 - M_1 = \int_1^2 V\,dx \tag{2-19}$$

Note that the term to the right expresses the area of the shear diagram between 1 and 2. Although this area can be computed by calculus if need be, it is often convenient to compute it by simple arithmetic. The following equation expresses this relationship:

$$M_2 = M_1 + \text{area of shear diagram between points 1 and 2} \tag{2-20}$$

---

* In calculus one must always examine the end points or any points of discontinuity of the interval of a curve under consideration for a maximum or minimum, since these may exist despite the fact that the derivative has no zeros in the interval.

† When the load w is zero, it may seem that this would indicate a point of maximum or minimum shear; however, this case rarely arises in useful structures. The maxima or minima occur at the ends of the beam (interval) or at the reaction or concentrated load locations (discontinuities in moment curve), and thus these points must be located separately. This is in accordance with the preceding footnote.

2–4. Additional Examples. As another example and illustration of the finding of maximum moment, consider the structure of Fig. 2–8. The sketch represents a vertical-sheet piling wall which is supported by wale frames B and C. The load is triangular, due to the combined soil pres-

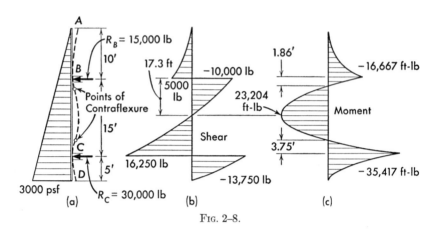

FIG. 2–8.

sure and hydrostatic pressure, which increases 100 psf for each foot of depth. A maximum pressure of 3000 psf exists at the bottom of the piling. Although the piling is considered to run continuously for some distance perpendicular to the plane of the sketch, a strip 1 ft in length is used in the analysis.

REACTIONS:

$$15R_C = \frac{3000 \times 30}{2} \times 10, \qquad R_C = 30,000 \text{ lb}$$

$$\text{(2–21)}$$

$$15R_B = \frac{3000 \times 30}{2} \times 5, \qquad R_B = 15,000 \text{ lb}$$

SHEARS:

$$V_{AB\,(\text{origin at } A)} = 100x \cdot \frac{x}{2} = 50x^2$$

$$V_{(x=10-\Delta x)} = 50 \times 10^2 = 5000 \text{ lb}$$

$$V_{(x=10+\Delta x)} = 50 \times 10^2 - 15,000 = -10,000 \text{ lb}$$

$$V_{BC\,(\text{origin at } A)} = 50x^2 - 15,000$$

$$V_{(x=25-\Delta x)} = 50 \times 25^2 - 15,000 = 16,250 \text{ ft-k}$$

$$V = 50x^2 - 15,000 = 0$$

$$x^2 = 300$$

$$x = 17.3 \text{ ft}$$

The last calculation indicates the point of zero shear and point of maximum or minimum moment, to be checked later.

$$V_{CD\,(\text{origin at } D)} = 3000x - 50x^2$$
$$V_{(x=5-\Delta x)} = 3000 \times 5 - 50 \times 5^2 = 13{,}750 \text{ k}$$

Note that the sum of the shears at the left and right sides of each support (C and D) totals to the reaction itself. The maximum shears have been calculated; the shear diagram itself, Fig. 2–8b, consists of segments of a parabola.

MOMENTS:

$$M_{AB\,(\text{origin at } A)} = -100 \cdot \frac{x}{2} \cdot \frac{x}{3} = -16.667x^3$$
$$M_{(x=10)} = -16.667 \times 10^3 = -16{,}667 \text{ ft-lb}$$
$$M_{BC\,(\text{origin at } A)} = -16.667x^3 + 15{,}000\,(x - 10)$$
$$M_{(x=17.3)} = -16.667 \times \overline{17.3}^3 + 15{,}000\,(17.3 - 10)$$
$$= 23{,}204 \text{ ft-lb}$$
$$M_{(x=25)} = -16.667 \times 25^3 + 15{,}000\,(25 - 10) = -35{,}417 \text{ ft-lb}$$
$$M_{CD\,(\text{origin at } D)} = \frac{-3000x^2}{2} + 16.667x^3$$
$$M_{(x=5)} = -15{,}000 \times 5^2 + 16.667 \times 5^3 = -35{,}417 \text{ ft-lb}$$

Oftentimes it is necessary to know the points of zero moment because these points are obviously the points at which to splice structural members since only shear forces need be resisted. These points are also known as *points of contraflexure* because the direction of curvature due to the deflection of the beam changes from concave to convex (or vice versa) at this point. In this case there are obviously two points of contraflexure, and they can be found by extracting the roots of the moment equation when it is equated to zero; thus:

$$M_{BC} = -16.667x^3 + 15{,}000\,(x - 10) = 0 \qquad (2\text{--}22)$$

Since this is a cubic equation, it is most easily solved by trial to find that $x = 11.86$ ft and 22.25 ft.

Fig. 2–9 illustrates a case which is somewhat confusing to the average student. It consists of a simple beam with a moment applied at a point x from the left end. The reactions can be found by taking moments about either end.

$$\Sigma M_A = 0, \qquad R_B L - M = 0$$
$$R_B = \frac{M}{L} \text{ (up)} \qquad (2\text{--}23)$$

Likewise,

$$R_A = -\frac{M}{L} \text{ (down)}$$

The shear diagram is shown in Fig. 2–9b. It is constructed by taking the usual free-body diagrams from the left and noting that there are no vertical forces to modify shear at any point for any section taken. The shear is constant across the entire beam.

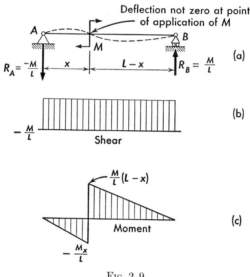

FIG. 2–9.

The moment diagram is constructed by using the free body both to the left of M and to the right of M to find that

$$M_{(x-\Delta x)} = -\frac{Mx}{L}$$

$$M_{(x+\Delta x)} = \frac{M}{L}(L-x)$$

(2–24)

Eq. 2–20 can also be used to calculate the moment.

$$M_{(x-\Delta x)} = 0 + \text{area of shear diagram between 0 and } x$$

$$= \frac{Mx}{L}$$

Likewise,

$$0 = M_{(x+\Delta x)} + \text{area of shear diagram between } x \text{ and } L$$

(2–25)

$$M_{(x+\Delta x)} = \frac{M}{L}(L-x)$$

Note also that

$$M_{(x-\Delta x)} + M_{(x+\Delta x)} = M$$

so that the two beam moments properly add to the applied moment at M.

The relationship between the moment and shear diagram is further illustrated by recomputing the moments of the beam of Fig. 2–6. Utilizing Eq. 2–20, the moments at B, C, D, and E are computed.

$$M_B = 0 + (26.07 \times 10) = 260.7 \text{ ft-k}$$

$$M_C = 260.7 - (3.93 \times 10) = 221.4 \text{ ft-k}$$

$$M_D = 221.4 - \left(\frac{18.93 + 28.93}{2} \times 10\right) = -18.0 \text{ ft-k}$$

$$M_E = -18.0 + \left(\frac{6 \times 6}{2}\right) = 0 \quad (Check!)$$

(2–26)

Note also that the point of maximum moment is at the point where the shear diagram passes through zero. This is in accord with Eq. 2–16, which specifies this relationship. This relationship is not strictly applicable at a point of discontinuity, however, since the derivative dM/dx does not exist at such a point. Nevertheless, if one considers the case where the load of 30 k, for example, is spread over a distance Δx on the beam, the shear passes through zero at the identical point, although the shear diagram would have a sloping line through the distance Δx. The moment diagram would be slightly rounded at point B in accordance with this assumption. As Δx approaches zero, the relationship approaches the one illustrated in the example, so that even at a discontinuity, a zero shear indicates a maximum or minimum in the moment diagram. In connection with this it should be noted that true concentrated loads are almost impossible to find in actual structures; however, the simplification of the computations is achieved by substituting them for certain loads applied in limited areas.

The use of Eq. 2–20 should not be limited to shear diagrams which involve straight lines only. Many times parabolic curves and others which have standard formulas for the area under the curve may be utilized for rapid solutions. Both the direct solution for moments and the shear diagram area method may be used as a check.

2–5. Rigid Frames. Many useful structures consist of members which are not straight. Fig. 2–10 illustrates a structure which is of this type. In this case the structure may be a grandstand or bleacher structure where seats are placed on the sloping side and the interior utilized for some other purpose. The sections AB, BC, and CD are connected rigidly at the joints B and C so that moment and shear can be transmitted directly through the connection. Because of this feature this type of structure is referred to as a *rigid frame*. The need for shear and moment diagram is the same as that for the simpler beam structures.

As an example, the moment and shear diagrams for the frame of Fig. 2–10 will be found, loaded with a single concentrated load at B, as shown. The reactions can be found in the usual manner by taking moments about A and D. The moments and shears in each portion of the frame can be found by analysis of each portion separately. The free-body

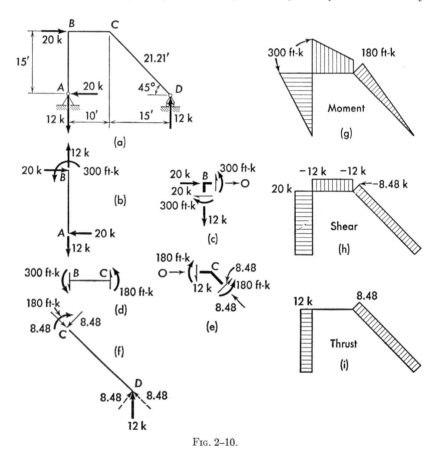

Fig. 2–10.

diagrams of the segments are drawn in Figs. 2–10b, d, and f and of the rigid corners in Figs. 2–10c and d. Since all frames involve thrust as well as shear and moment, three types of diagrams must be drawn. In Fig. 2–10b there are three unknown forces at the severed end B. These can be found by applying the three equations of statics.

$$\Sigma F_x = V_B - 20 = 0, \qquad V_{BA} = 20 \text{ k}$$

$$\Sigma F_y = T_B - 12 = 0, \qquad T_{BA} = 12 \text{ k} \qquad (2\text{--}27)$$

$$\Sigma M_B = M_B - 20 \times 15 = 0, \qquad M_B = 300 \text{ ft-k}$$

Since there are no other loads, the shear for the leg AB is constant, as illustrated in Fig. 2–10h. M_B can also be computed from the shear diagram to be

$$M_B = 20 \text{ k} \times 15 \text{ ft} = 300 \text{ ft-k}$$

In plotting the moment, the beam connection can be used again by picturing the exterior of the frame as the top of the beam. Thus positive moments cause compression on the exterior, and negative moments cause compression on the interior of the frame.

The free body of the other leg is shown in Fig. 2–10d. The reaction at D is resolved into its components perpendicular and parallel to the direction of the members as shown.

$$\Sigma F_{DC} = 8.48 + T_D = 0, \qquad\qquad T_D = -8.48 \text{ k compression}$$

$$\Sigma F (\perp \text{ to } DC) = 8.48 - V_D = 0, \qquad V_D = 8.48 \text{ k} \qquad\qquad (2\text{–}28)$$

$$\Sigma M_D = M_D - 8.48 \times 21.2 = 0, \quad M_D = 180 \text{ ft-k}$$

Once the moments are found at the joints, the top segment can be analyzed. The fact that the moments carry directly around the rigid corner is proved by consideration of the free body of the corner section as shown in Fig. 2–10c or d. Moments are taken about the intersection, and since the thrusts and shears pass through the center of moments and the lever arms of the shears approach zero as the corner approaches zero, the equality $M_{BA} = M_{BC}$, for example, is evident. Consideration of the free body, Fig. 2–10c, yields the following:

$$\Sigma M_C = 300 - 180 - 10V_{BC} = 0$$

$$V_{BC} = 12 \text{ k}$$
$$(2\text{–}29)$$
$$\Sigma F_y = V_{CB} - 12 = 0$$

$$V_{CB} = 12 \text{ k}$$

There are no thrusts in the top segment. This may be found by analysis of the forces at the top of Fig. 2–10b or d. The applied force of 20 k is exactly counterbalanced by the shear of 20 k in Fig. 2–10b, while the summation of forces in the horizontal direction at the top of Fig. 2–10f indicates that the horizontal component of the shear (8.48 k) will exactly counterbalance the horizontal component of thrust (8.48 k).

With this calculated information, the shear and moment diagrams can be easily constructed as shown. One deviation from formerly described practice is evident in the construction of the shear diagram. The shear is plotted on the positive side for the BCD segment to avoid the confusing overlap at C which would otherwise result. The values have been marked negative in accordance with their proper sign.

A slightly more complicated frame is illustrated in Fig. 2–11. The structure is broken up into the three free bodies illustrated in Fig. 2–11b, c, and d. The following calculations are used to find the necessary data.

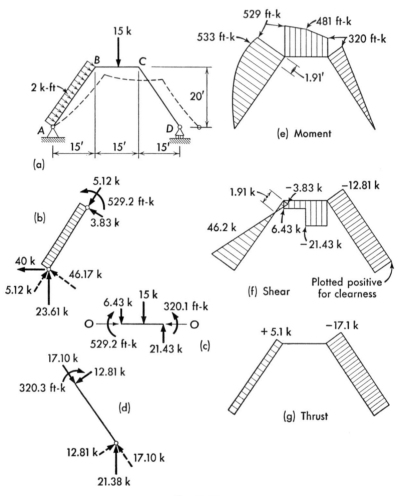

FIG. 2–11.

REACTIONS:

$$D_y = \frac{(50 \times 12.5) + (15 \times 22.5)}{45} = 21.39 \text{ k}$$

$$A_y = \frac{(15 \times 22.5) + (50 \times 14.5)}{45} = 23.61 \text{ k} \qquad (2\text{–}30)$$

$$A_x = 2 \times 25 \times \frac{4}{5} = 40 \text{ k}$$

These reactions are resolved into components collinear and perpendicular to the members, as shown by the dashed forces in Fig. 2–11b and d, and these in turn are used in the following calculations.

FROM FIG. 2–11b:

$$\Sigma M_B = (2 \times 25 \times 12.5) - (46.17 \times 25) - M_B = 0$$

$$M_B = 529.2 \text{ ft-k}$$

$$\Sigma M_A = (2 \times 25 \times 12.5) - 529.2 - 25V_{BA} = 0$$

$$V_{BA} = 3.83 \text{ k} \tag{2-31}$$

$$\Sigma F_{AB} = 5.12 - T_{BA} = 0$$

$$T_{BA} = 5.12 \text{ k compression}$$

FROM FIG. 2–11d:

$$\Sigma M_C = -(12.81 \times 25) + M_{CD} = 0$$

$$M_{CD} = 320.3 \text{ ft-k}$$

$$\Sigma F(\perp \text{ to } CD) = 12.81 - V_{CD} = 0$$

$$V_{CD} = 12.81 \text{ k} \tag{2-32}$$

$$\Sigma F_{CD} = 17.10 - T_{CD} = 0$$

$$T_{CD} = 17.10 \text{ k compression}$$

FROM FIG. 2–11c:

$$\Sigma M_B = 529.2 - 320.1 + (15 \times 7.5) - 15V_{CB} = 0$$

$$V_{CB} = 21.43 \text{ k}$$

$$\Sigma F_y = 21.43 - 15.0 - V_{BC} = 0 \tag{2-33}$$

$$V_{BC} = 6.43 \text{ k}$$

The moment is calculated at the 15-k load as follows:

$$M_{15} = 529.2 - (6.43 \times 7.5) = 481 \text{ ft-k}$$

In plotting the shear diagram for AB, one finds a zero shear at 1.91 ft from B. This is a point of maximum moment, which is calculated as follows:

$$M_{max} = 46.17(25.0 - 1.91) - 2 \times \frac{(25 - 1.91)^2}{2} = 533 \text{ ft-k} \tag{2-34}$$

Note again that the shear diagram is not plotted according to sign, to avoid confusing overlap in the diagram.

PROBLEMS

NOTE: When moment and shear diagrams are requested, points of zero shear and points of contraflexure should be shown.

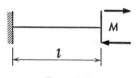

PROB. 2–1.

2–1. A moment M is applied to the end of a cantilever beam of length l, as shown in the accompanying diagram. Draw shear and moment diagrams.

2–2. Draw shear and moment diagrams for member ACD in Problem 3–10.

2–3. Draw shear and moment diagrams for the beam in Problem 3–11.

2–4. Draw shear and moment diagrams for the beam in Problem 3–12.

2–5. Draw shear and moment diagrams for the beam in Problem 3–13.

2–6. Draw shear and moment diagrams for the beam in Problem 3–14.

2–7. Draw shear and moment diagrams for the beam in Problem 3–18.

2–8. Draw shear and moment diagrams for the beam in Problem 3–21.

2–9. Draw shear and moment diagrams for the beam in Problem 3–22.

2–10, 2–11. Draw shear and moment diagrams for the structures shown in the two accompanying illustrations.

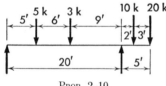

PROB. 2–10.

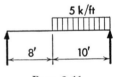

PROB. 2–11.

2–12. The double, cantilever, simple beam represents a loading dock which can have all or any portion loaded at one time. For example, referring to the sketch, areas 1 and 3, 1, 2, and 3, 1 and 2, 2 and 3, or 1, 2, or 3 singly are possibilities. Draw an envelope curve of all possibilities. The resulting curve is convenient to have in designing the beam, since it specifies both the negative and positive extreme moments at each point.

2–13. Compute the maximum moment in the beam shown in the illustration.

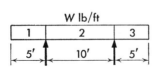

PROB. 2–12.

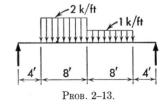

PROB. 2–13.

2–14, 2–15. Draw the shear and moment diagrams for the beam in the accompanying sketch.

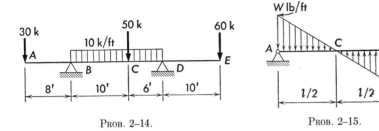

PROB. 2–14.   PROB. 2–15.

2–16. Compute the maximum moment and points of contraflexure for Problem 3–25.

2–17. Compute the distances x at which R_1 and R_2 must be placed from the end of this beam in order to have a minimum moment.

2–18. A channel carrying water is cast monolithically with a wall of reinforced concrete as shown. Consider one linear foot of wall, and draw the shear and moment diagrams for the combined structure.

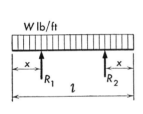

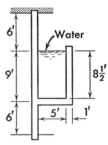

PROB. 2–17.   PROB. 2–18.

2–19. A temporary dam is built as shown in the illustration. Draw the shear and moment diagram due to the hydrostatic pressure on the face of the dam.

2–20. Draw the shear and moment diagram of the structure due to the cable tension of 10 k between B and C.

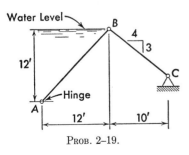

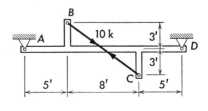

PROB. 2–19.   PROB. 2–20.

2–21. Draw shear and moment diagrams for the compound beam shown in the figure here.

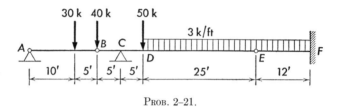

PROB. 2–21.

2–22. Deduce the shear diagram and the loaded beam from this moment diagram. The beam is simply supported.

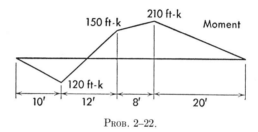

PROB. 2–22.

2–23, 2–24. Deduce the moment diagram and the loaded beam from the shear diagram. The beams are simply supported.

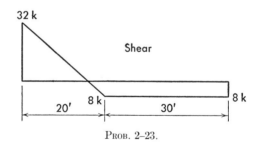

PROB. 2–23.

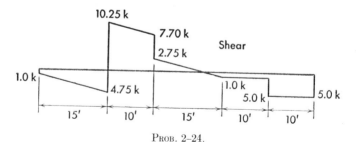

PROB. 2–24.

2–25. Draw the shear and moment diagrams for this cantilever beam. Express the equations of the curves in algebraic form.

2–26. A simple beam is loaded with a parabolically varying load. Sketch the shear and moment diagrams, and express their curves algebraically.

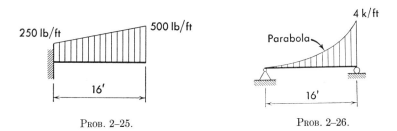

PROB. 2–25.   PROB. 2–26.

2–27. In the analysis of a large building the moments on the ends of one of the floor girders were found as shown in the figure. Complete the analysis by sketching the shear and moment diagrams and finding the points of contraflexure.

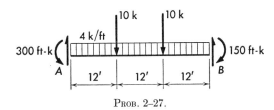

PROB. 2–27.

2–28. This girder is loaded through a system of floor beams which run laterally, and which in turn are spanned longitudinally by simple slabs. Draw the shear and moment diagrams for the girder (this represents a standard arrangement of components in bridge structures).

2–29. A semicircular arch of radius r is loaded with a load of w pounds per linear foot of horizontal projection. Express the shear and moment at each point in an algebraic expression. *Hint:* Use polar coordinates.

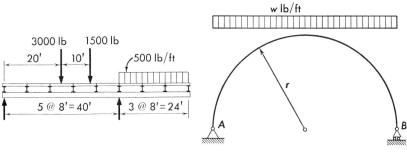

PROB. 2–28.   PROB. 2–29.

2-30. A compound beam is shown in the accompanying figure. Draw the shear and moment diagrams.

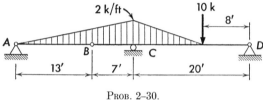

PROB. 2–30.

2-31. A footing which is 8 ft long and 18 in. wide is loaded with a wall column on the center 3 feet. Assuming uniform bearing pressure under the footing, draw the moment and shear diagrams.

2-32. A combined footing that supports two columns is shown. Because of the eccentric loading, the bearing pressure will have a trapezoidal distribution. Draw the moment and shear diagrams.

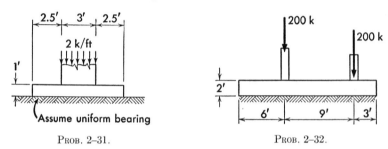

PROB. 2–31.   PROB. 2–32.

2-33. The two frames shown are identically loaded. Compare the effect on the frame of having the leg *AB* of the frame in the two positions shown, by sketching the shear and moment diagrams.

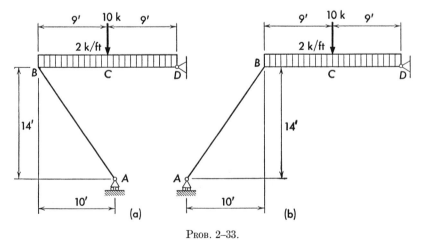

PROB. 2–33.

2–34, 2–35, 2–36, 2–37. Draw the shear, moment, and thrust diagrams for the frames shown.

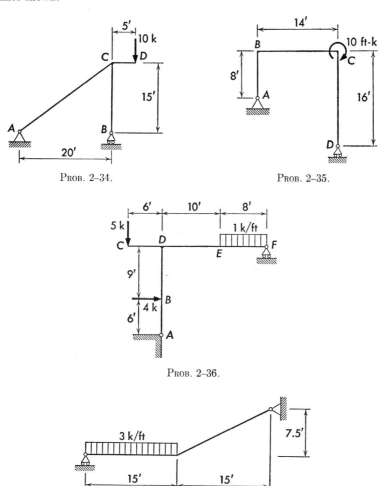

Prob. 2–34.   Prob. 2–35.

Prob. 2–36.

Prob. 2–37.

2–38. Draw shear, moment, and thrust diagrams for the frame in Problem 2–33, for a unit couple applied in place of the 10-k load.

2–39. Draw the shear moment and thrust diagrams for the frame in Problem 2–34, for a lateral load of 20 k applied at D in the direction of C.

CHAPTER 3

GRAPHIC STATICS

The science of graphic statics is based upon the fact that a force can be represented as a measured directional line, called *a vector*. The manipulation of vectors and the resolution or composition of forces by various graphical constructions is known as *graphic statics* and was first introduced about 1865 by Carl Culmann. Some graphical solutions are still referred to as Culmann solutions.

No new principles other than those already introduced are involved in the use of graphics, and the same results can be obtained either by algebraic or graphical methods. It is up to the engineer to select the more convenient of the two methods.

Actually in recent years the use of algebraic methods has replaced graphics in stress analysis. This is unfortunate, since many problems in structural engineering can be more easily solved by graphic statics. Usually the more complex the structure and the more complex or numerous its loads and spacing of members, the more advantageous is the use of graphics. Finding the stresses in curved chord or nonparallel chord trusses, evaluating the moments and reactions of nonuniformly loaded beams, and finding the centroids and moments of inertia of irregular sections are typical uses of graphic statics.

This chapter has a great value to the student, therefore, even if he has been using algebraic methods. The understanding of the algebraic method is enhanced by the "picture" of the solution. Many times a "rough" sketch of the graphical solution makes the algebraic solution easier.

In this chapter simple structures and beams are used to illustrate the use of graphic statics in order to make the methods clear. This is done in some cases where algebraic methods would be more suitable but in which graphics are used in order to illustrate the point.

3–1. Graphic Resolution and Composition. The three characteristics of a force (magnitude, direction, and point of application) are represented by the length of the vector, its direction, and its location. In Fig. 3–1a force P is represented by the vector AF. When the force AF is broken down into its components, this process is known as *resolution*. Several possible resolutions are shown in the figure by the double vectors ADF,

ACF, *ABF*, and *AEF*. An infinite number of other combinations of vectors may also be resolved from vector *AF*. No proof of this construction is needed, since it is self-evident that the projections of *AD* and *DF* on *AF* must add to *AF*. In fact, such constructions are often used to prove the algebraic methods.

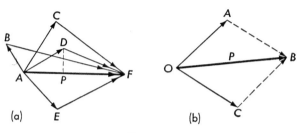

Fig. 3–1.

The reverse of resolution is known as *composition*. It is illustrated in Fig. 3–1b. The vectors *OA* and *OC* are added by forming a parallelogram of forces, with opposite sides of the parallelogram formed by the forces themselves. The vectors *OAB* or *OCB* are two possible resolutions of the force *P*. It can also be seen that joining the two forces *OA* and *OC* "head to tail" to form *OAB* will result in *P* as the resultant. This is often referred to as a *triangle of forces*. The relationship between the sides of the triangle has already been represented by trigonometric expressions (Chapter 1).

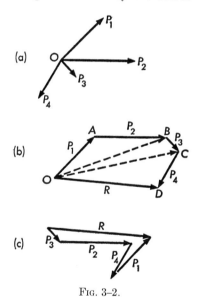

Fig. 3–2.

3–2. Force Polygon or Diagram. Suppose it is desired to find the resultant of the several concurrent forces shown in Fig. 3–2a. The idea of the force triangle can be applied repeatedly, as is illustrated in Fig. 3–1b. In Fig. 3–2b, first, the forces P_1 and P_2 are combined to form *OB* as a resultant; next, *OB* forms a triangle with P_3, and this resultant, *OC*, forms a triangle with P_4 to obtain the final resultant of all the forces *R* or *OD*. This triangle specifies both the magnitude and direction of the resultant.

From examination of the diagram it is evident that the same result could be obtained by merely joining the forces P_1, P_2, P_3, and P_4, "head to tail," and drawing the closing line R. Furthermore it makes no difference in what order the vectors are joined; the resultant will always be the same, as is illustrated in Fig. 3–2c by another arrangement of the forces. The resulting shape formed by the forces and their resultant is called the *force polygon*, or *force diagram*. Any number of forces can be joined in this fashion if drawn to scale to obtain the magnitude of the resultant. In this case the resultant must pass through the common point O of all forces. The magnitude of the resultant of nonconcurrent (all forces do not pass through a common point) systems may be found in a similar manner, but the location of the resultant must be located by a method to be presented in Article 3–3.

3–3. Composition of Nonconcurrent Forces; Equilibrium or String Polygon. Consider the three forces N, P, and Q applied to the body in Fig. 3–3a. Since the forces are nonconcurrent, the line of action of the resultant is not defined by the force diagram shown in Fig. 3–3b. Only its direction and magnitude can be found in this manner.

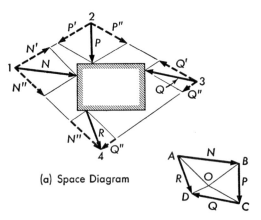

(a) Space Diagram

(b) Force Diagram (Polygon)

Fig. 3–3.

One may find the line of action, magnitude, and direction of the resultant by successive application of the parallelogram construction for the resolution or composition of the forces (Fig. 3–3a). First, N is resolved into N' and N'' along two arbitrary directions. Next, P is moved along its line of action, due to its property of transmissibility, to point 2 and is there resolved into two components, P' and P''. The component P' is selected to be equal and opposite to N', so that they cancel each other. The direction of P'' is controlled by the selection of the direction of P'. The force Q is now resolved into Q' and Q'' at point 3. The force Q' is selected to be equal and opposite to P'', and the direction of Q'' is controlled by the selection of Q'. The only forces not countered by equal and opposite forces are N'' and Q'', which are now moved along their line of action to 4 and combined by the parallelogram construction to find the resultant R. If R is not in a convenient position, it can be moved to a new position on its line of action.

Although the method described is theoretically correct, it may become unwieldy for use on systems of many forces. Furthermore the forces may not be positioned properly for convenient resolution or accurate intersection of the lines of action. Consequently, an ingenious construction has been devised to accomplish the same process more rapidly.

Each of the forces in the .force diagram can be resolved into components by drawing rays from the joints of the forces to a point O, known as the *pole*. The rays AO and OB represent N' and N'' if O is chosen in the proper location. The force P is resolved into BO and OC. Likewise, Q is resolved into CO and OD. The fact that OB and BO (N'' and P') are equal and opposite is expressed automatically in the force diagram, Fig. 3–3b. Each of the rays AO, BO, CO, and DO are parallel to the lines 1–4, 1–2, 2–3, and 3–4 in Fig. 3–3a. Further study indicates that if the pole O had been selected first, the polygon 1–2–3–4 could have been constructed without the resolution of forces previously described. The polygon 1–2–3–4 is known variously as the *funicular polygon, string polygon, or equilibrium polygon.* The last term will be used throughout this text.

The equilibrium polygon can be found by first arbitrarily locating the pole O and drawing in the rays. Next, at some arbitrary point 1 on the line of action of N, the strings 1–2 and 1–4 are projected parallel to the corresponding rays AO and OB on the force diagram (Fig. 3–3b). The string 1–2 is projected until it intersects the line of action of P at point 2, where 2–3 is projected parallel to ray OC to intersect the line of action of Q at 3. From this point, string 3–4 is projected parallel to ray OD to intersect the string 1–2. This intersection lies on the line of action of the resultant. A resultant vector can be drawn through this point parallel to the vector AD, representing the resultant in the force diagram, to complete the solution. The diagram containing the equilibrium polygon and location of forces, shown in Fig. 3–3a, is known as the *space diagram.*

3–4. Equilibrium Polygon Using Bow's Notation. Another example of the composition of forces is shown in Fig. 3–4. The use of a special notation, known as Bow's notation, is used to facilitate the construction and to avoid confusion. The forces are denoted by lettering the joints of the force diagram; thus, the letters AB denote the force P_1. In the space diagram the line of action of the force is denoted by the letters A and B placed in the area between the forces. Thus the force P_1 is "between" A and B in both the space diagram and the force diagram. The notations P_1, P_2, and P_3 are therefore not needed to denote the forces. The letters *oa, ob,* ⋯ are used to relate the lines in the equilibrium polygon of the space diagram to the parallel rays of the associated force diagram denoted by *OA, OB,* etc.

Each of the steps described hereinafter refer to the example illustrated in Fig. 3–4. Each step, however, is general and could be applied to any problem. The student should compare the resulting solutions with the more fundamental concepts described in the preceding article. Two possible solutions are shown for two arbitrary selections of the pole (solid or dashed construction).

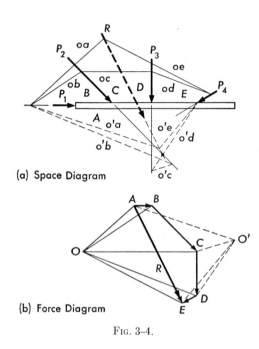

(a) Space Diagram

(b) Force Diagram

Fig. 3–4.

STEP 1. Draw the space diagram to scale, locating the lines of action of the forces accurately. The forces need not be drawn to scale in this diagram.

STEP. 2. Draw the force diagram to scale by drawing the force vectors "head to tail" and parallel to the lines of action in the space diagram. The closing line of the force diagram is the resultant and can be scaled directly from the diagram. The direction of *R* can also be taken from the diagram, but its location in the space diagram is not defined by the force diagram.

STEP 3. Choose a pole *O* or *O′* at some convenient location. The choice of the pole is dependent only upon keeping the construction within the bounds of the worksheet and upon obtaining angles which are not too acute for accurate determination of the intersection point.

STEP 4. From pole O, draw the rays from the joints of the force diagram to the pole $(OA, OB, OC, \cdots)$.

STEP 5. At an arbitrary point on the line of action of the extreme left force in the space diagram, draw a string of the equilibrium polygon parallel to ray OB in the force diagram. This line will be denoted by ob. At the point where it intersects the line of action of the force BC, another ray is drawn parallel to ray OC, toward force CD, and is labeled oc. At the next intersection the same process is repeated until the last ray OE is encountered. By drawing the lines oa and oe parallel to rays OA and OE, an intersection is obtained which lies on the line of action of the resultant R.

STEP 6. Draw the force R through the point obtained and parallel to the resultant shown in the force diagram.

Another point of intersection is obtained on the line of action of R when the pole O' is chosen. Obviously there are an infinite number of choices for the pole, the resulting equilibrium polygons and intersection points. In Art. 3–5 this construction is further extended to obtain unknown reactions.

3–5. Reactions of a Simple Beam. The beam shown in Fig. 3–5 has three known loads and is supported by two vertical reactions R_1 and R_2. The force diagram $ABCD$ is laid off in the ordinary fashion, and the pole O is arbitrarily selected. Since the system is in equilibrium, the force diagram must close, and this is accomplished by the reactions R_1 and R_2

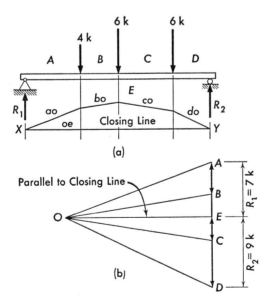

FIG. 3–5. Graphical determination of beam reactions.

directed upward, forming the closed polygon $ABCDA$. Thus the distance DA represents the sum of the two reactions. It remains only to establish the point E in the diagram to determine the magnitude of each.

The construction proceeds in the ordinary sequence. The lines of the equilibrium polygon are drawn parallel to the rays in the force diagram, commencing from an arbitrary point X on the line of action of R_1. When the point Y is obtained on the line of action of R_2, the connecting line oe is drawn to close the equilibrium polygon. The corresponding ray in the force diagram is drawn parallel to the closing line of the equilibrium polygon. The resultants can be scaled directly from the force diagram as indicated.

Confusion may be avoided by using Bow's notation to identify each reaction. Since R_2 lies between D and E on the space diagram, the vector DE defines the reaction in the force diagram. Likewise, R_1 lies between E and A on the space diagram and is defined by the vector EA. The direction of the forces can be obtained by reading the letter designations in rotation (A, B, C, D, E). Thus the reactions DE and EA have the upward direction in order to close the force diagram.

3–6. Reactions: One Reaction with Defined Direction. Fig. 3–6 illustrates an example in which the direction of one of the reactions is fixed. The upper chord of the truss has the reaction R_1 acting in the same direction as the chord, since the chord member is a two-force member and can

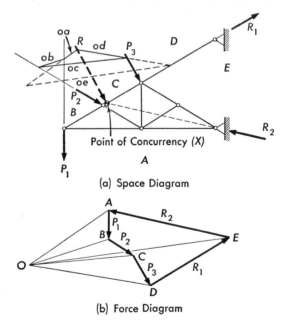

(a) Space Diagram

(b) Force Diagram

FIG. 3–6. Graphical determination of reactions with one direction defined.

transmit only tension or compression. The direction of the reaction at the lower bracket is not defined.

The first step is to find the resultant of the three forces, P_1, P_2, and P_3, acting on the truss. This is done by the method described in Art. 3-4. The equilibrium polygon associated with the determination of this resultant is shown in solid lines (oa, ob, oc, od). The magnitude and line of action of R are thus determined. Since it is an axiom of statics that any three forces in a plane, in equilibrium, are concurrent, this fact can be used to proceed with the problem.

The intersection of the lines of action of R and R_1 occurs at X on the upper chord of the truss and defines the point of concurrency. The line of action of the third force must also intersect at X, as shown by the dashed line at R_2. The directions of the reactions are now known, and they can be drawn in the force diagram parallel to the lines of action to find E. The reactions can be directly scaled from the diagram without further work. However, as a check on the accuracy of the construction, the final ray oe can be drawn, and the equilibrium polygon can be completed, as shown by the dotted line, to make sure it closes.

3-7. Graphic Moments. Fig. 3-7 shows four forces, P_1, P_2, $\cdots$, having arbitrary directions. It is desired to find the moment of the forces about an arbitrarily selected point v. An equilibrium polygon is constructed in the ordinary way to find the location and magnitude of the resultant R of the four forces. The line vu is then drawn parallel to the line of action of the resultant. It is now seen that the triangle uvw in the space diagram is similar to the triangle OAE in the force diagram, since

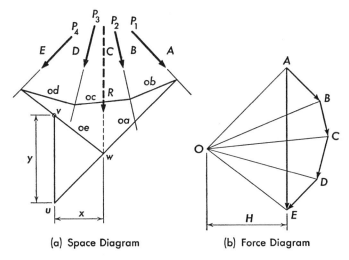

(a) Space Diagram   (b) Force Diagram

FIG. 3-7. Determination of moment by graphics.

each of the sides is parallel to one of the sides in the other triangle, due to the manner of construction. Thus an equation of similarity may be written

$$\frac{H}{AE} = \frac{x}{y}$$

or

$$AE \cdot x = Hy$$

$$M = Hy \tag{3-1}$$

That is, the moment of a group of coplanar forces about any point in the plane may be found by multiplying the pole distance H, taken perpendicular from the resultant R to the pole O by the intercept distance y, as measured vertically between the strings of the equilibrium polygon which intersect on the line of action of R. The units of moment (ft-lb, in.-lb, etc.,) are maintained, since H represents a force (scaled from the force diagram) and y represents a length or lever arm (scaled from the space diagram).

The method presented is general and may be used to find the moment of any group of coplanar forces about any point in the plane.

3-8. Moment and Shear Diagrams by Graphics. The property of the equilibrium polygon described in Art. 3-7 is often used to construct, graphically, the moment diagram of a beam under vertical loads only. Fig. 3-8 shows a beam loaded with the forces N, P, and Q. An equilibrium polygon has been drawn for an arbitrarily selected pole O. Consider the moment at the point M in the beam. The moment may be described algebraically as

$$M = R_1 x - Nx_1 - Px_2 \tag{3-2}$$

The moments of each of the forces can also be described by the various intercept distances and the pole distance in the equilibrium polygon construction; thus:

$$M = (H \cdot rv) - (H \cdot vu) - (H \cdot us)$$

$$M = H(rv - vu - us) \tag{3-3}$$

$$M = Hy$$

Likewise, the moment may be calculated from the other end of the beam:

$$M = (H \cdot rt) - (H \cdot ts) = H(rt - ts)$$

$$M = Hy \tag{3-4}$$

It may be similarly shown that the moment at any location can be found by multiplying the ordinate of the equilibrium polygon by the pole distance. In fact, if the pole distance is selected as unity, the equilibrium polygon will be the moment diagram without modification. Although selection of $H = 1$ is not usually practical, the selection of H as some multiple of ten is usually advantageous for mental arithmetic when scaling the moments from the diagram directly.

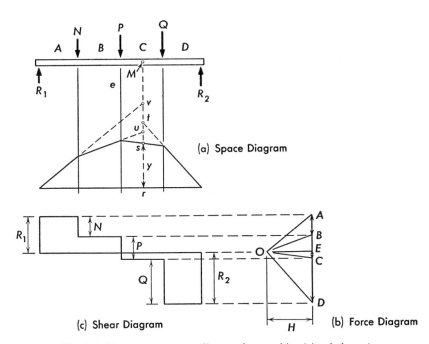

FIG. 3–8. Shear and moment diagram by graphics (simple beam).

The shear diagram can be found by projecting the forces from the force diagram to the lines of action of the space diagram. First, R_1 is laid off at the left side, and then N, P, and Q are graphically subtracted in that order at their point of loading. As a check the final ordinate will be $R_2 = R_1 - N - P - Q$. In some problems the order in which the forces occur in the force diagram will not be the same as that in which they occur in the space diagram. Consequently, the forces must be laid off in the shear diagram in the order in which they occur in the space diagram when moving from left to right.

Figs. 3–9 and 3–10 show additional examples of moment diagram construction for a cantilever beam and an overhanging beam. In the case of the overhanging beam (Fig. 3–10), the moment diagram has been replotted to put it in a more recognizable shape. This procedure is not necessary, however.

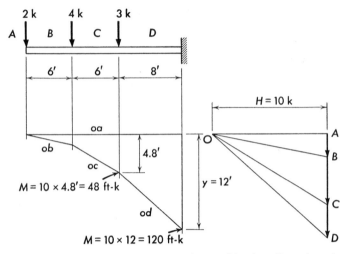

FIG. 3-9. Shear and moment diagram by graphics (cantilever beam).

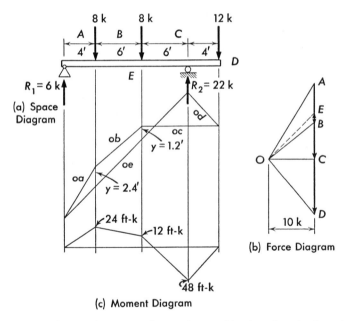

FIG. 3-10. Shear and moment diagram by graphics (overhanging beam).

Fig. 3-11 illustrates a compound beam for which a moment diagram is desired. Each of the parts of the compound beam can be solved in sequence by overlapping the force diagrams. Since the moment must be zero at the pins of the center beam, it may be solved prior to the end spans.

A layout of all the forces of the force diagram, A through H, is done first. Then, a pole O_2 is established for the center beam, the reactions are found, and the equilibrium polygon is completed. The reactions, however, are also part of the loading forces on the cantilever end spans. Therefore new poles O_1 and O_3 are selected, the reactions of the middle beam are incorporated into the other force diagrams, and the construction is completed. The moment diagram is replotted in more familiar form in Fig. 3–11b.

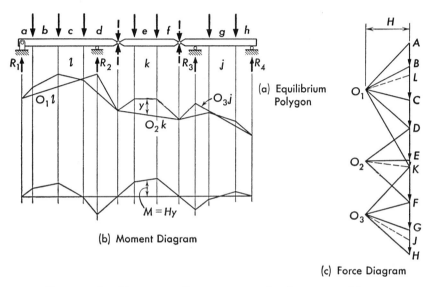

(a) Equilibrium Polygon

(b) Moment Diagram

(c) Force Diagram

FIG. 3–11. Graphic moment diagram construction for compound beam.

3–9. Distributed Loads; Effect of Continuity.

In order to treat distributed loads by graphics, the load must be divided into a series of concentrated loads. The action of the concentrated loads approximates the distributed load, and the greater the number of concentrated loads used, the closer will be the approximation.

Fig. 3–12 illustrates a beam with uniform load over the left 14 ft and two concentrated loads. A substitution of a 6-k concentrated load will be used every 2 ft to approximate the uniform load of 3 k per foot. The force diagram is constructed in the ordinary fashion. If the reactions are at the ends of the beam, the equilibrium polygon in Fig. 3–12a will be constructed. The moment diagram will be identical in shape to the equilibrium polygon, and although theoretically the diagram should vary smoothly throughout the distributed load zone, it is approximated by a series of straight lines. Study of the manner of construction indicates that the moment diagram is overestimated slightly. A more exact approximation could be obtained by inscribing a curve tangent at the mid-points of the equilibrium polygon in this zone.

The graphical construction also lends itself to (1) the study of the moment diagram when the reactions are moved, and (2) the effect of continuity. Three cases are illustrated. In Fig. 3–12b it is assumed that the reaction R_2 is to be moved in toward the center of the beam in order to reduce the center moments. The optimum condition will be reached when the moment over the support is equal to the moment between the supports; this occurs when the reaction is at R'_2. The only change in the

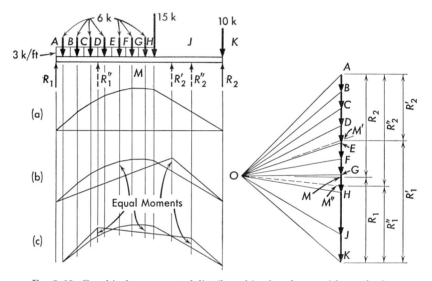

Fig. 3–12. Graphical treatment of distributed load on beam with continuity.

equilibrium polygon will be the inclination of the closing line. Likewise, further economies, as far as the strength of the beam cross-section is concerned, could be accomplished by moving both supports (R''_1 and R''_2) to new positions so that the moments would be equal at the location of the two supports and in the center portion of the beam, as illustrated in Fig. 3–12c. The effect of continuity is directly illustrated by this construction, and the location of the reactions can be scaled from the diagram.

3–10. The Linear Arch; Suspension Systems. Consider the problem of supporting with a structure a number of coplanar forces such as the three forces P_1, P_2, and P_3 shown in Fig. 3–13. Choose an arbitrary pole location O and draw the rays completing the force diagram. Note again that the rays of the force diagram, such as BO and OA, are the equilibrants of the force P_1; likewise, CO and OB, and DO and OC are the equilibrants of P_2 and P_3, respectively. In the force diagram the forces OB and BO as well as CO and OC cancel each other to leave the closed polygon $OABCD$. It is evident that DO and OA are the equilibrants of P_1, P_2, and P_3 combined, and as such, are one possible set of reactions supporting the forces.

An equilibrium polygon 1–2–3–4–5 is constructed, based on the selected force diagram. To reiterate the facts presented in Art. 3–3, the strings of the string polygon represent the lines of action of the various forces denoted by the rays in the force diagram. Consequently, if one were to insert structural members along these lines of action between the forces as shown, these members would be subjected to direct stress only. This is known as a *linear arch*. The actual stress in each member can be scaled

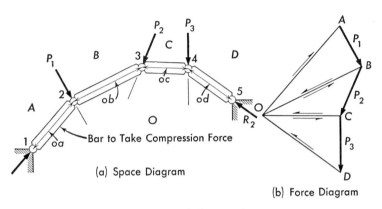

(a) Space Diagram

(b) Force Diagram

Fig. 3–13. A linear arch.

from the force diagram. If Bow's notation is used, the direction of the force can be obtained by following the vectors around the force diagram in the same order that the letters occur around the joint in the space diagram. Thus OA (oa) is compression toward the joint 4, or P_1 is compression toward the joint, as is BO (bo). This method of describing the direction of the forces of the members will be valuable in the more complex force diagrams for the graphical solutions of stresses of truss members described in a subsequent chapter.

Obviously, many equilibrium polygons could be drawn which would support the forces shown in Fig. 3–13. If the pole had been chosen on the opposite side of the diagram, the equilibrium polygon would have been convex downward. In this case a cable-type suspension would result, in which the segments of the equilibrium polygon would be subjected to tension only. Note that pure tension or compression in these members is dependent upon the forces remaining as originally described. Any movement or nonuniform change in magnitude of the forces will result in instability of the arch or introduction of moments.

FIG. 3–14. A gabled roof frame of a school gymnasium at San Mateo, California, utilizes the equilibrium polygon shape for roof bracing. Designer, Alexander G. Tarics of John Lyon Reid and Partners, San Francisco. (Photo by Phil Fein, San Francisco.)

Fig. 3–14 illustrates a unique use of a linear arch in a building roof framing. Ordinarily the rafter-type framing would have cross-ties, resulting in an A-frame truss, but the use of a linear arch results in an open-type ceiling without obstruction, thus eliminating these ties. The thrust, or reaction, of the arch is carried to the end frames of the building (see Prob. 3–30). The suspension bridge and stone or masonry arches are examples of structures which make use of the shape of the equilibrium polygon to maintain direct stress in the members. In stone arches the stones are held in place by mortar or dry joints. Consequently they can take no moment, and adherence to the equilibrium polygon shape (line of resistance) must be fairly exact.

In order to use the equilibrium polygon to advantage, it is necessary to make the polygon pass through certain preselected points at the supports and usually at mid-span too. The arch shown in Fig. 3–14, for example, must pass through the corners of the building and be tangent at the middle of the ridge line. Special graphical constructions are available to solve this problem.

3–11. Equilibrium Polygon Through Two Points. Fig. 3–15 shows four forces, P_1, P_2, P_3, and P_4, at random directions in a plane. It is desired to construct an equilibrium polygon for the system such that the strings will pass through two specified points, X and Y. First a force diagram is constructed, and the equilibrium polygon is drawn for an arbitrarily selected trial pole O_1. The polygon (dotted line) is started at the point X; it does not end on point Y as wanted but on another point Y'.

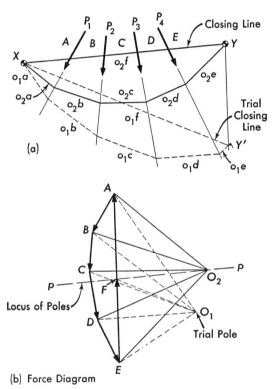

(a)

(b) Force Diagram

Fig. 3–15. Equilibrium polygon through two points.

The point Y' is found by drawing the line YY' parallel to the reactions EA in the force diagram and intersecting it with the string o_1e. The equilibrium polygon must be rotated up to point Y by some means.

In order to do this, assume that the forces are supported on some structure (solution is independent of the shape of the structure) with supports at X and Y'. Establish the reactions at each of the two points by drawing the line O_1F in the force diagram parallel to the trial closing line o_1f on the equilibrium polygon.

Suppose the structure was supported at the points X and Y instead of at X and Y'. Then the closing line XY (o_2f) must also define the point F

in the force diagram, and thus a line pp parallel to o_1f is drawn through point F. A pole O_2 is chosen on this new line, and a new set of rays is constructed (solid lines). The equilibrium polygon, started through X, then passes through point Y as shown. Upon further examination it can be seen that any pole on the line pp will have an equilibrium polygon associated with it which passes through the points X and Y. Therefore there are an infinite number of equilibrium polygons and pole locations which satisfy the requirements. The only criterion is that the pole must be on the locus of poles pp.

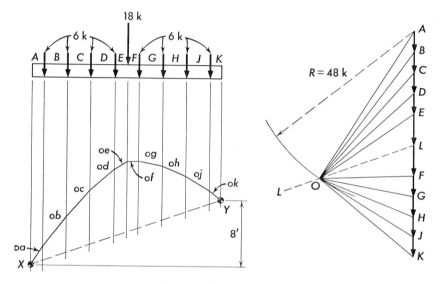

Fig. 3–16. Voussoir arch.

A practical application of the principle is shown in Fig. 3–16. A stone (voussoir) arch is to be constructed 24 ft wide to carry the uniformly distributed load of 2 k per foot and a concentrated center load of 18 k. The springings of the arch are to be at two points, X and Y, with a vertical difference in elevation of 8 ft. As an added restriction, the total stress in the arch at any point is not to exceed 48 k. A trial pole is not needed, since the reactions of the hypothetical structure used to locate the point of intersection L of the locus of the poles and the force diagram may be done mentally. The locus of the poles will be the line LL drawn parallel to the closing line XY of the equilibrium polygon. An arc is drawn with a radius of 48 k, with the point A as origin. The intersection of the arc and the locus of poles LL is the origin to satisfy the specified requirements. The rays OA, OB, $\cdots$, are established, and the equilibrium polygon is completed. The arch must be constructed so that the equilibrium polygon (line of resistance of the arch) falls in the kern (center third) of the cross-section as drawn.

3–12. Equilibrium Polygon Through Three Points. There are an infinite number of equilibrium polygons to fit two specified points, but only one will fit three specified points. Fig. 3–17 indicates a continuation of the problem described in Fig. 3–15 and in Art. 3–11. In addition to X and Y, the polygon must also pass through point Z. To continue, it is

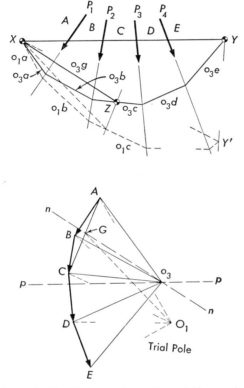

FIG. 3–17. Equilibrium polygon through three points.

necessary to locate the locus of poles for the forces to the left of point Z alone (P_1 and P_2), which will pass the equilibrium polygon through X and Z. The locus of poles nn is therefore thus located. The intersection of nn and pp locates the point which will satisfy both combinations of forces, and thus O_3 can be established. The rays are again drawn, and the equilibrium polygon is completed in the ordinary way.

In Fig. 3–18 an oil pipe line is to span a chasm 30 ft wide. A cable suspension is proposed, with suspenders to the pipe line at every 5 ft along its line. The pipe is on a slope that has a difference of 12 ft in elevation between the ends. In addition the anchorage points for the cable are to be at elevations of 24 ft and 30 ft above the pipe, as shown. Find the path of the cable and the maximum tensions in it.

The pipe filled with oil weighs 100 lb per foot, so that each suspender will have a 500-lb load. The two loci of poles pp and nn are established by first using the entire force group and drawing the line pp parallel to XY through G and then drawing nn parallel to ZY through E. Both G and E are the locations of reaction intersections on the force diagram for each of the force groupings indicated. Each intersection is found by the method

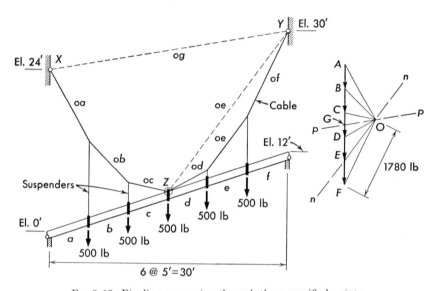

Fig. 3–18. Pipeline suspension through three specified points.

indicated in Fig. 3–15. The origin O is at the intersection of nn and pp. The strings of the equilibrium polygon are drawn, and the location of the cable is completed. The stress in each of the segments of the cable can be scaled from the force diagram, and the maximum stress of 1780 lb is found in segment of (OF), as indicated. The length of cable and suspenders as well as the elevation of the connections can also be scaled from the drawing.

The principles established in this article have further application in the solution of three-hinged arches (Chapter 11).

3–13. Centroids by Graphics. Many structures have irregular cross-sections and shapes which cannot be described mathematically, or if so, only in a complicated form. Dam cross-sections, arches with variable cross-sections, and various types of structural rolled shapes, such as bulb angles and aluminum extrusions, are examples of these cross-sections. It is sometimes convenient to find the centroid and moment of inertia of these shapes by graphical constructions.

Fig. 3–19 illustrates such a case (portion of an arch). The shape shown is divided into six segments of equal length. Each of the areas may be treated as a force (A_1, A_2, $\cdots$) located at the centroid of each of the nearly rectangular segments. The actual area of each segment is not needed, since the area of each will be proportional to its width.

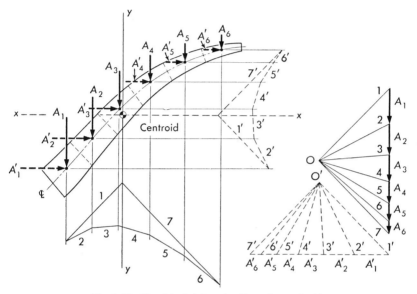

Fig. 3–19. Graphical determination of a centroid.

A force diagram is laid out with these widths of segments as forces, and an equilibrium polygon is constructed to locate the resultant of the forces (areas). If two such equilibrium polygons are constructed as shown in the figure, the intersection of the two resultant lines yy and xx will mark the centroid. The forces A and A' are equal in magnitude for each segment, since they both represent the same area in the two force diagrams.

The two force diagrams need not be at right angles to each other, but this is usually the most convenient and accurate method. Greater accuracy can be obtained by dividing the shape into smaller segments.

3–14. Moment of Inertia. Two methods are commonly used to find the moment of inertia of an area or group of forces about an axis: (1) Mohr's method and (2) Culmann's method. Only the latter will be described. The moment of inertia of an area about an axis may be written as

$$I_{MM} = \int x^2 \, dA \tag{3–5}$$

where x is the variable lever arm to the element dA, perpendicular to the axis about which the moment of inertia is desired. A numerical integration can be performed by dividing the area into several segments, as was

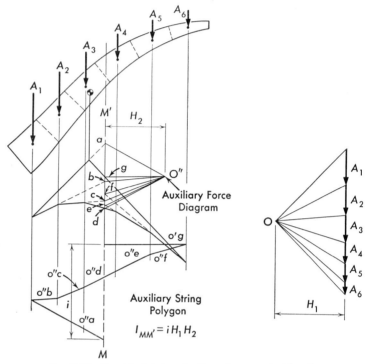

FIG. 3–20. Graphical determination of moment of inertia.

illustrated in finding the centroid of the area. Fig. 3–20 illustrates the construction for finding the moment of inertia about an arbitrary axis MM'. The moment of inertia, or second moment, can be approximated by

$$I_{MM} = A_1x_1^2 + A_2x_2^2 + A_3x_3^2 + \cdots \tag{3–6}$$

the sum of the second moments for each of the forces. The procedure is to find the first moments about the axis MM' by the method described in Arts. 3–7 and 3–13, and then by a similar construction superimposed upon the first, to find the moment of the first moments.

As indicated in Fig. 3–20, the strings of the equilibrium polygon are projected to intersect the axis MM'. Then the first moment of A_1 about MM equals $H_1 \cdot ab$; moment of A_2 equals $H_1 \cdot bc$; moment of A_3 equals $H_1 \cdot cd$, etc.

In order to find the second moments, the intercepts ab, bc, cd, de, $\cdots$, on MM' will be used to form a new auxiliary force diagram with the arbitrary pole distance H_2 and the origin at O''. An auxiliary equilibrium polygon is constructed, as shown in the lower portion of the figure. As before, the moment will be the product of the intercept i on the axis MM' and the pole distance H_2. Since the forces of the auxiliary force diagram need to be multiplied by H_1 to obtain the first moments, the moment of inertia will be the product of the final intercept i and both pole distances; thus:

$$I_{MM'} = iH_1H_2 \tag{3-7}$$

This value of the moment of inertia is not theoretically exact, since each of the areas $A_1, A_2, \cdots$ have a moment of inertia about a centroidal axis which is omitted from the construction; i.e., the second moment of A_1 about MM' is $I_g + A_1x_1^2$. This error will be eliminated by choosing the segments small enough to make I_g negligible. Other more exact methods can be found in the literature.*

PROBLEMS

All problems listed below are to be solved graphically. In addition, the problems at the end of Chapters 1 and 2 may also be used as exercises in graphic statics.

3–1. Find the resultant of the concurrent force system shown in the illustration.

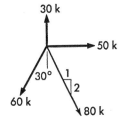

PROB. 3–1.

3–2, 3–3, 3–4, 3–5. Find the resultant of the force systems by the use of the equilibrium polygon.

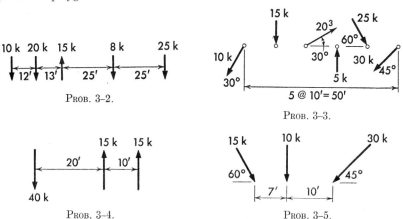

PROB. 3–2.

PROB. 3–3.

PROB. 3–4.   PROB. 3–5.

* For example, T. Merriam and T. H. Wiggin, *American Civil Engineers Handbook,* 5th ed. (New York: John Wiley & Sons, Inc., 1946), p. 106.

3-6, 3-7. Find the resultant of the force systems by the use of the equilibrium polygon. *Hint:* The resultant is a couple, since the equilibrium polygon does not close but results in two parallel lines. The magnitude of the couple is the perpendicular distance between the lines multiplied by the magnitude of one of the force rays represented by the two parallel strings.

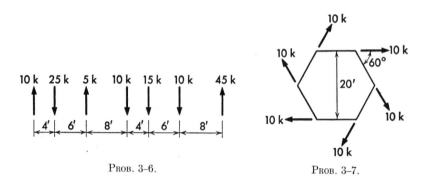

PROB. 3-6.   PROB. 3-7.

3-8. Find the magnitude of the two unknown forces B and C in this structural joint if one force (A) is known to be 40 k.

3-9. Find the stresses in the cable and post of this derrick.

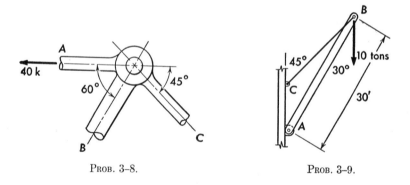

PROB. 3-8.   PROB. 3-9.

3-10. Find the reactions at A and B.

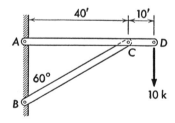

PROB. 3-10.

3–11, 3–12, 3–13, 3–14. Find the reactions of the beams by use of the equilibrium polygon.

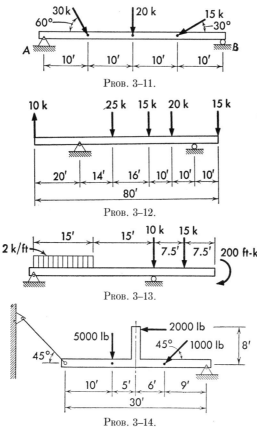

PROB. 3–11.

PROB. 3–12.

PROB. 3–13.

PROB. 3–14.

3–15, 3–16, 3–17. Find the reactions of the trusses by the use of the equilibrium polygon.

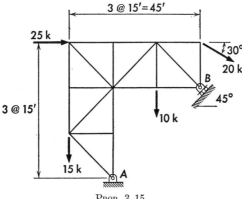

PROB. 3–15.

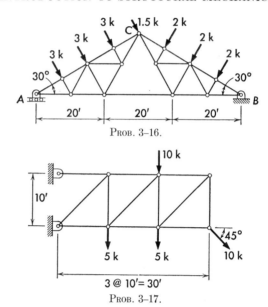

PROB. 3–16.

PROB. 3–17.

3–18. Find the moment at point M of the beam, using the methods of Art. 3–7.

3–19. Find the moment and shear diagrams for the beam of Problem 3–12.

3–20. Find the moment and shear diagram for the beam of Problem 3–13.

3–21. Find the reactions and draw the moment diagrams of the parts of the compound beam. The link can transmit no moment.

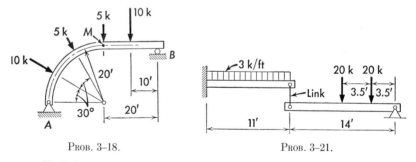

PROB. 3–18.   PROB. 3–21.

3–22. Find the moment and shear diagram of the compound beam.

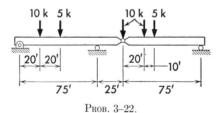

PROB. 3–22.

3–23. Find the moment diagram and reactions of the compound beam consisting of two cantilever-trussed end spans and a simply supported center K-truss span.

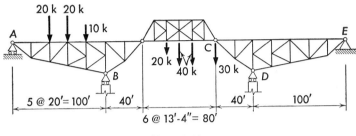

20 k 20 k

10 k

A

20 k
40 k

C

30 k

B

D

E

5 @ 20′= 100′   40′   6 @ 13′-4″= 80′   40′   100′

PROB. 3–23.

3–24. A wall of a cofferdam which resists a triangular loading due to hydrostatic and soil pressures is supported on two wale frames providing reactions R_1 and R_2. The frames may be located at any distance x and y from the ends of the frame. (a) Construct a moment diagram for x and y equal to zero, and find the maximum moment. (b) Find the value x such that the moment over the reaction R_1 will be identical in magnitude to the maximum moment between R_1 and R_2. (c) Find the value of x and y such that the moments will be equal at reactions R_1 and R_2 and at a point between the reactions.

3–25. Find the reactions and construct the moment diagram due to the parabolic loading on the cantilever span.

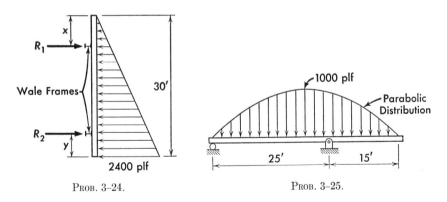

R_1

x

Wale Frames

30′

1000 plf

Parabolic
Distribution

R_2

y

2400 plf

25′   15′

PROB. 3–24.   PROB. 3–25.

3–26. A cantilever beam made of reinforced concrete varies in depth parabolically from 1½ ft at the end to 3 ft at the fixed end. The beam is 3 ft wide. If concrete weighs 150 pcf, construct the moment diagram for the beam.

3–27. A cable suspension is to support the three forces shown and is to be anchored at points A and B. The total force in the cable at any point is not to exceed 30 k. Draw the location of the cable, and find its total length and the forces in each segment.

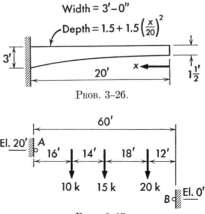

Width = 3'-0"

Depth = $1.5 + 1.5 \left(\frac{x}{20}\right)^2$

Prob. 3–26.

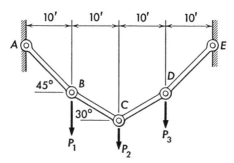

Prob. 3–27.

3–28. The eye-bar suspension is to support the three forces P_1, P_2, and P_3. If the location of the joints (B, C, and D) is to be unchanged, what must be the relationship between the forces?

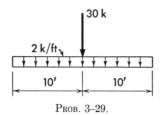

Prob. 3–28.

3–29. A stone arch is to support the loads shown in the diagram and is to pass through three specified points. The ends of the arch will be on the same level, but the center of the arch will be at an elevation 25 ft above the springing of the arch. Locate the line of resistance of the arch, and find the maximum force the arch must resist.

30 k

2 k/ft

10'   10'

Prob. 3–29.

3–30. Find the location of the centerline of the roof bracing in the panel as shown. The bracing is similar to that shown in Fig. 3–14. If the load on the roof is 30 psf, what will be the maximum stress in the bracing?

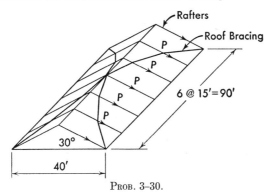

PROB. 3–30.

3–31. Find the location line of the lower chord of the truss shown, such that all other members of the truss except the verticals will be inactive. Find the maximum stress in the lower chord as a proportion of P.

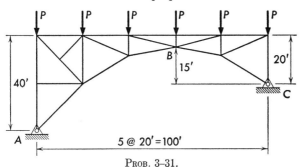

PROB. 3–31.

3–32. A special structural connection requires the use of twelve 1-in. diameter bolts arranged as shown. (a) Find the centroid of the bolt group. (b) Find the moment of inertia of the group about the y-y centroidal axis.

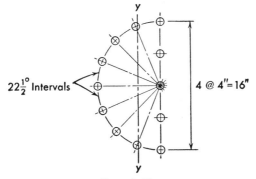

PROB. 3–32.

3–33. The drawing represents the cross-section through a concrete shell structure for a north-light industrial building. (a) Find the centroid of the section. (b) Find the moment of inertia about the x-x centroidal axis. (c) Find the moment of inertia about the y-y centroidal axis.

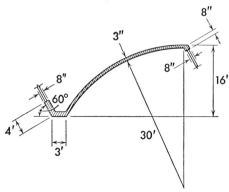

PROB. 3–33.

3–34. Find the moment of inertia of the force group of Problem 3–4 about the extreme right-hand force.

CHAPTER 4

THE STRESS DIAGRAM

It has been shown in Chapter 3 that for a truss under load, it is possible to draw for each joint a closed force polygon whose sides will represent the forces transmitted by the various members of the joint. These forces are usually referred to as *stresses*, but the term should not be confused with unit stresses. In 1864 J. Clerk-Maxwell, a British physicist, invented the stress diagram for trusses which unites into a single figure all the force polygons for the individual joints.

If the stress diagram is used for graphical measurements of the stresses, it is necessary that it be drawn accurately to scale. It will be shown in the discussion here, however, that once the shape of the stress diagram is outlined, then the various stresses can be readily computed from this figure without the necessity of having an accurate drawing.

4–1. General Procedure. Consider the truss shown in Fig. 4–1a to be subjected to the action of a single vertical load at mid-span and, because of symmetry, to equal reactions at the ends. In order to identify the external forces, the area bounded by the right reaction, the right half of the bottom chord, and the center load has been designated A; the area bounded by the load, the left half of the bottom chord and the left reaction, has been designated B. The rest of the area outside the truss, bounded by the two reactions and the top chord, has been labeled C. Similarly the inside areas bounded by members of the truss have been labeled $1, 2, 3, \cdots$.

If a section is passed around joint x, it will be seen that there are three forces intersecting at this point, namely, the reaction (known direction and magnitude) and the stresses in the two members (known directions and unknown magnitudes). A force polygon for this joint can now be constructed, as shown in Fig. 4–1b, and because the forces maintain equilibrium, they will form a closed polygon. The arrows indicate the directions of the forces.

Although the forces corresponding to the various members of a joint can be taken in any order, they are usually laid off in the sequence which follows a clockwise rotation around the joint. This convention has been followed throughout this volume. The vectors in the force polygon are designated by the letters and numbers corresponding to the areas in the truss diagram, between which the member lies. Thus for joint x the length bc in the force polygon is laid off to correspond to 50 k. It is in an upward direction because the reaction at x in the truss is the boundary line between areas B and C going around the joint in a clockwise direction. It can now be seen that the stress in the sloping end post at the left end of the truss will carry a stress represented by the length $c\text{--}1$ in the

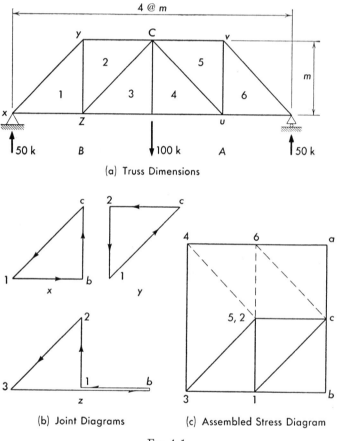

(a) Truss Dimensions

(b) Joint Diagrams   (c) Assembled Stress Diagram

Fig. 4–1.

force polygon. It is pushing against this joint (it is a compression stress) because, by going from area c to area 1 in the clockwise direction around the joint in the truss, the observer moves toward this joint in the force polygon. Likewise, it is seen that the stress in the bottom chord panel next to the left support is represented by the length $1\text{--}b$ in the force polygon. Furthermore this stress must be tension because a rotation around joint x in the clockwise direction crosses this member by moving from area *1* to area *B*, and the corresponding length, *1–b*, in the force polygon represents a movement away from this joint, i.e., it pulls on the joint.

After the stress in *c–1* (or *xy*) has been determined, a force polygon can be drawn for joint *y*. Here again, all directions of the forces are known and two magnitudes (*c–2* and *2–1*) are unknown. Because the stress in the sloping end post was found to be compression, the force polygon is started with a line *1–c* pointing toward the joint corresponding to a clockwise rotation around *y* in the truss. Point *2* in the force polygon is found by intersecting a line through *c* parallel to *C–2* (the top chord) and through *1* parallel to *2–1* (the vertical). The directions of these stresses are such that a closed force polygon is produced. Thus it is seen that *c–2* is toward joint *y* (a compression stress) while *2–1* is away from it (a tension stress).

Joint *z* can now be treated in a similar manner. Of the four forces intersecting at this point, one has been determined from joint *x* and one from joint *y*. These two known forces, *b–1* and *1–2* are laid off in the order in which they are encountered in moving around the joint in a clockwise rotation. Both are tension stresses and therefore have directions away from joint *z*. Because the directions of *2–3* and *3–B* are known, they are found by intersecting lines parallel to them through points *2* and *b* in the force polygon. Their directions must be such that an observer going around the perimeter of the force polygon will proceed uninterruptedly in the same direction.

Instead of drawing separate force polygons for the various joints, time and space can be saved by combining these into one figure, the stress diagram. As each polygon is completed, it is seen that it will contain one or more stresses which will be used for building up force polygons for subsequent joints.

In order to combine the joint diagrams in Fig. 4–1b into the single diagram in Fig. 4–1c, the force polygon *abca* for the outside force and the reactions should be drawn first. Next the polygon *b–c–1* for joint *x* should be added, followed by *1–c–2* for joint *y* and *b–1–2–3* for joint *z*. Then the polygon *b–3–4–a* for the center joint can be drawn, which will determine the stresses in the members *3–4* and *4–a*. It is now possible to proceed to joint *u* and joint *v* and complete the diagram for the entire truss. All stresses are finally found by measuring the various lengths in Fig. 4–1c, using the same scale as was used for the outside force and reactions. The stresses (in kilopounds) are indicated in Fig. 4–2, where the compression stresses are preceded by a minus sign.

The stress diagram is self-checking. Thus, when point *6* in the diagram has been located, it is seen that the line *c–6* in the stress diagram must be parallel to member *C–6* (the right end post) in the truss.

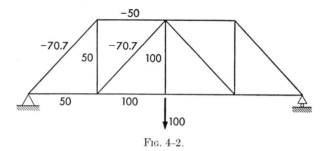

Fig. 4–2.

4–2. Computations of Stresses. If the stress diagram is drawn to scale, it is possible to mark off the stresses with considerable accuracy. It is also possible from the general outline of the diagram to compute the various stresses. This procedure is illustrated in Fig. 4–3 for the

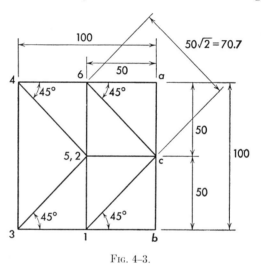

Fig. 4–3.

loaded truss shown in Fig. 4–1. With known forces and reactions and all angles known (found from the dimensions of the truss), it is readily seen that all the lengths can be computed by the well-known trigonometric relations.

If the stresses are computed in this manner, no great accuracy is necessary in the drawing of the stress diagram. It is essential, however, to incorporate in it the features of closure. This is illustrated in Fig. 4–3 by the fact that point *6* lies on the horizontal line connecting points *a* and *4*.

4–3. Examples of Stress Diagrams. Fig. 4–4 shows a symmetrical tower frame subjected to the action of a horizontal force of 25 k. The arrangement of the interior members (web members) is the so-called K-system.

The reactions are first found by taking moments about one of the supports; thus $R = 25 \times 50 \div 42 = 29.8$ k. At each of the supports there are then two unknowns, and the polygons b–c–d–6 and d–a–4 will correspond to the right and left support, respectively. The equilibrium polygon for the joint midway between the two supporting joints is found by drawing lines in Fig. 4–4b through points 4 and 6 parallel to the two lower diagonals. At each of the two end joints of the intermediate horizontal member, there are now only two unknown stresses. The points 1 and 3 in the stress diagram corresponding to the triangles 1 and 3 in the tower

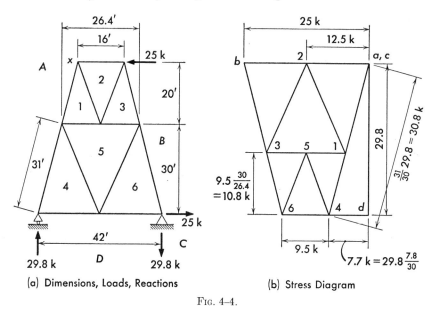

(a) Dimensions, Loads, Reactions   (b) Stress Diagram

Fig. 4–4.

frame are found by drawing a horizontal line through point 5 and intersecting it with lines a–4 and b–6. The only point lacking in Fig. 4–4b is that corresponding to the triangle 2 in Fig. 4–4a; this is located as the point of intersection of lines through point 1 parallel to the left upper diagonal and through point 3 parallel to the right upper diagonal. Because the member A–2 is horizontal, it follows that point 2 in Fig. 4–4b must lie on the line a–b.

The stresses in the various members can now be found by scaling off all lengths in Fig. 4–4b. Their signs (whether tension or compression) are determined by noting the directions of the vectors in the stress diagram. Thus for the member A–1 in the frame, it is seen that in going around the lower joint of this member in the clockwise direction, the sequence is from A to 1. The corresponding movement in the stress diagram is from a to 1, a direction against the lower joint, i.e., a compression stress.

If the upper joint of this member is selected for inspection, it is found that a clockwise rotation about the joint gives the sequence *1* to *A;* and in the stress diagram, from *1* to *a*, which represents a movement in a direction opposite to that on the lower joint, toward the upper joint, i.e., compression.

Proceeding around this upper joint *x* in the clockwise direction, the next member (the horizontal top member) is crossed by passing from *A* to *2*, and *a–2* in the stress diagram indicates a movement toward the joint (also a compression stress).

The clockwise rotation around the upper left joint is finally completed by moving from area *2* to area *1* in Fig. 4–4a. In Fig. 4–4b the corresponding vector is representing a movement from *2* to *1*, away from the joint. Hence this member is in tension.

If it is desired to compute the stresses in the various members from the stress diagram, the lengths of the vectors in Fig. 4–4b can be readily evaluated. Thus the stress in the member *A–4* can be found by dividing the length of *d–a* in the stress diagram by the cosine of the angle made by the member with a vertical line. Likewise, the stress in *4–D* can be found by multiplying the quantity (29.8) by the tangent of this angle.

The vector *4–6*, which represents the difference between stresses in the two members making up the lower horizontal member, can be found by subtracting twice the length of *d–4* from the length of *ab*.

The vertical distance of point *5* above line *4–6* in Fig. 4–4b is determined from the two similar triangles: *4–5–6* in the stress diagram, and the one made up of the intermediate horizontal member and two lower interior diagonals in the tower. Expressing proportionality between corresponding heights and bases indicates that this vertical distance equals 10.8 k. Subsequently the vertical distance of point *2* above line *1–3* in the stress diagram is found to equal 19 k.

Other vectors in the stress diagram are now found as follows:

$$5 - 1 = 3 - 5 = \frac{1}{2}\left[9.5 + \frac{10.8}{29.8}(25 - 9.5)\right] = 7.6 \text{ k}$$

$$4 - 5 = 5 - 6 = \frac{9.5}{26.4}\sqrt{30^2 + 13.2^2} = 11.8 \text{ k} \tag{4–1}$$

$$1 - 2 = 2 - 3 = \frac{15.1}{16}\sqrt{20^2 + 8^2} = 20.4 \text{ k}$$

As a second typical example of the construction of a stress diagram, consider the cantilever truss in Fig. 4–5a subjected to the action of four concentrated loads as shown. It is desired to find all stresses in terms of *P*.

In the case of a cantilever truss, it is not necessary to determine the reactions before commencing the construction of the stress diagram. The diagram can usually be drawn immediately and the reactions can be found as part of it. The stress diagram is begun at the right end of the truss. Going around the first joint in the clockwise direction, the triangle *ba1* is constructed, having a side $ba = \frac{1}{2}P$ and all angles known. It is seen that points *1* and *2* must coincide and that the polygon *b–c–3–2–1* can be next constructed. The stress diagram (Fig. 4–5b) is completed by alternating between bottom chord joints and top chord joints.

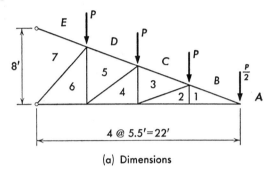

(a) Dimensions

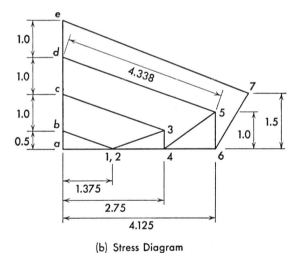

(b) Stress Diagram

FIG. 4–5.

The stresses in the various members can now be computed from the stress diagram, as shown by the following equations. The bottom chord stress *a–1* will equal

$$S_{a-1} = \frac{P}{2} \times \frac{22}{8} = 1.375P \tag{4–2}$$

Because the angle between the horizontal and each of three lines *b–1*, *2–3*, and *c–3* is the same, the stress in the vertical *3–4* must equal $\frac{1}{2}P$, and the bottom chord stress *a–4* must be twice that of stress *a–2*, or **2.75P**.

The stress in the top chord represented by the vector c–3 can be found as the hypotenuse in a right triangle; thus:

$$S_{c\text{-}3} = P\sqrt{1.00^2 + 2.75^2} = 2.93P \tag{4–3}$$

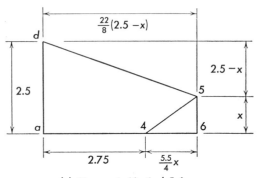

(a) Stresses in Vertical 5-6

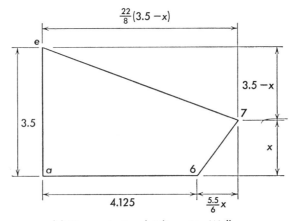

(b) Stresses in Panel Adjacent to Wall

Fig. 4–6.

Fig. 4–6a shows a portion of the stress diagram in Fig. 4–5b. From this portion the lengths of the various vectors can be computed. If x denotes the stress in the vertical *5–6*, it is seen that

$$\frac{5.5}{4}x + 2.75 = \frac{22}{8}(2.5 - x); \qquad x = 1.00P \tag{4–4}$$

Because the length of the diagonal *4–5* in the truss is 6.8 ft, the length of the vector in Fig. 4–6a is equal to

$$S_{4\text{-}5} = \frac{6.8}{4}P = 1.7P \tag{4–5}$$

The length of the vector d–5 can be found by dividing its horizontal projection, $4.125P$, by the cosine of the angle between the top and bottom chords of the truss; thus:

$$4.125P\frac{23.4}{22} = 4.388P \tag{4-6}$$

Similar computations can be made for the portion of the stress diagram representing the panel of the truss adjacent to the wall. If in Fig. 4–6b the vertical projection of vector 6–7 is designated x, it is seen that

$$\frac{5.5}{6}x + 4.125 = \frac{22}{8}(3.5 - x); \qquad x = 1.5P \tag{4-7}$$

and that the length of the vector e–7 will equal

$$S_{e-7} = \left(4.125 + 1.5\frac{5.5}{6}\right)\frac{23.4}{22}P = 5.85P \tag{4-8}$$

4–4. Subdivided Trusses. Truss systems which consist of large triangles on which smaller triangles have been superposed are called *subdivided* trusses or trusses with subdivided panels. The stress diagrams for subdivided trusses usually present special problems, as will be shown in the following discussion.

The truss shown in Fig. 4–7a consists of equilateral triangles (all angles everywhere in the truss are 60°). It is statically determinate, having 11 joints and 19 members, which will satisfy the relation. (See Art. 5–1 for complete explanation of equation.)

$$m = 2j - 3 = 2 \times 11 - 3 = 19$$

If subjected to two loads of 60 k and 120 k, the truss will develop the reactions shown, which can be arrived at graphically by drawing a force polygon and an equilibrium polygon, or the reactions can be developed analytically by taking moments about one end of the truss. Next the areas bounded by forces, reactions, and truss members are labeled, and the polygon a–b–c–d–a corresponding to outside forces and reactions is drawn.

The triangle b–1–a in the stress diagram corresponding to the joint over the left support can be readily constructed. A continuation of the stress diagram necessitates construction of stress polygons for either joint x or joint y. Each of these joints, however, has three unknown stresses.

In order to complete the diagram, it is assumed that the stress in member B–3 is known, and the corresponding point $3'$ is marked in Fig. 4–7b. The tentative polygon for joint x is then b–$3'$–$2'$–1–b. Joint z is treated next by starting at point $2'$ and going around the joint in the clockwise direction; the polygon is $2'$–$3'$–$5'$–$4'$. Because the member D–4 is horizontal, line d–4 in the stress diagram must also be horizontal. The correct position of point $4'$ is therefore found by moving it up to point 4, as indicated in Fig. 4–7b. The final diagram in Fig. 4–7c shows how points 4 and 6 can be found directly without any preliminary assumptions. From these points the remainder of the stress diagram can be readily constructed.

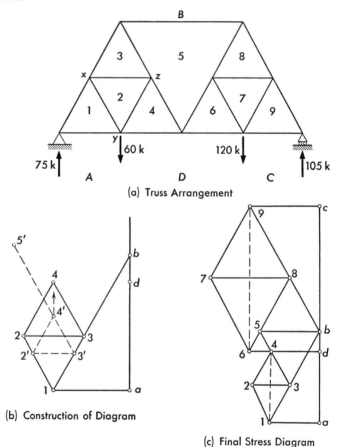

(a) Truss Arrangement

(b) Construction of Diagram

(c) Final Stress Diagram

Fig. 4–7.

The lengths of the vectors in the stress diagram can be now computed. As an example it can be shown that the stresses in the two web members which connect to the mid-span bottom chord joint will have the same numerical value; this will equal

$$(120 - 105) \div \cos 30° = 17.3 \text{ k} \qquad (4\text{–}9)$$

The diagram also shows that this is compression for member 5–6 and tension for member 4–5.

4–5. The Baltimore Truss. A parallel-chord Pratt truss with subdivided panels is called a *Baltimore truss*. The procedure for construction of the stress diagram is similar to the one discussed in Art. 4–4.

Fig. 4–8a shows a Baltimore truss subjected to equal loads at all panel points. It is desired to draw a stress diagram. Due to symmetry of geometrical arrangement and loading, the two reactions will be equal. The areas enclosed by forces and truss members are labeled in the usual manner, and a force polygon is drawn for the outside forces and reactions.

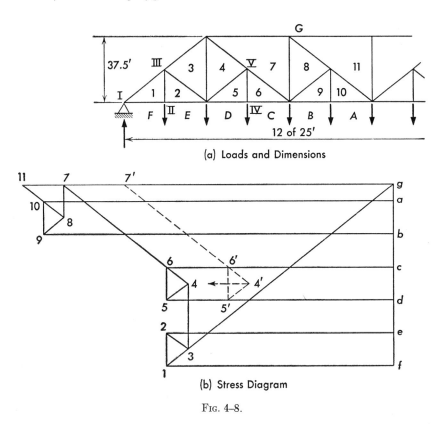

(a) Loads and Dimensions

(b) Stress Diagram

Fɪɢ. 4–8.

The stress diagram is commenced at the left-end joint *I*. With only two unknowns, the triangle corresponding to this joint can be readily drawn. Next the portions representing joint *II* and joint *III* are completed, each having two unknowns in this succession. Proceeding to either the next top-chord joint or the next bottom-chord joint, it is seen that in both cases three unknowns exist; another approach must be found.

Assuming that the stress in the third and fourth panel of the bottom chord is known, the diagram can be continued at joint *IV* and joint *V*.

Going around these joints in the clockwise direction, the points *4′*, *5′*, *6′*, and *7′* are located, but it is observed immediately that the line connecting points *3* and *4* must be vertical; the correct position of point *4′* is therefore vertically above point *3*. Points *4′*, *5′*, *6′*, and *7′* are thus moved sideways so that this requirement can be satisfied. The complete diagram for one-half of the truss is shown in Fig. 4–8b.

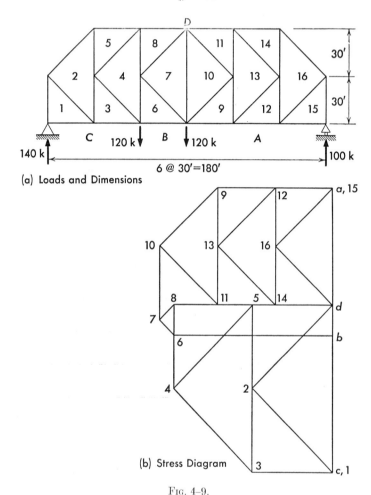

(a) Loads and Dimensions

(b) Stress Diagram

Fig. 4–9.

4–6. The K-Truss. The stress diagram for the K-truss, such as that shown in Fig. 4–9a, can be drawn by starting first at one end and completing it up to the mid-span vertical, and then constructing the remainder from the other end. The two parts are finally connected by the line *7–10*, which (as a check) must be parallel to the center vertical.

The magnitudes of the stresses are readily computed from Fig. 4–9b. Thus it is seen that the center vertical 7–10 has a tension stress amounting to

$$S_{7-10} = 120 - \tfrac{1}{2}(100) - \tfrac{1}{2}(120 - 100) = 60 \text{ k} \qquad (4\text{--}10)$$

4–7. Substitute Members. It has already been pointed out that difficulties are often encountered in the drawing of a stress diagram because no joint that has only two unknown stresses can be found in the course of construction. It has also been shown (Figs. 4–7 and 4–8) how these difficulties can be overcome by assuming an arbitrary value for one of these unknowns, then continuing the construction, and subsequently adjusting the diagram to conform to the geometrical realities of the truss. Another approach to completion of these diagrams is by the use of substitute members. This method will be illustrated for a Fink truss.

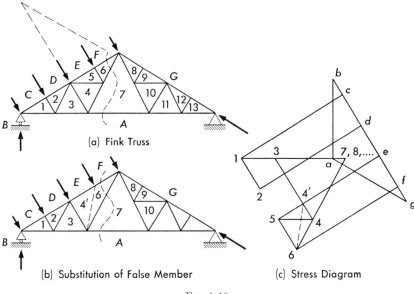

(a) Fink Truss

(b) Substitution of False Member

(c) Stress Diagram

Fig. 4–10.

Fig. 4–10a shows a roof truss subjected to a number of forces on one side (the resultants of wind pressure) and the two reactions resulting from these forces. The stress diagram is readily constructed for the first three joints (left-end joint, top-chord joint, and bottom-chord joint), but the next joint has three unknown stresses and is therefore more difficult to compute. The construction can now be continued by assuming the two members 4–5 and 5–6 in Fig. 4–10a to be replaced by the dotted member in Fig. 4–10b. It is apparent that this substitution will not affect the stresses in the three members *F–6, 6–7,* and *7–A,* for if they are cut by a section, the stresses in these three members in both trusses are determined by identical moment equations. The stress diagram is therefore completed for Fig. 4–10b, so that point *4′* corresponds to the area *4′.* The points *6* and *7* thus found can be used for the completion of the stress diagram for the original Fink truss in Fig. 4–10a.

4–8. Irregular Trusses. Statically determinate trusses consisting of triangles and quadrangles are often called *irregular.* Fig. 4–11a shows an irregular truss having 12 joints and 21 members. Consequently because

$$m = 2j - 3 = 24 - 3 = 21 \qquad (4\text{–}11)$$

it is statically determinate. It is desired to construct a stress diagram for this truss. This can be done, since it is possible to complete the stress diagram for the two bottom-chord joints adjacent to the end. Subsequent joints will have three unknowns. If the long diagonal in Fig. 4–11a is

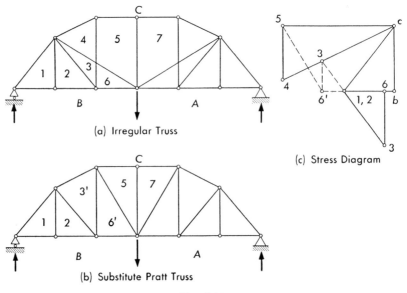

(a) Irregular Truss

(c) Stress Diagram

(b) Substitute Pratt Truss

Fig. 4–11.

shifted to the third panel, as shown in Fig. 4–11b, it is found that the irregular truss and the substitute Pratt truss will have a number of identical stresses. The center portion of the top chord will not change stress due to this shift. The stress in *C–5* can therefore be found by continuing the stress diagram with the diagonal shifted until point *5* in Fig. 4–11c has been located. This part of the diagram has been shown with dotted lines. Next, point *4* is found, and subsequently, points *3* and *6.*

A check of the accuracy of the construction is provided by the requirement that the length of vector *4–5* must equal the length of vector *3–6*.

PROBLEMS

4–1. Find the stresses in the Baltimore truss shown in the sketch by drawing a stress diagram and scaling off the lengths of the vectors.

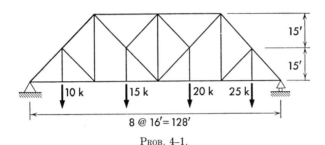

PROB. 4–1.

4–2. The truss in the accompanying illustration has an overhang with a force of 100 k acting at its end. Find the two reactions graphically and analytically, and draw a complete stress diagram for the truss.

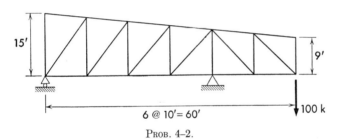

PROB. 4–2.

4–3. Draw the stress diagram for the cantilever truss shown in the sketch, and compute the stresses in the various members from the diagram.

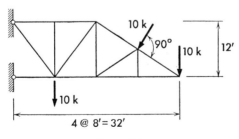

PROB. 4–3.

4–4. Draw the stress diagram for the Z-truss shown in the illustration, and compute from the stresses in all members the diagram. *Hint:* The stresses in the three sloping members in any panel are numerically equal and their vertical components must add up to reaction at right.

4–5. Draw the stress diagram for a tower (see sketch) subjected to a force of 18 k. Find the stresses by scaling on the diagram.

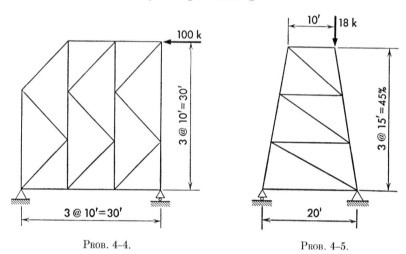

PROB. 4–4.   PROB. 4–5.

4–6. The truss in the illustration is made up of two equilateral triangles *ABC* and *abc*, connected by members *Aa*, *Bb*, and *Cc*. Show that this truss is statically determinate, and by drawing a stress diagram, find the stresses in all members due to a unit load at *b*.

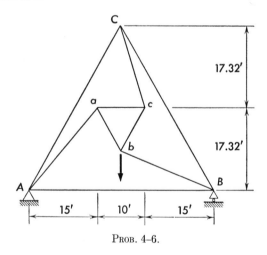

PROB. 4–6.

CHAPTER 5

TRUSSES: ALGEBRAIC METHODS

The student should be well aware of the characteristics of a truss after progressing this far in his professional education. He may nevertheless have a stereotyped conception of them and possibly may think of them as a series of triangles of bars or structural members connected together. Actually, trusses can be very complicated structures, and the usual triangular relationship is not necessarily an identifying characteristic. Over the years many useful forms of trusses have fallen into disuse because of the difficulty of solving stresses in certain types. In recent years the development of digital computers has made the solution of numerous simultaneous equations less laborious, and many trusses such as the "complex" trusses described subsequently may come back into use because of the simplification of computation.

A Brief History of Truss Analysis. The development process of the science of truss structures is interesting and therefore a short review is given here. The invention of the truss is usually credited to Andrea Palladio (1518–1580), a Venetian architect of some fame, since several types of architectural details such as the Palladian window have been named after him. Being somewhat modest, he credited German builders with the idea, and hence the true originator will probably remain unknown. His bridges were usually made of wood and were so strong "because all their parts mutually support each other." Before Palladio's use of the truss, Leonardo da Vinci apparently had also developed the idea, since a drawing of a truss appeared in his sketch book (as did many other engineering principles which are considered contemporary). Throughout the history of structural engineering, which was obscure until the sixteenth century, scattered applications of trusses have been found.

About 1750, French, German, and Swiss builders were creating truss structures of various types. However, it is evident that they could not have understood the principles of truss structure or have known how to analyze them, since there was no clear-cut use of the triangular principle, and struts and ties were combined in irregular fashion. Even so, a bridge of a span of 200 ft was built by Grubenmann in Zürich in 1764. It is likely that other examples were destroyed by wars and fires.

Starting about 1800, truss bridges of many types were invented. Theodore Burr (1771–1822), Lewis Wernwag (1769–1843), Ithiel Town (1784–1844), and Squire Wipple (1804–1888) were active in this period, building many bridges. Wernwag's bridge across the Delaware River was of particular significance because it started the trend toward using wood posts and iron rods in many types of trusses. Although one does not think of trusses as patentable devices, the records show that Town patented his lattice truss in 1820 and became a rich man from the royalties of one dollar or more per foot of structure. One of these bridges at Richmond, crossing the James River, was 2900 ft long. Several bridges of this type are still in use but are no longer constructed.

Many trusses were invented in the years following these first inventors. Most of their inventions were based upon a special use of materials. Thus, in 1840 William Howe (1803–1852) invented a truss which used timber diagonals under compression and vertical iron members under tension, whereas Caleb and Thomas Pratt sloped the diagonals opposite to those in the Howe truss, to put the verticals in compression. Squire Wipple patented a bridge using cast-iron top chords which were always under compression while all the other members were under tension. These trusses now bear the inventors' names.

The first writings on the subject of rational analysis of stresses in trusses appeared during this inventive period. Wipple wrote his *Essay on Bridge Building* in 1847; Herman Haupt (1817–1905), one of the first professors of engineering, wrote his *General Theory of Bridge Construction* in 1851; Robert Bow, a Scotsman, published his *Treatise on Bracing* in 1851; and William Doyne and William Blood wrote on lattice trusses in the *Minutes of the Institution of Civil Engineers* in 1851–1852. These engineers almost simultaneously created the link between theory and practice.

A lesson is to be learned from this history. Steven, in 1586, with his "triangle of forces," and Pierre Varignon (1654–1722) in 1687, with his "principle of moments," made clear the mathematical principles necessary for the analysis of trusses, but these engineering developments were not applied until almost two centuries later. Engineers should be practical to be sure, but in this case their fumbling experimentation could have been saved if they had been theoreticians first and practical engineers second. It is in this spirit that this chapter is written. A theoretical approach will first be made, followed by practical analysis of roof trusses and bridge trusses in subsequent chapters.

5–1. The Simple Truss. Consideration of the fundamental construction of a truss will lead to a deeper insight of its basic behavior. Certain understanding makes it possible to create almost numberless different forms of trusses for different purposes. Although the most prevalent and useful forms are named in honor of their inventors, the engineer should guard against learning techniques which fit a particular type of truss and rather should practice the methodical application of the equations of statics to all shapes and forms.

The simplest form of a truss is illustrated in Fig. 5–1a, resulting in the constraint of the point C (joint C) in the plane. It is, of course, obvious that two bars are necessary, since the removal of either bar would permit

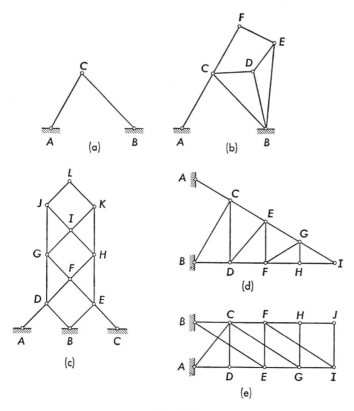

Fig. 5–1.

C to rotate about one of the foundation points. It is also apparent that the addition of extra bars will not add to the rigidity. A more extensive truss can be created by constraining additional joints. However, the array of interconnecting bars cannot be random but must be connected in some orderly method in order to have a stable structure. As an example, the structure of Fig. 5–1a is extended in Fig. 5–1b as follows: Joint D is constrained by the two bars BD and CD so that C and D are now rigid with respect to one another as well as to the foundation points A and B. Likewise, E is constrained, with the two bars DE and BE extending from previously constrained joints. Joint F is in turn constrained by EF and CF. Thus the truss can be extended without limit as long as one adheres to the method. A truss so constructed, regardless of the number of bars, will be statically determinate and stable. The relationship of the number of bars to joints may be written in the form of an equation:

$$2j = m \tag{5–1}$$

where j is the number of joints (exclusive of foundation constraints) and m is the number of members. If $m < 2j$, the truss is unstable, since there are insufficient bars to constrain all the joints; whereas, if $m > 2j$, the truss is statically indeterminate, and some bars are redundant. The equa-

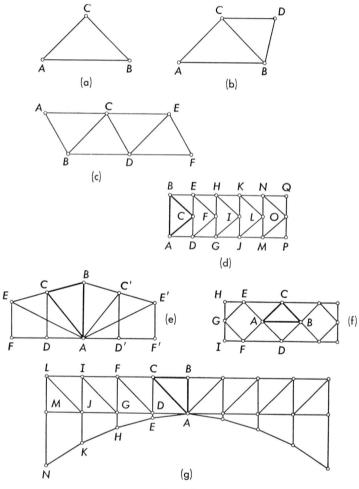

Fig. 5–2.

tion can be used to check the stability of the truss only if a logical order of constraint of joints can be set up. The equation is thus a necessary but not sufficient condition for stability.

Other examples of simple trusses which are connected by bars directly to foundation points are illustrated in Figs. 5–1c, d, and e. The reader will benefit from tracing the order of formation of these trusses by locating each joint in succession and also by checking to see if Eq. 5–1 is satisfied. The joints are alphabetically lettered in the order of constraint.

The simplest form of a self-contained or "free" truss is illustrated in Fig. 5–2a. It is a triangle of bars joined at the ends, thus constraining three joints relative to one another. If one attempts to constrain the joints of a polygon, as illustrated in Fig. 5–2b (ABCD), obviously an unstable structure will be obtained. This condition can be corrected only by addition of the diagonal member CB, which divides the trapezoid into two triangles again. Indeed the triangle is the building block of the simple truss. Fig. 5–2c illustrates this process. ABC is the initial triangle, and in alphabetical order, the other joints are constrained by two bars for each joint; i.e., joint D by the bars BD and CD from the base triangle, and likewise, E by CE and DE from the now constrained joint D, etc. Again the relationship may be expressed as an equation:

$$2j - 3 = m \qquad (5\text{–}2)$$

Any self-contained truss which satisfies the equation and for which the order of joint constraint can be established is statically determinate and stable. As before, the equation is a necessary but not sufficient condition for stability; this will be discussed in connection with complex and compound trusses described subsequently. Also, sometimes the order of constraint is not obvious, and the analyst must examine the truss very carefully in order to determine whether a simple truss exists. Several examples are shown in Figs. 5–2d to g. The reader should study the construction

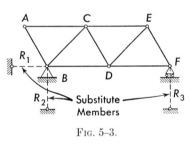

Fig. 5–3.

of these trusses by following the order of joint constraint. The joints are lettered alphabetically in order of constraint from the base triangle ABC in each case.

Eqs. 5–1 and 5–2 can be reconciled to a common form applicable to all forms of trusses, whether it is from the group represented by the former or the latter. Consider the truss in Fig. 5–3, which is identical with Fig. 5–2c except that the pin support at B and the roller at F have been added. Imaginary bars can be attached to substitute for the supports, as shown by dashed lines in the figure, attaching one bar for each component of reaction. Now the modified truss is of the first type mentioned, in which $m' = 2j$, but in this case $m' = m + r$, where m is the number of real bars and r is the number of reaction components. Substituting in the equation, one finds that 9 bars $+ 3$ reactions $= 2 \times 6$ joints. Using this idea, Eq. 5–1 can be used to check the correct relationship between bars, reactions, and joints for all trusses.

5–2. The Ideal Truss. In the light of the preceding discussion, a truss may be defined as an orderly arrangement of interconnected pin-ended bars in a plane so arranged as to support loads. In the calculation of stresses due to these loads, certain idealizations must be made. First, in practice, the members may be riveted or welded together at the joints to give conditions other than the frictionless pin which is assumed in the analysis. The actual condition gives partial rigidity to the connection which introduces moment into the members and distortion of the bars. The stresses due to this bending are known as *secondary* stresses, whereas those in the idealized truss are called *primary* stresses. Secondary stresses are seldom computed, but in some types of trusses they may be large. These computations are treated elsewhere.*

Secondly, the members are assumed to be weightless, and all loads are assumed to act at the joints. Computations for dead loads can be accomplished by assuming the weight of each member to be concentrated at the ends near the joint. Ordinarily the members of a bridge truss do not carry flexural loads except for the relatively small dead loads and wind loads on each member. Roof-truss chord members are often required to transmit loads from their point of application to a joint and thereby may develop sizable flexural stresses. These stresses are analyzed separately from the primary truss stresses, and the two are superimposed upon each other in the design and selection of the member to take the stress. To summarize, the members of the truss are assumed weightless and are connected by frictionless pins at joints where all loads are assumed to act.

5–3. Statically Indeterminate Structures. When a structure has more members than necessary for stability, i.e., $(m + r) > 2j$, it is said to be statically indeterminate. This means that although a solution may be possible by more advanced analysis, it is not possible with the tools at hand. These tools, of course, are the three equations of statics: $\Sigma F_x = 0$, $\Sigma F_y = 0$, and $\Sigma M_o = 0$.

When $(m + r) - 2j = 1$, the truss is said to be statically indeterminate to the first degree. When the difference $(m + r) - 2j = n$, it is said to be statically indeterminate to the nth degree. The symbol n specifies the

* For example, L. E. Grinter, *Theory of Modern Steel Structures* (2d ed.; New York: The Macmillan Co.), p. 149.

number of redundant bars or reactions one may remove and still have a stable structure. There must, of course, be at least three components of reaction forces to support the structure. The structures of Fig. 5–4 are all of the statically indeterminate type. The bar and joint counts are shown in the figure, and the degree of the indeterminacy is computed by Eq. 5–2. Such structures are said to be indeterminate internally or externally, depending on whether there is an excess of internal bars or an excess

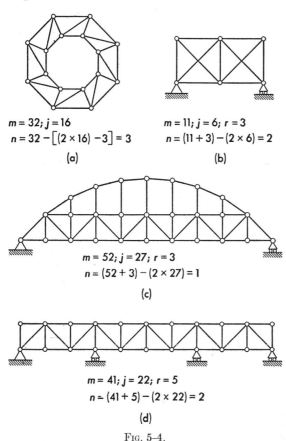

$m = 32;\ j = 16$
$n = 32 - \left[(2 \times 16) - 3\right] = 3$

(a)

$m = 11;\ j = 6;\ r = 3$
$n = (11 + 3) - (2 \times 6) = 2$

(b)

$m = 52;\ j = 27;\ r = 3$
$n = (52 + 3) - (2 \times 27) = 1$

(c)

$m = 41;\ j = 22;\ r = 5$
$n = (41 + 5) - (2 \times 22) = 2$

(d)

FIG. 5–4.

of external reaction components. Figs. 5–4a to c illustrate trusses statically indeterminate internally, whereas Fig. 5–4d illustrates one which is externally statically indeterminate and which has two excess reaction components. It is evident that some trusses may have both redundant bars and reactions. One such possibility could be illustrated if extra diagonal bars were placed in each panel of Fig. 5–4d so that X-bracing existed as in Fig. 5–4b. The degree of indeterminacy would increase by one for each extra diagonal.

The rudimentary knowledge of statically indeterminate forms presented in this article is necessary so that the beginning student does not fruitlessly attempt to solve a statically indeterminate structure by the equations of statics.

5–4. Simple Trusses: Method of Joints. Each joint of a truss is a point of intersection of two or more two-force members, and thus each joint is a concurrent force system in equilibrium. One may find the

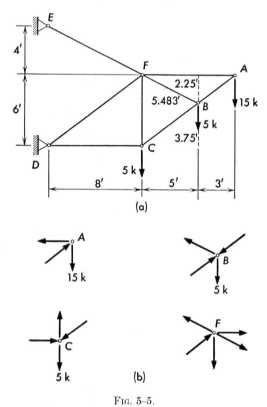

FIG. 5–5.

stresses in members which meet at a joint by applying the equations of statics to the free body of the joint. By selection of joints in the proper sequence, eventually all the stresses in the truss can be found by reapplying the equations to each joint. The two equations

$$\Sigma F_x = 0$$
$$\Sigma F_y = 0$$

(5–3)

are sufficient to describe equilibrium of forces for the coplanar, concurrent force system involved. Thus, with only two independent equations, a joint with only two unknown member stresses must be found for a starting point. According to the method of construction of a simple truss in Art. 5–2, there is always one such joint (the last one formed). The joints must be selected for calculation in the reverse order of formation. The method is best illustrated by the solution of an example.

Find the stresses in the cantilever structure of Fig. 5–5 due to the three vertical loads shown. The joint A has only two unknown stresses and is the starting point. A free body is created by cutting AF and AB to sever the joint in Fig. 5–5b. As a necessary part of the solution one must find whether the members are in compression or tension. The tension force is represented by a force directed away from the joint; compression, by a force directed toward the joint. Since it is not always possible to detect the direction before calculation, the stresses are not always assumed to be in tension.* When a negative solution is the result of solving Eqs. 5–3, this indicates a compression force. The forces are summed for each joint to give two equations in the horizontal and vertical directions.

AT JOINT A (Fig. 5–5b):

$$\Sigma F_v = \frac{3}{5} AB + 15 = 0$$

$$AB = -25\text{-k compression}$$

$$\Sigma F_h = AF - \frac{4}{5} \times 25 = 0$$ (5–4)

$$AF = +20\text{-k tension}$$

AT JOINT B:

$$\Sigma F_v = \frac{3}{5} BC - \frac{2.25}{5.483} BF + 5.0 + \left(\frac{3}{5} \times 25\right) = 0$$

$$\Sigma F_h = \frac{4}{5} BC + \frac{5}{5.483} BF + \left(\frac{4}{5} \times 25\right) = 0$$ (5–5)

Simultaneous solution yields

$$BC = -30.210\text{-k compression}$$

$$BF = +4.570\text{-k tension}$$

* It is not always necessary to rely on the calculations only to determine the direction of the forces. The student will be able to predict the proper direction in most cases by visual examination. It may be easier for many to assume a direction for the stress, and if the sign of the force is reversed by the solution, one knows that the stress is in the opposite direction from that chosen. No time is lost at this point, since the force may be reversed on the free-body diagram and the solution continued. For continuity in this text, however, the member will always be assumed as being in tension, and the plus or minus sign will determine the state of stress and direction of force for each member.

At joint C:

$$\Sigma F_v = CF - \left(\frac{3}{5} \times 30.21\right) - 5.0 = 0$$

$$CF = +23.130\text{-k tension}$$

$$\Sigma F_h = CD + \left(\frac{4}{5} \times 30.21\right) = 0$$

$$CD = -24.17\text{-k compression}$$

(5–6)

At joint F:

$$\Sigma F_v = \frac{8}{\sqrt{80}} EF + \frac{4}{5} DF - 20.0 - \left(\frac{5}{5.483} \times 4.570\right) = 0$$

$$DF = -12.917\text{-k}$$
$$\text{compression}$$

$$\Sigma F_h = \frac{4}{\sqrt{80}} EF - \frac{3}{5} DF - 23.125 - \left(\frac{2.25}{5.483} \times 4.570\right) = 0$$

$$EF = +38.572\text{-k}$$
$$\text{tension}$$

(5–7)

Note that the trigonometry is always expressed in terms of the truss geometry. It is unnatural to solve for the angles of the truss members and then look up the handbook values of the trigonometric functions for use in the solution. The use of the geometry of the truss directly is more convenient and probably more accurate because intermediate steps have been eliminated.

The simple bridge truss shown in Fig. 5–6 will serve as another example. The bridge is symmetrically loaded so that only half of the joints need be analyzed.

Joint L_0:

$$\Sigma F_v = \frac{3}{5} L_0 U_1 + 20 = 0$$

$$L_0 U_1 = -33.3\text{-k compression}$$

$$\Sigma F_h = L_0 L_1 - \left(\frac{4}{5} \times 33.3\right) = 0$$

$$L_0 L_1 = 26.67\text{-k tension}$$

(5–8)

Joint U_1:

$$\Sigma F_h = U_1 U_2 + \left(\frac{4}{5} \times 33.3\right) = 0$$

$$U_1 U_2 = -26.67\text{-k compression}$$

$$\Sigma F_v = U_1 L_1 - \left(\frac{3}{5} \times 33.33\right) + 15 = 0$$

$$U_1 L_1 = 5.0\text{-k tension}$$

(5–9)

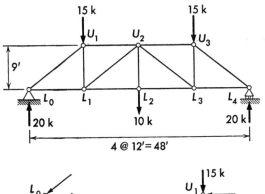

Fig. 5–6.

Joint L_1:

$$\Sigma F_v = 5.0 + \frac{3}{5} L_1 U_2 = 0$$

$$L_1 U_2 = -8.33\text{-k compression}$$ (5–10)

$$\Sigma F_h = L_1 L_2 - \left(\frac{4}{5} \times 8.33\right) - 26.67 = 0$$

$$L_1 L_2 = 33.3\text{-k tension}$$

Joint L_2:

$$\Sigma F_v = U_2 L_2 - 10 = 0$$ (5–11)

$$U_2 L_2 = 10\text{-k tension}$$

Still another example further illustrates the method of joints. The analysis of the structure in Fig. 5–7 must begin at one of the supports.

Joint A:

$$\Sigma F_v = 0.707 AB + \frac{10}{\sqrt{500}} AF + 2 = 0$$ (5–12)

$$\Sigma F_h = 0.707 AB + \frac{20}{\sqrt{500}} AF - 10 = 0$$

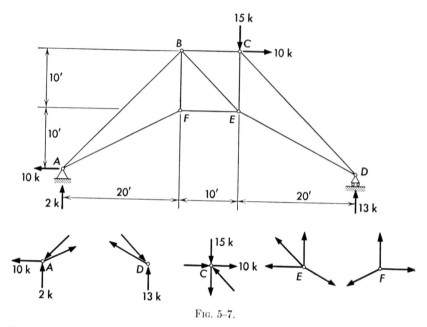

Fig. 5–7.

Simultaneous solution yields

$$AF = +26.83\text{-k tension}$$
$$AB = -19.80\text{-k compression}$$

JOINT D:

$$\Sigma F_v = 0.707DC + \frac{10}{\sqrt{500}}\,DE + 13 = 0$$

$$\Sigma F_h = 0.707DC + \frac{20}{\sqrt{500}}\,DE = 0 \qquad (5\text{–}13)$$

$$DE = +29.07\text{-k tension}$$
$$DC = -36.77\text{-k compression}$$

JOINT C:

$$\Sigma F_h = BC - 10 + (0.707 \times 36.77) = 0$$

$$BC = -16.0\text{-k compression}$$
$$\Sigma F_v = CE + 15 - (0.707 \times 36.77) = 0 \qquad (5\text{–}14)$$

$$CE = +11.0\text{-k tension}$$

JOINT E:

$$\Sigma F_v = 11.0 - \left(29.07 \times \frac{10}{\sqrt{500}}\right) + 0.707\,BE = 0$$

$$BE = +2.83\text{-k tension} \qquad (5\text{–}15)$$

JOINT F:

$$\Sigma F_h = EF - \left(26.83 \times \frac{20}{\sqrt{500}}\right) = 0$$

$$EF = 24.0\text{-k tension}$$

(5–16)

$$\Sigma F_v = BF - \left(26.83 \times \frac{10}{\sqrt{500}}\right) = 0$$

$$BF = 12.0\text{-k tension}$$

In solving for bar stresses, it is very advantageous to be able to recognize by direct observation those with zero stress. Usually these can be recognized by a typical arrangement of bars at a joint, as illustrated in Fig. 5–8. The joint F of the structure is selected for analysis and is shown in Fig. 5–8b. Summation of the forces perpendicular to EFG at F proves that the stress in bar DF is zero. This is the case whenever a third bar joins two other collinear members at a joint. Further examination of the truss shows that DG also is zero because the same state of bar arrangement exists at joint D, now that DF has been found to be zero. One may progress from joint to joint to prove that $CG = CH = BH = BJ = 0$ and that the only members having a stress are the chord members.

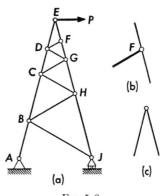

FIG. 5–8.

Suppose that the load P is now assumed to be located at F. The condition previously described is no longer the case, and all web members are stressed. The joint E is isolated in Fig. 5–8c. It is apparent that this is a special case of the bar arrangement shown in Fig. 5–8b. Summation of forces perpendicular to either one of the two bars results in a proof of zero stress in both these members. The analyst should watch for these two types of bar arrangements, to simplify his solutions.

5–5. Method of Sections. It is customary to separate the discussion of analysis of trusses "joint by joint" from that of using larger sections involving two or more joints. The student will not become confused by this process if he remembers that in reality one is only applying the three equations of statics to a free-body diagram cut from the truss. These equations are, of course, $\Sigma F_x = 0$, $\Sigma F_y = 0$, and $\Sigma M_0 = 0$. Since forces at a joint represent a concurrent force system only, the first two equations are applicable. For larger sections of trusses, all three may be used. The method is best illustrated by examples.

Consider again the cantilever truss of Fig. 5–5. It is proposed to find the stresses in members *EF*, *FD*, and *DC* without progressing from joint

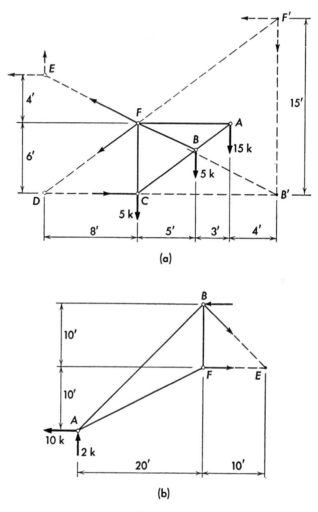

(a)

(b)

Fig. 5–9.

to joint as before. A free body is isolated by passing a section through the three members to give the free body in Fig. 5–9a. There are three unknowns and three equations. It is convenient to sum moments about *D*, since both *DF* and *DC* pass through *D* and thus do not enter into the equation. In addition, if the force representing stress *EF* is moved to *E*, the vertical component will also pass through D. Thus the moment equation is as follows, assuming that EF is tension:

$$\left(\frac{8}{\sqrt{80}} EF \times 10\right) - (5 \times 8) - (5 \times 13) - (15 \times 16) = 0 \tag{5–17}$$

$$EF = +38.57\text{-k}$$
$$\text{tension}$$

If one chooses the point of moments at the proper location, all the "unknowns" except the stress in question can be eliminated. There is no rule for this selection, but the experienced analyst soon recognizes the proper points. One must look for the intersection points of all but one of the unknown stresses. The problem is continued by using the same section to find the stress in DC by taking moments about F. This eliminates EF and DF from the equation, since they both pass through the center of moments.

The stress in the final severed member DF can be found by taking moments about the intersection of EF and DC. Remembering also that any force can be moved along its line of action, DF is moved to F' for purposes of analysis, since its vertical component will then pass through B'.

$$\Sigma M_{B'} = (15 \times 4) + (5 \times 7) + (5 \times 12) + \left(\frac{4}{5} DF \times 15\right) = 0 \tag{5–18}$$

$$DF = -12.92\text{-k}$$
$$\text{compression}$$

Alternately, the stress DF can be found by summing the stresses vertically on the entire section shown; thus:

$$\Sigma F_v = 15 + 5 + 5 - \left(\frac{4}{\sqrt{80}} \times 38.57\right) + \frac{3}{5} DF = 0 \tag{5–19}$$

$$DF = -12.92\text{-k}$$
$$\text{compression}$$

Another example illustrates the advantage of the method of sections in certain cases. Consider the truss of Fig. 5–7. It is desired to find the stresses in BC, BE, and FE. A section is passed through these three members, and the portion to the left is taken as a free body, as shown in Fig. 5–9b. To find the stress in BC, sum the moments about E because the other two unknowns have been eliminated.

$$\Sigma M_E = (10 \times 10) + (2 \times 30) + 10BC = 0 \tag{5–20}$$

$$BC = -16\text{-k compression}$$

Likewise, the stress in FE can be found by taking moments about B; thus:

$$\Sigma M_B = (10 \times 20) + (2 \times 20) - 10EF = 0$$
$$EF = +24\text{-k tension} \tag{5-21}$$

The diagonal stress BE can be found by summing the vertical forces on the section.

$$\Sigma F_v = 2.0 - 0.707BE = 0$$
$$BE = +2.83\text{-k tension} \tag{5-22}$$

For a solution for the rest of the bar stresses, one may proceed through joints F and B, in that order, using the method of joints. This illustrated solution is easier than starting at joint A by the method of joints, which would require the solution of simultaneous equations. The indicated combination of both methods would involve equations with only one unknown.

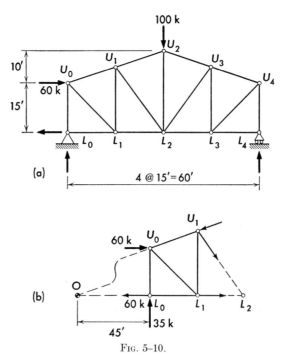

Fig. 5–10.

The truss with sloping upper chord or lower chord members is often pointed out as a special case of the method of sections. A truss of this type is shown in Fig. 5–10. Suppose it is desired to find the stresses in the members of the second panel from the left. The section cuts three members, as shown in Fig. 5–10b. One may find the stresses in U_1U_2 by taking moments about L_2, thus eliminating two unknowns from the equation and making it possible to solve for U_1U_2 directly.

$$\Sigma M_{L_2} = (60 \times 15) + (35 \times 30) - \left(\frac{15}{\sqrt{250}} U_1U_2 \times 25 \right) = 0$$

$$U_1U_2 = -82.2\text{-k}$$

compression

(5–23)

Likewise, the stress in L_1L_2 may be found by taking moments about U_1, thus eliminating U_1U_2 and U_1L_2 from the equation and leaving only one unknown, U_1L_2.

$$\Sigma M_{U_1} = (60 \times 15) + (35 \times 15) - 20L_1L_2 = 0$$

$$L_1L_2 = +71.2\text{-k tension}$$

(5–24)

The process is no different in finding U_1L_2. In order to find the stress directly, one must somehow eliminate the other two forces from the moment equation. This can be done by properly selecting the point of moments. By projecting U_1U_2 and L_1L_2 to the left, the intersection O is determined. By taking moments about this point, two forces are eliminated. The force U_1L_2 is moved along its line of action to L_2 in order to eliminate its horizontal component from the equation also.

$$\Sigma M_0 = (60 \times 15) - (35 \times 45) + \left(\frac{4}{5} U_1L_2 \times 75 \right) = 0$$

$$U_1L_2 = +11.25\text{-k}$$

tension

(5–25)

This same system can be used when the slope of the chords changes in each panel; of course the point O for the moment equation to determine the stress in the diagonal member changes for each panel in this case.

The stress in the diagonal could be found in another manner by summing the vertical forces on the section in Fig. 5–10b, once U_1U_2 and L_1L_2 are known. Thus:

$$\Sigma F_v = 35.0 - \left(\frac{5}{\sqrt{250}} \times 82.2 \right) - \frac{4}{5} U_1L_2 = 0$$

$$U_1L_2 = +11.25\text{-k tension}$$

(5–26)

5–6. Solution by Mixed Methods. The student should not be confused by the preceding explanation, where either the method of joints or the method of sections is used exclusively on certain problems. Both methods are based on the same principles of statics; only the free-body diagrams are different. In most solutions it is convenient to intermix the methods at the convenience of the analyst. The K-truss of Fig. 5–11 will serve as an example. Suppose it is assumed that only the stresses in M_1U_2 and M_1L_2 are wanted. Since the truss is symmetrically loaded with

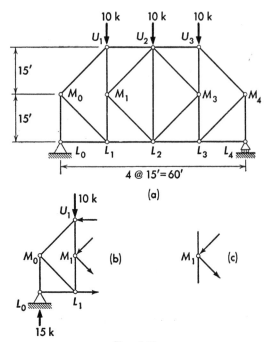

FIG. 5–11.

three 10-k loads, each reaction will be 15 k vertically. The stresses in the members can be found by the method of joints by working through the joints L_0, M_0, U_1, L_1, and M_1 in that order. An easier method would be to cut a section vertically through the second panel of the truss to give the free-body diagram in Fig. 5–11b. Of course four members are cut, and obviously these cannot be determined from the three equations available. Next consider joint M_1 in Fig. 5–11c. The summation of forces in the horizontal direction yields

$$\Sigma F_h = 0.707M_1U_2 + 0.707M_1L_2 = 0$$
$$M_1U_2 = -M_1L_2 \qquad (5\text{--}27)$$

This relationship indicates that if one force is toward the joint, the other must be directed outward from the joint (one compression, one tension). Returning now to Fig. 5–11b, the summation of forces in the vertical direction is

$$\Sigma F_v = 15 - 10 - 0.707M_1U_2 - 0.707M_1L_2 = 0$$
$$5 - (2 \times 0.707M_1U_2) = 0 \qquad (5\text{--}28)$$
$$M_1U_2 = 3.53\text{-k compression}$$

and

$$M_1L_2 = 3.53\text{-k tension}$$

If a solution is desired for U_1U_2 directly, moments may be taken about L_1. Note that the vertical components of M_1U_2 and M_1L_2 pass through L_1, whereas the horizontal components cancel each other.

$$M_{L_1} = (15 \times 15) + 30U_1U_2 = 0$$

$$U_1U_2 = -7.5\text{-k compression}$$

(5–29)

5–7. The Compound Truss. Compound trusses are formed by connecting two or more simple trusses together. This type of truss finds many varied uses in bridges, roof trusses, and other structures. The connection

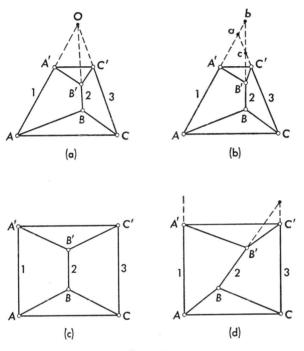

Fig. 5–12.

between two trusses can be made in one of three ways. In the first, the two trusses are connected by three bars much as if one truss were the base which supported the other. A typical connection of this type is shown in Fig. 5–13b, where the simple truss ABC is connected to the simple truss DEF by the three bars 1, 2, and 3. Since these connecting bars must give complete rigidity of one truss to the other, care must be taken to get a proper arrangement. Fig. 5–12 illustrates the common danger. In Fig. 5–12a the connecting bars 1, 2, and 3 have an imaginary intersection point outside the truss. The forces in the members then form a concurrent force system which has no moment resisting quality, and one truss can rotate with respect to the other about the point O. The situation can be corrected by arranging the lines of action so that their projected intersection form a triangle, as shown in Fig. 5–12b. The larger the triangle abc becomes, the more stable the connection is. On the other hand, as the triangle approaches zero area, the connection becomes unstable.

A similar situation is shown in Fig. 5–12c, where all three connecting bars, *1*, *2*, and *3*, are parallel. Obviously, truss $A'B'C'$ can move laterally with respect to ABC. This can be corrected by rearranging the truss so

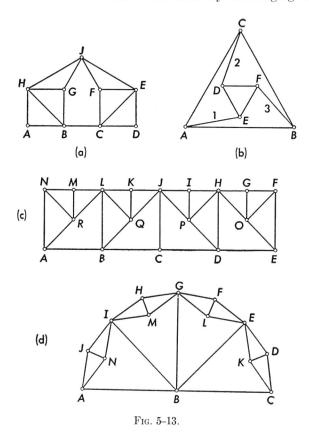

Fig. 5–13.

that one of the bars is not parallel, thus forming a nonconcurrent, non-parallel force system which can resist both moments and forces in the x and y direction, as illustrated in Fig. 5–12d.

Still another common method of connecting one truss to another is by a pin and one bar. This is illustrated in Fig. 5–13a. Here the truss ABJ is connected to CDJ at the pin J and by the bar BC. Since the pin provides both an x and y component of force, essentially the same effect as having three bars is obtained. Fig. 5–13c illustrates a deck-type bridge truss, which may be considered to be a series of four trusses joined one after another by a pin and an additional bar. On the other hand, it may be considered a simple truss, too.

Fig. 5–13d illustrates a third type of compound truss. In each of the segments, such as BCE, the outer member EC has been removed and a truss $EDCK$ has been substituted. This is often done to improve the economy of a truss. Since the member EC would ordinarily be heavily loaded with (for example) roof loads, there would be excessive bending in the member. This loading could be taken better by the truss substituted for the individual member.

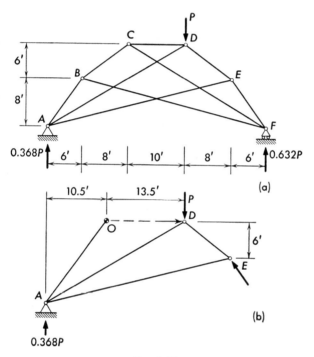

FIG. 5–14.

5–8. Numerical Examples: Compound Trusses. Sometimes the fact that one has a compound truss is not obvious. The truss illustrated in Fig. 5–14 shows a case in point. Here two trusses ADE and FBC are connected by the three bars AB, CD, and EF. It is impossible to proceed to a solution for the bar stresses by the method of joints, since there are three members at each joint. Likewise it is impossible to cut a section without cutting more than three members, unless one isolates one of the simple trusses forming the compound. When one locates the two simple trusses ADE and FBC, tied together by the three connecting members, one may easily proceed. The truss ADE is isolated as a free body, as shown in Fig. 5–14b; then

$$\Sigma M_0 = 13.5P + (0.368P \times 10.5) + (0.8EF \times 21.5)$$
$$- (0.6EF \times 6) = 0$$
$$EF = -1.277P \text{ compression}$$
$$\Sigma F_v = P - 0.368P - (0.8 \times 1.277P)$$
$$- 0.8AB = 0 \tag{5–30}$$
$$AB = -0.487P \text{ compression}$$
$$\Sigma F_h = CD + (0.6 \times 0.487P)$$
$$+ (0.6 \times 1.277P) = 0$$
$$CD = -1.058P \text{ compression}$$

The solution may now proceed to completion by the method of joints.

Fig. 5–15 illustrates a different type of compound truss. Examination will show again that it is impossible to commence a solution by either the

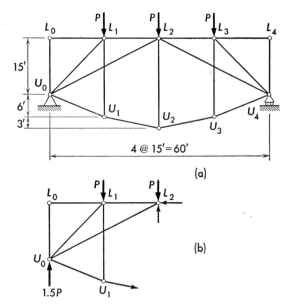

Fig. 5–15.

method of sections or joints. It is noted, however, that the truss consists of the two trusses, $L_0L_2U_2U_0$ and $L_2L_4U_4U_2$, connected by the pin at L_2 and the member U_1U_2 (the trusses may be alternately selected so that U_2U_3 is the connecting link, depending on which truss the joint U_2 is placed). The solution proceeds by isolating the left-hand simple truss shown in Fig. 5–15b and solving for the link stress U_1U_2; thus:

$$U_0U_1 = 16.16 \text{ ft}; \qquad U_1U_2 = 15.30 \text{ ft}; \qquad U_0L_2 = 33.54 \text{ ft}$$

$$\Sigma M_{L_2} = 30 \times 1.5P - 15P - 24 \times 0.98U_1U_2 = 0 \tag{5-31}$$

$$U_1U_2 = 1.275P \text{ tension}$$

The solution now proceeds by joints.

Joint U_1:

$$\Sigma F_x = 0.980 \times 1.275P - 0.928U_0U_1 = 0$$

$$U_0U_1 = 1.346P \text{ tension}$$
$$\tag{5-32}$$

$$\Sigma F_v = L_1U_1 + 0.371 \times 1.346P - 0.196 \times 1.275P = 0$$

$$L_1U_1 = -0.250P \text{ compression}$$

Joint U_2:

$$\Sigma F_y = L_2U_2 + 2 \times 0.196 \times 1.275P = 0$$
$$\tag{5-33}$$

$$L_2U_2 = -0.500P \text{ compression}$$

Joint L_2:

$$\Sigma F_y = 0.500P - P - 2 \times 0.447U_0L_2 = 0$$
$$\tag{5-34}$$

$$U_0L_2 = -0.559P \text{ compression}$$

Joint L_1:

$$\Sigma F_y = P - 0.250P + 0.707U_0L_1 = 0$$
$$\tag{5-35}$$

$$U_0L_1 = -1.061P \text{ compression}$$

Also

$$L_0U_0 = L_0L_1 = L_3L_4 = L_4L_4 = 0$$

The last example of a compound truss is illustrated in Fig. 5–16. The three individual trusses similar to $ABB'C$ are substituted for members in the Warren trusses shown in Fig. 5–16b. The solution can be achieved by superimposing the solutions for the separate trusses. The truss $CDD'E$ acts as a distributor for the centerline load P, imposing a load $P/2$ on joints C and E in addition to the load P already carried directly at these points. The Warren truss in Fig. 5–16b is solved first, using the section to the left, and noting that all angles are $60°$.

$$\Sigma M_H = (0.866 \times 15CE) - (1.5 \times 7.5)$$

$$+ (1.5P \times 15) = 0 \tag{5-36}$$

$$CE = -0.866P \text{ compression}$$

At joint A:

$$AC = \frac{-1.5P}{0.866} = -1.732P \text{ compression}$$

The truss in Fig. 5–16d must carry the compression in AC as indicated in the preceding equation.

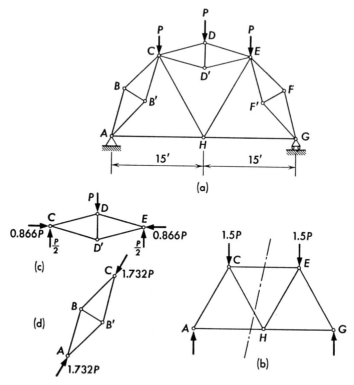

Fig. 5–16.

Joint C in Fig. 5–16d:

$$CB = CB'; BCB' = 30°$$

$$(0.966 \times 2CB) + 1.732P = 0 \tag{5-37}$$

$$CB = -0.897P \text{ compression}$$

From the other joint relationships, $CB = CB' = AB = AB'$.

Joint B in Fig. 5–16d:

$$BB' - (2 \times 0.897P \times 0.259) = 0$$
$$BB' = 0.464P \text{ tension} \tag{5-38}$$

The truss $CDD'E$ is more complicated because it carries both the thrust taken by CE of the truss in Fig. 5–16b and also the centerline lateral load as shown in Fig. 5–16c.

At joint E in Fig. 5–16c:

$$0.258DE - 0.258D'E + 0.5P = 0$$

$$0.966DE - 0.966D'E + 0.866P = 0$$

$$DE = -1.414 \text{ compression}$$

$$D'E = +0.518P \text{ tension}$$

(5–39)

From other joint relationships, $DE = DC$ and $D'C = D'E$.

Joint D in Fig. 5–16c:

$$DD' + (2 \times 0.518P \times 0.258) = 0$$

$$DD' = -0.267P \text{ compression}$$

(5–40)

5–9. The Complex Truss. Consider the truss of Fig. 5–17a and b. A simple truss is illustrated in Fig. 5–17a that satisfies not only the equation $m = 2j - 3$ but also the method of construction described in Art. 5–2 for simple trusses. That is, if ABC is considered the base triangle, it can be shown that each joint is constrained by two added bars in some consecutive order. The solution for bar stresses can be carried out by either the method of joints or the method of sections, or by a combination of both methods. Now examine Fig. 5–17b. Here is a truss identical to Fig. 5–17a except for a single bar; AC has been removed and AG substituted. Note that the number of bars and number of joints remains the same, so that $m = 2j - 3$. Apparently a rigid structure is obtained, but the solution is impossible by the elementary methods; i.e., method of joints or method of sections. One finds that each joint has at least three connecting bars, and thus, with only two equations of statics for the concurrent force system at a joint, a direct solution for bar stresses is not possible. Likewise, if one tries to cut a section, one finds that this is impossible without cutting at least four bars. Consequently one again lacks enough equations for a direct solution by the method of sections, since only three independent equations exist for a nonconcurrent system of forces.

Two more examples of such structures are shown in Figs. 5–17c, d, e, and f. In Fig. 5–17c a simple truss is constructed on a base triangle ABC in the ordinary way. By removing AC and substituting BF, as shown in Fig. 5–17d, the same situation exists as previously described in Fig. 5–17b. Still another example is illustrated in Figs. 5–17e and f, where bar BD of the simple truss in Fig. 5–17e is replaced by AF. In both cases the equation $m = 2j - 3$ is satisfied. Such structures are known as *complex trusses*.

Complex trusses are not in extensive use, although they are as useful as the more common compound and simple trusses. The authors suspect that these trusses are not popular because many engineers do not know what they are or how to analyze them and consequently avoid them in favor of other forms. Most of the useful space trusses are of this type, however, and thus it is best to understand the plane complex form before studying the complex space truss.

In order to find the stresses for any complex truss, one must examine the truss as a unit. Thus, for Fig. 5–17b, there are 7 joints, and $2 \times 7 = 14$ independent equations of statics; there are also 11 unknown bar stresses and 3 possible external reactions. Simultaneous solution of

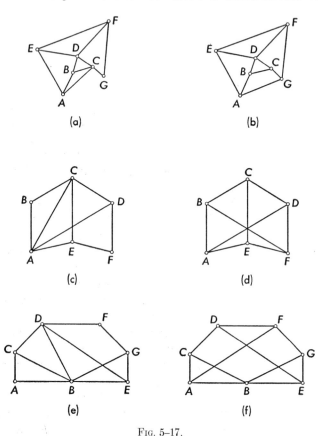

Fig. 5–17.

the 14 equations will yield the solution. Study of the trusses in Figs. 5–17d and f will show that solutions are possible if 12 equations and 14 equations are solved, respectively. The solution of such a large number of simultaneous equations is, of course, time-consuming, and tedious. These trusses illustrate some of the simpler types of complex forms; the addition of each additional joint adds two more equations. Since it is not uncommon to have, say, 40 joints and thus 80 equations of statics for a truss, some other method must be sought to implement the solution. The digital computer can be used to solve the simultaneous equations directly; however, in the absence of such equipment, special methods can be used as illustrated in the subsequent articles.

5–10. The Critical Form. In following the methods described for the formation of complex trusses, one may obtain a *critical form*, which is a configuration of bars so arranged as to give instability. Some critical forms may be discovered by inspection whereas others are obscure. One of the simplest critical forms is shown in Fig. 5–18. Fig. 5–18a shows a stable, totally constrained, joint in the plane. Let the angle of repose of the constraining bars decrease until they are horizontal, as in Fig. 5–18b. A stable form exists for all but the horizontal position in which excessive lateral movement, Δ, may be obtained under very small loads. In fact the structure is statically indeterminate. If one pictures a turnbuckle mounted in one of the bars, it is apparent that an infinite number of bar stresses can exist for this bar configuration and that a unique solution does not exist. Such a situation does not present itself for any other but the horizontal arrangement of the two bars. If a structure can be shown to be a simple truss or a compound truss, then the analyst is assured that a unique solution exists for the stresses in the bars and that therefore an ambiguous situation such as that described here cannot exist.

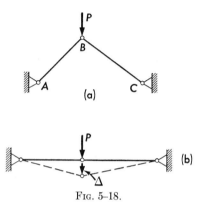

FIG. 5–18.

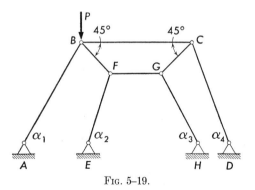

FIG. 5–19.

Fig. 5–19 illustrates a complex truss which may have a critical form. Determination of this fact is not apparent by observation alone. One must resort to simultaneous solution of $2j$ equations of statics in order to find the bar stresses. These equations are given on page 116.

$$+ AB \sin \alpha_1 + BF \sin 45° = -P \tag{5-41a}$$

$$-BC + AB \cos \alpha_1 + BF \cos 45° = 0 \tag{5-41b}$$

$$+ CD \sin \alpha_4 + CG \sin 45° = 0 \tag{5-41c}$$

$$+ CD \cos \alpha_4 + CG \cos 45° = 0 \tag{5-41d}$$

$$EF \sin \alpha_2 - BF \sin 45° = 0 \tag{5-41e}$$

$$+ EF \cos \alpha_2 + BF \cos 45° = 0 \tag{5-41f}$$

$$-FG + GH \sin \alpha_3 - CG \sin 45° = 0 \tag{5-41g}$$

$$-FG + GH \cos \alpha_3 + CG \cos 45° = 0 \tag{5-41h}$$

Eqs. 5–41a and b are for joint B, Eqs. 5–41c and d for joint C, Eqs. 5–41e and f for joint F, and Eqs. 5–41g and h for joint G. One may solve the set of equations by the use of Cramer's rule, i.e.,

$$S_n = \frac{D_n}{D} \tag{5-41}$$

where D is the determinant formed by the coefficients of the unknowns and D_n is the determinant obtained when the elements of the nth column of D are replaced by the constants on the right side of the equations, provided $D \neq 0$.* However, if $D = 0$, then

$$S_n = \frac{D_n}{0} \tag{5-42}$$

and S_n may have any value, i.e., a unique solution does not exist; or if $D_n = 0$, also, then

$$S_n = \frac{0}{0} \tag{5-43}$$

an indeterminant form. Thus the existence of a vanishing determinant indicates a critical form, since many solutions are possible. On the other hand, if a solution exists, satisfying all equations, the structure is stable and is a useful truss.

In order to find the angles α when a critical form exists, the determinant is equated to zero; thus:

$$D = \begin{vmatrix} 0 & 0 & \sin\alpha_1 & 0 & \sin 45° & 0 & 0 & 0 \\ 0 & -1 & \cos\alpha_1 & 0 & -\cos 45° & 0 & 0 & 0 \\ 0 & 0 & 0 & 0 & 0 & \sin\alpha_4 & 0 & \sin 45° \\ 0 & -1 & 0 & 0 & 0 & \cos\alpha_4 & 0 & -\cos 45° \\ 0 & 0 & 0 & \sin\alpha_2 & -\sin 45° & 0 & 0 & 0 \\ -1 & 0 & 0 & \cos\alpha_2 & \cos 45° & 0 & 0 & 0 \\ 0 & 0 & 0 & 0 & 0 & 0 & \sin\alpha_3 & -\sin 45° \\ -1 & 0 & 0 & 0 & 0 & 0 & \cos\alpha_3 & \cos 45° \end{vmatrix} = 0 \tag{5-44}$$

Solution of this determinant results in

$$-\sin\alpha_1 \, \sin\alpha_2 \, \cos\alpha_3 \, \sin\alpha_4 - \cos\alpha_1 \, \sin\alpha_2 \, \sin\alpha_3 \, \sin\alpha_4$$
$$-\cos\alpha_1 \, \sin\alpha_2 \, \cos\alpha_3 \, \sin\alpha_4 + \sin\alpha_1 \, \sin\alpha_2 \, \sin\alpha_3 \, \cos\alpha_4 = 0 \tag{5-45}$$
$$+\sin\alpha_1 \, \cos\alpha_2 \, \sin\alpha_3 \, \cos\alpha_4 + \sin\alpha_1 \, \cos\alpha_2 \, \sin\alpha_3 \, \sin\alpha_4$$

* See, for example, H. Sohon, *Engineering Mathematics* (Princeton, N. J.: D. Van Nostrand Co., Inc., 1944.)

It can be shown by examination that $D = 0$ and that a critical form exists for the following combinations of angles:

1. All legs vertical, $\alpha_1 = \alpha_2 = \alpha_3 = \alpha_4 = 90°$. It is also obvious that the form is statically indeterminant.

2. Outside legs vertical, $\alpha_1 = \alpha_4 = 90°$. Equal angles in internal legs, $\alpha_2 = \alpha_3$.

3. Inside legs vertical, $\alpha_2 = \alpha_3 = 90°$. Outside legs, equal angles, $\alpha_1 = \alpha_4 = 90°$.

4. Any three legs vertical, for example: $\alpha_1 = \alpha_2 = \alpha_4 = 90°$. Other leg horizontal, for example: $\alpha_3 = 0$.

5. All legs horizontal, $\alpha_1 = \alpha_2 = \alpha_3 = \alpha_4 = 0$.

6. Pairs of legs on each side equal: $\alpha_1 = \alpha_2 = \alpha$ and $\alpha_3 = \alpha_4 = \beta$.

Perhaps the reader can discover other combinations of angles that will give a critical form. Still it is obvious that many combinations occur which do not yield $D = 0$ and for which a unique solution exists. One does not wish to go again through the preceding analysis to prove $D = 0$, however, since most complex structures are more complicated and would involve excessive labor. One may deduce whether $D = 0$ by a simpler method described in Art. 5–11.

5–11. The Zero Load Test. The fact that $D = 0$ is always an indication of a critical form. The vanishing determinant is also indicative that an infinite number of combinations of stress can exist independent of the load conditions; i.e., stresses can exist under no load at all. If such a condition can be shown, a critical form exists. For example, consider the structure of Fig. 5–20a which has already been shown to be a critical form. Imagine a turnbuckle installed in member FG and tightened to produce a tension. The tension induces equal tensions in EF and GH, equal tensions in BF and CG, equal compressions in AB and CD, and compatible compressions satisfying statics at each end of BC. The magnitude of the stresses are dependent upon the turnbuckle setting; therefore an infinite number of combinations is possible, consistent with $D = 0$. An internal stress condition can exist with no external load, and the structure again can be proved to have a critical form.

Consider next the structure in Fig. 5–20b. Again induce a tension in member FG by a turnbuckle. Equal stresses are necessary again in BF and GC to keep the inner frame in balance. These equal forces cannot be the resultant of two different sets of forces at the joints B and C; i.e., the stress CB is incompatible with BC. This inconsistency indicates that no internal stresses can exist under zero load, a unique solution exists under load, and the structure is stable.

5–12. Solution by Special Conditions. In analyzing any truss, but especially complex trusses, one must look for special conditions such as symmetry, which may substantially reduce the labor in a solution. This may be in connection with a particular joint or the truss as a whole. For example, the Z-truss (so-called because of the Z-pattern of web members) in Fig. 5–21a is a complex truss, since there are at least three bars joining at each joint.

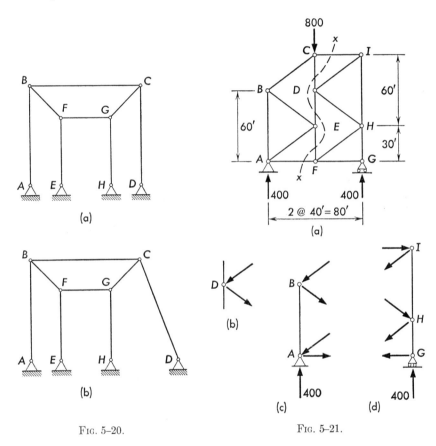

Fɪɢ. 5–20.   Fɪɢ. 5–21.

A special condition exists at joint D, however (Fig. 5–21b). By summing forces in the horizontal direction one finds $DI = -DH$. Likewise, at joint H, $DH = -FH$, or $DI = -DH = HF$.

Consider next the section cut by passing a plane vertically through panel FG shown in Fig. 5–21d. It is now known that the three diagonal web members have the same numerical value even though one may be in compression and another in tension. By summing forces vertically in Fig. 5–21d, one obtains

$$3 \times \frac{3}{5} DI = 400$$

and thus,

$$DI = 222\text{-k tension}$$

$$DH = -222\text{-k compression} \qquad (5\text{--}46)$$

$$FH = 222\text{-k tension}$$

Likewise, for a section taken on the left side

$$BC = -222\text{-k compression}$$

$$BE = 222\text{-k tension} \qquad (5\text{--}47)$$

$$AE = -222\text{-k compression}$$

The method of joints or sections can now be continued to complete the solution. Note that the solution would have been possible also if the angles CDI and EDH, for example, had been unequal. The top and bottom chord stresses can be found directly by section xx in Fig. 5–21a.

5–13. Solution by Multiple Substitute Members. Fig. 5–22a illustrates a typical complex structure which may be solved by the substitute member method. It will be noted that every joint has at least three members, and thus the equation $2j - 3 = m$ is satisfied. It is obvious that removal of a member from the outer chord would ease the situation by leaving two joints with only two members; this is accomplished by removing $G'F'$ and replacing it with BC'. If one pictures the progression of a solution by the method of joints, assuming that the stress in $G'F'$ is known, progress from joint to joint is blocked by joint E', which still has three unknowns. DE' is now removed and replaced by CF. It is immediately evident that the structure is now a simple truss, and a solution can be made by progressing from joint to joint, if it is assumed that S_1 and S_2, the two unknown stresses, are known. The resulting loaded structure is shown in Fig. 5–22b.

The solution of the stresses for each load, P, S_1, or S_2, is made separately, as illustrated in Figs. 5–22c, d, and e. The members obviously having zero stress are shown by dashed lines. In the case of S_1 and S_2, Figs. 5–22d and e, the stresses for a unit load will be found, and the stresses in any member can be multiplied by S_1 or S_2 to find the actual stresses due to that load. Since the actual conditions demand that the substitute members x and y have zero stress, equations of compatibility should be set up. Let S_x and S_y be the stresses in x and y due to the load P in Fig. 5–22c and u be the stresses due to the unit loads along S_1

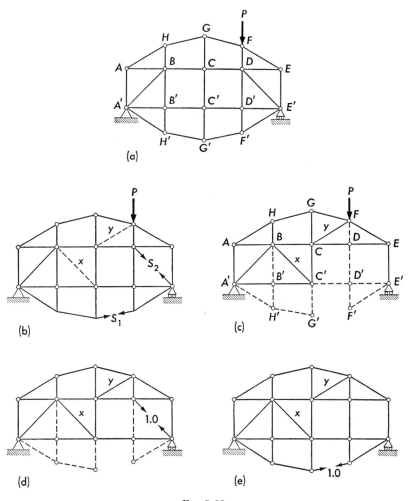

Fig. 5–22.

or S_2. The first subscript will designate the member stressed and the second subscript the application line of the unit load.

$$X = S_x + u_{x,1}S_1 + u_{x,2}S_2 = 0$$
$$Y = S_y + u_{y,1}S_1 + u_{y,2}S_2 = 0$$

(5–48)

Since S_1 and S_2 are the only unknowns in the equations, the equations can be solved directly for them. Once numerical values are thus established for S_1 and S_2, the solution may proceed directly for the other stresses by the method of joints or moments.

PROBLEMS

5–1, 5–2. The structures shown in the illustration represent idealized diagrams of engine mounts for aircraft and similar structures. Find the stresses due to the dead weight, thrust, and moment as shown in each case.

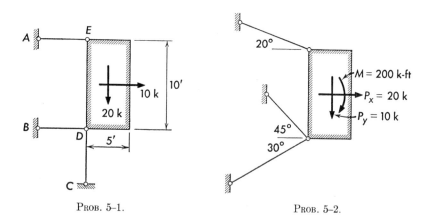

PROB. 5–1.   PROB. 5–2.

5–3. Ordinarily a bar would be placed in the U_1L_2 position in the truss shown in the accompanying illustration; however, to provide area for duct work, the bar has to be placed in the position U_1L_3 as shown. Is the truss stable? Simple? Find the stresses in the members due to the loads shown.

5–4. A turnbuckle is tightened in the rod GH to provide a load P, as shown in the figure, in the stiffening truss for a large bin. Find the stresses in the members.

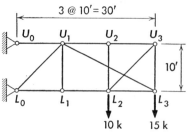

PROB. 5–3.

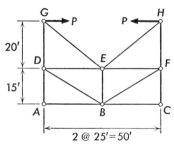

PROB. 5–4.

5–5. Find the stresses due to the concentrated load of 4000 lb, as shown in the illustration, on the truss supporting a conveyor belt.

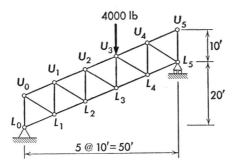

PROB. 5–5.

5–6. Find the stresses in the aircraft undercarriage shown in the figure.

5–7. Find the stresses in the simple truss shown in the figure. *Note:* Before computing any stresses, be sure to eliminate those bars having zero stress.

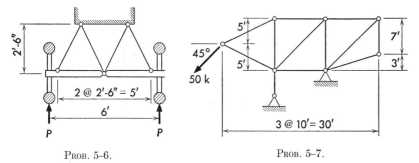

PROB. 5–6.   PROB. 5–7.

5–8. The joints of the upper and lower chord of the camel'sback truss in the illustration lie on a parabolic curve. Find the stresses in the bars.

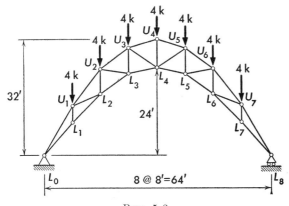

PROB. 5–8.

5–9. Find the stresses in the bars joining at U_1 and at U_4 in the compound truss shown in the accompanying figure.

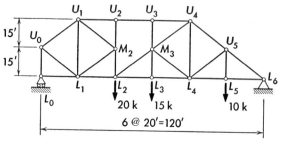

PROB. 5–9.

5–10. Find the stresses in the members of the camel'sback roof truss, due to the wind loads shown on the sketch.

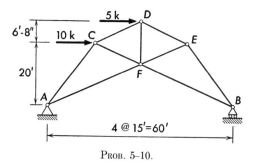

PROB. 5–10.

5–11 to 5–13. Find the stresses in the trusses of Problems 3–15, 3–16, and 3–17 by (a) methods of joints, (b) methods of sections, and (c) most convenient mixing of (a) and (b).

5–14 to 5–21. Find the stresses in Problems 4–1 to 4–8 of Chapter 4 by the most convenient method.

5–22, 5–23, 5–24. Three compound trusses are shown in the illustration. Determine whether the compounding connection between the simple trusses is a stable one, and if it is, find the stresses in these connecting members.

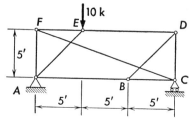

PROB. 5–22.

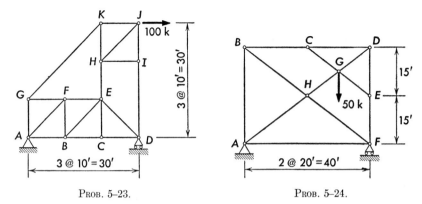

PROB. 5–23.   PROB. 5–24.

5–25. The figure here shows a Bollman truss, invented by Wendell Bollman about 1850. Although this truss is no longer built because of its long diagonals, it had one advantage, i.e., the upper chord had the same stress throughout for any given load no matter what panels or combination of panels was loaded. Can you prove that this was so?

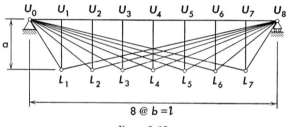

PROB. 5–25.

5–26. The Fink truss was invented by Albert Fink about 1852. It was used frequently for long spans in that era. In reality this truss is a trussed beam. Still common today is a version of this truss used for building roofs. Find the stresses due to the 10-k load shown in the sketch.

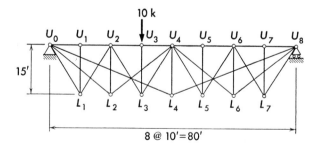

PROB. 5–26.

5-27. Find the stresses in the Baltimore (Pettit) truss due to the dead-load forces shown. Although the dead load is distributed along each beam, it is common practice to concentrate it at the panel points for design calculations.

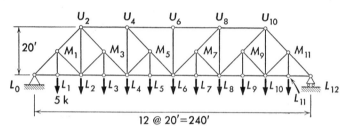

PROB. 5-27.

5-28. Three similar trusses are shown in the figure. The trusses (a) and (c) are compound trusses. Discuss the stability of each. Note that if the truss DEF of truss (a) is gradually reduced, it approaches the form of truss (b) in the limit. What is the specific difference between these two forms? What effect does the rotation of DEF of truss (a) to a new position, as shown in truss (c), have on its analysis?

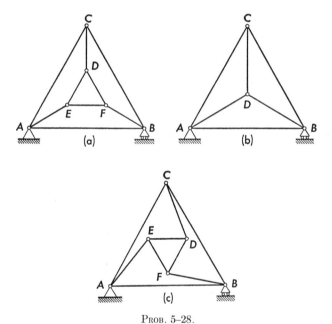

PROB. 5-28.

5-29. The truss shown in the sketch is a Warren truss with subdivided panels. Such subdivision braces the long diagonals of the ordinary Warren truss, usually resulting in materials being saved in the struts. Treat the truss as a compound structure, and find the stresses in all members joining at the joints A, B, C, and E.

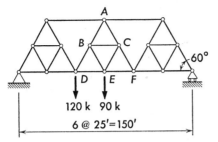

PROB. 5–29.

5–30, 5–31. Find the stresses in these forms of the Baltimore truss by (a) ordinary treatment as a compound truss and (b) superposition.

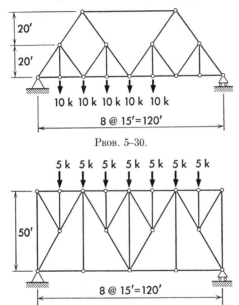

PROB. 5–30.

PROB. 5–31.

5–32. Discuss which of these three trusses are stable. Use the following methods: (a) by simultaneous solution of the equations of statics at each joint; (b) by the use of the zero load test.

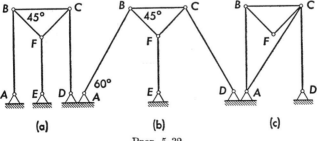

PROB. 5–32.

5–33. A hexagonal truss used for supporting tunnel lining during construction is shown at the left in the accompanying illustration. Is it statically determinate and stable? What would be the effect of the introduction of a pin G where the members cross as shown at the right?

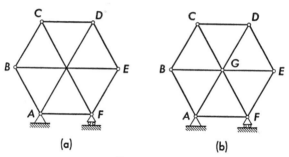

(a)   (b)

PROB. 5–33.

5–34. A load P is placed horizontally at the corner C of the hexagonal truss of Problem 5–33. Find the stresses.

5–35. Use the zero load test to check the stability of the truss in the sketch.

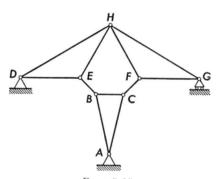

PROB. 5–35.

5–36, 5–37, 5–38. Find the stresses in DF and BG in this complex truss.

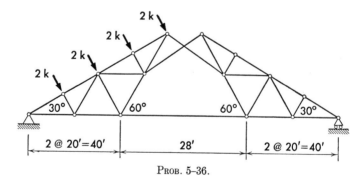

PROB. 5–36.

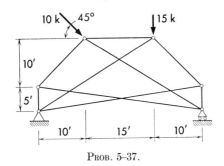

PROB. 5–37.

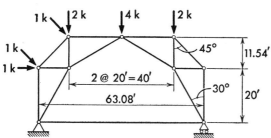

PROB. 5–38.

5–39. Find the stresses in DF and BG in this complex truss.

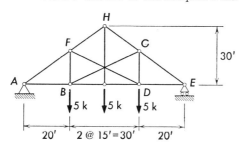

PROB. 5–39.

5–40. Find the stresses in this bridge truss for all the web members in the two center panels U_2–U_3–U_4.

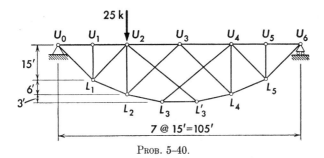

PROB. 5–40.

5–41. Find the stresses in members *CD*, *DE*, *CJ*, and *EJ* of the truss shown for this problem.

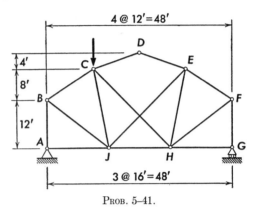

PROB. 5–41.

CHAPTER 6

ROOF TRUSSES

Roof trusses are used over areas that must be free of interior walls and columns. They may be supported by masonry walls or be a part of the structural frame of either steel or wood. A roof truss is usually economical for spans in excess of 40 ft. This chapter discusses stress analyses for trusses which are supported on masonry walls or piers.

Roof trusses are usually simply supported at the ends. One end is anchored to the wall by bolts, which will not allow translation, while at the other end slotted holes in the base plate and circular holes in an underlying masonry plate permit horizontal movement due to expansion or contraction of the truss. This arrangement is satisfactory for span lengths up to about 70 ft. For longer spans, roof trusses should be hinged at one end and should rest on rollers at the other end.

A general arrangement of roof construction is shown in Fig. 6–1. A series of parallel trusses are supported on masonry walls or on columns embedded in the walls. The distance between the supports is called the *span* of the truss, and the distance from these to its highest point is termed the *rise*. The roofing is generally carried on longitudinal beams called *purlins*, which rest on the top chord, and preferably, at the truss joints.

The purlins and the roofing also serve as longitudinal bracing, which is supplemented by additional top and bottom chord bracing. The function of this bracing is to resist forces such as wind pressures that act perpendicularly to the planes of the trusses. Another purpose of the bracing is to reduce the lateral lengths of the unsupported truss members and thus prevent their lateral buckling.

In the plane of the top chord the bracing usually consists of diagonals in the form of rods or light angles in every third or fourth bay. These diagonals may be placed just underneath the purlins. The bottom chord bracing may consist of diagonals and struts. The struts should ordinarily continue through all the bays, and the diagonals should be placed in the same bays as the top chord diagonals.

6–1. Types of Roof Trusses. Roof trusses are usually divided into equal panels along the top chord upon which the purlins rest. Fig. 6–2 shows the common types of trusses which support roofs of comparatively steep slopes. In the Pratt truss, Fig. 6–2a, the diagonals will develop tension and the verticals will exert compression due to the dead and live loads. In the Howe truss, Fig. 6–2b, the situation is reversed; the diagonals will be in compression and the verticals in tension. These truss arrangements are named after the inventors who secured patents for these

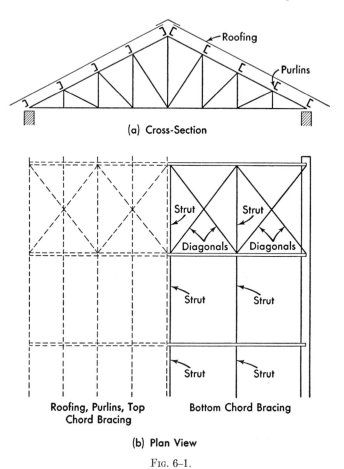

(a) Cross-Section

(b) Plan View

Fig. 6–1.

systems more than a century ago (Thomas and Caleb Pratt in 1844; William Howe in 1840).

The most economical truss and the one most widely used is the Fink truss, shown in Fig. 6–2c. The Fan truss, Fig. 6–2d, is less frequently used because it is not economical except for very short spans.

If additional lighting and ventilation of the interior of the building are required, it is feasible to add a *monitor* along the ridge of the roof, as shown in Fig. 6–2e. It should be noted that all the various types of

Fig. 6–2 can be provided with a monitor. The addition of six members and three joints will maintain the statical determinacy of the trusses.

For comparatively flat roofs the truss types in Fig. 6–3 can be used. A Pratt truss (Fig. 6–3a) is the most economical if all members are of structural steel. The long web members (the diagonals) are in tension, whereas the shorter ones (the verticals) are in compression. In the Howe

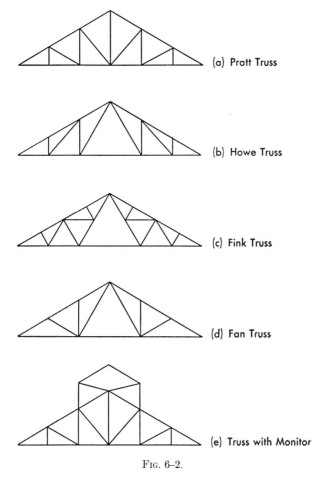

Fig. 6–2.

truss, Fig. 6–3b, where these stresses are reversed, economy of construction can usually be achieved by making the diagonals of wood and the verticals of steel rods. In the Warren truss, Fig. 6–3c, the diagonals will be in tension or compression, depending upon whether the slope is toward the center or the ends.

For long-span roofs, the trusses should be of the arch type, in order to be economical. Fig. 6–4 shows a three-hinged arch. For very steep

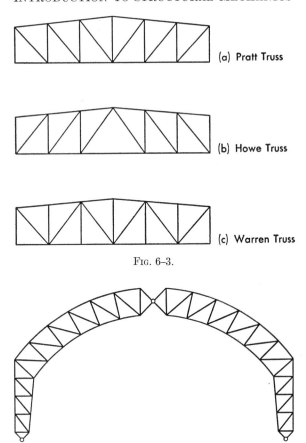

FIG. 6–3.

FIG. 6–4.

roofs, such as those used in church construction, the scissors truss, Fig. 6–5, can be used to advantage. For cantilever roofs, all the types shown in Fig. 6–2 can be used. Fig. 6–6 shows a Fink cantilever truss. The cantilever can also be made part of a simply supported truss, as indicated in Fig. 6–7.

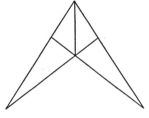

FIG. 6–5.

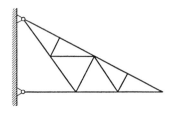

FIG. 6–6.

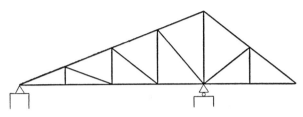

Fig. 6–7.

6–2. Loads on Roof Trusses. The members of roof trusses will develop stresses due to dead load, live load, and wind load. These loads are initially resisted by the roofing and are transmitted to the panel points of the truss in the form of concentrated forces.

The dead load comprises the weight of the completed roof, including the truss, and must be evaluated before the stresses in the members can be determined. Table 6–1 lists the approximate weights of some com-

TABLE 6–1

WEIGHTS OF ROOFING MATERIALS

Roofing felt, 3-ply and gravel	5½ #/□′
Roofing felt, 5-ply and gravel	6½ "
Wood shingles	3 "
Asbestos shingles	4 "
Corrugated steel, 12 gage	5 "
Corrugated steel, 18 gage	2½ "
Corrugated steel, 24 gage	1½ "
Wood planking, ¾ in. thick	2½ "
Wood planking, 1⅝ in. thick	5½ "
Asphalt shingles	2 "
Ceiling, metal lath and plaster	10 "

monly used roofing materials. In addition to evaluating the over-all weight, it is necessary to make a preliminary estimate of the weight of the truss itself, which can be checked after the design has been completed. Several empirical formulas are available for determining the weight of trusses when the span is known, taking into account also the type of material, allowable working stresses, and types of connections (such as welded, riveted, or bolted). A simple and approximate rule is to assume the weight as $0.05L + 1.5$ psf of horizontal projection of the roof (L = span in feet). This figure includes the weight of the trusses and also of all top and bottom chord bracing.

The live load on roofs may be due to accumulated snow or to weight of additional roofing material stored temporarily during repairs, as well as the weight of persons working on such repairs. The actual snow load will depend on the slope of the roof (a great deal of snow can accumulate on a flat roof and only small amounts on a steep roof). Local building codes usually specify live load-intensities either in the form of snow load or as an allowance that will take care of various contingencies. Live loads on trusses are generally specified as 30 to 40 psf of horizontal projection of the roof.

6–3. Wind Load. The effects of wind on a structure are significant, and it is important that the forces on the structure, which can be assumed to be equivalent to the wind pressure, be correctly evaluated. Wind forces, though dynamic, can be assumed static for most engineering structures. These static forces are usually determined by the designer from specifications and building codes.

The wind pressure on an exposed surface is a function of the air velocity. The velocity pressure is the product of one-half the air density times the square of the air velocity and represents the kinetic energy per unit volume of moving air. For an air density of 0.07651 pcf, corresponding to 15° C at 760 mm of mercury, and the velocity V expressed in miles per hour, the velocity pressure in pounds per square foot is given by

$$q = \frac{1}{2} \times \frac{0.07651}{32.2} V^2 \left(\frac{5280}{3600}\right)^2$$
$$q = 0.002558V^2 \tag{6–1}$$

For buildings with plane surfaces normal to the wind, the total combined pressure on the outside of the windward and leeward faces will average 1.3q, of which 0.8q is the pressure on the windward wall and 0.5q is the suction on the leeward wall. Therefore

$$p = 1.3q = 1.3 \times 0.002558V^2$$
$$p = 0.0033V^2 \tag{6–2}$$

According to this equation a wind velocity of 77.8 mph will correspond to a total pressure of 20 psf. A total pressure of 30 psf will be produced by a wind velocity of 95 mph.

A committee of the American Society of Civil Engineers [*] has made a number of recommendations for wind pressures on buildings and roof surfaces. These recommendations are based on a total pressure on a vertical building at 20 psf.

For plane surfaces inclined to the wind, the recommended wind forces are as follows:

1. Windward Slope (α = angle with horizontal)
   a. For α not greater than 20°, a suction of 12 lb per sq ft.
   b. For α between 20° and 30°, a force of $p = 1.2\alpha - 36$ . . . . (3)

* "Wind Bracing in Steel Buildings," Final Report of Sub-committee 31, Committee on Steel of the Structural Division, *Trans. ASCE*, **105**, 1713 (1940).

c. For α between 30° and 60°, a force of $p = 0.30\alpha - 9$............(4)
the positive value indicating pressure.

d. For α greater than 60°, a pressure of 9 lb per sq ft.

2. Leeward Slope

a. For all values of α in excess of zero, a suction of 9 lb per sq ft.

The external wind forces applied to the windward slope are shown graphically in Fig. 6–8.

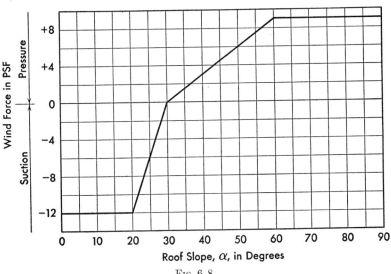

FIG. 6–8.

Recommendations were also made by the ASCE Committee on External Wind Forces for rounded, or approximately rounded, roof surfaces. Considering the rounded roof as represented roughly by a circular arc passing through the two eaves and the ridge, and letting the symbol r denote the ratio of rise of the arc to its span, the recommended wind forces for surfaces not more than 300 ft above ground level are as follows:

1. Windward Quarter of Roof Arc

a. For roofs resting on elevated vertical supports:
When r is less than 0.2, a suction of 12 lb per sq ft.
When r is greater than 0.2, a pressure of

$$p = 30r - 6 \tag{5}$$

Alternatively, when r is between 0.2 and 0.35, a force of

$$p = 80r - 28 \tag{6}$$

the negative sign indicating suction.

b. For roofs starting from ground level:
For all values of r, a pressure of

$$p = 19r \tag{7}$$

2. Central Half of Roof Arc
   a. For roofs resting on elevated vertical supports, a suction of

$$p = 15r + 11 \tag{8}$$

   b. For roofs starting from ground level, a suction of 11 lb per sq ft.

3. Leeward Quarter of Roof Arc—For all values of r greater than zero, a suction of 9 lb per sq ft.

The ASCE committee also recommended the use of internal pressures on roofs and walls. Even for buildings that are normally airtight, internal wind forces of either pressure or suction may exist. Large internal pressures may arise due to the breaking of windows. Still larger internal forces of pressure or suction may arise when the windward or leeward side of a building is completely open. The committee recommended that for buildings that are normally airtight, an internal pressure or suction of 4.5 psf should be considered as acting normal to the walls and the roof. For buildings with 30 per cent or more of the wall surfaces open, or subject to being open, an internal pressure of 12 psf or an internal suction of 9 psf was recommended. For buildings that have percentages of wall openings varying from 0 to 30 per cent of the wall space, the recommendation was an internal pressure varying uniformly from 4.5 to 12 psf, or an internal suction varying uniformly from 4.5 to 9 psf.

6–4. Numerical Example: Recommendations of ASCE. As a numerical application of the foregoing recommendations, assume that it is desired to evaluate the external wind forces on a semi-circular roof, starting from the ground level. The frames form 180° arcs, each with three hinges and each at 10 ft on center.

The ratio r for this roof is one-half, and substituting this into Eq. 6–7, it is found that the windward quarter of the roof arc is subjected to a normal pressure of 9.5 psf. The recommendations also indicate that the

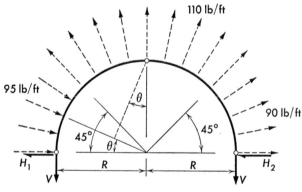

FIG. 6–9.

central half of the arc will sustain a suction of 11 psf and the leeward quarter a suction of 9 psf. With a distance of 10 ft between the frames, the forces will be as shown in Fig. 6–9.

Next let it be assumed that the frames are three-hinged arches. In addition to the two supporting hinges, there is also a top hinge on the centerline. It is desired to find the two reactions due to the external wind forces.

If the two reactions are each represented by a vertical and a horizontal component, it is found that by taking moments about the center of the semi-circle, the two vertical components must be equal. Projecting all forces and reactions on a vertical line gives

$$2V + \int_0^{45°} 95R \, d\theta \sin\theta = 2\int_{45°}^{90°} 110R \, d\theta \sin\theta + \int_0^{45°} 90R \, d\theta \sin\theta$$

$$2V = -5R \int_0^{45°} \sin\theta \, d\theta + 220R \int_{45°}^{90°} \sin\theta \, d\theta$$

$$2V = -(5R \times 0.293) + (220R \times 0.707) = 154.075R \qquad (6\text{–}3)$$

$$V = 77R$$

In order to find the two horizontal components, a horizontal line is projected to give

$$H_1 + H_2 = \int_0^{45°} 95R \, d\theta \cos\theta + \int_0^{45°} 90R \, d\theta \cos\theta$$

$$H_1 + H_2 = 185R \int_0^{45°} \cos\theta \, d\theta = 185R \sin 45° = 131R \qquad (6\text{–}4)$$

The component H_1 can be found by taking moments about the top hinge of all forces and reactions to the left of it; thus:

$$H_1 \times R - 77R \times R - \int_0^{45°} 95R \, d\theta \times R \cos\theta$$

$$+ \int_{45°}^{90°} 110R \, d\theta \times R \cos\theta = 0$$

$$H_1 = 77R + 95R \int_0^{45°} \cos\theta \, d\theta - 110R \int_{45°}^{90°} \cos\theta \, d\theta \qquad (6\text{–}5)$$

$$H_1 = R[77 + (95 \times 0.707) - (110 \times 0.293)] = 112R$$

6–5. Analysis of Fink Truss. Fig. 6–10a shows the general arrangement of a Fink truss and the dimensions for a span of 60 ft. The top chord is divided into equal panel lengths, and perpendiculars have been drawn through the panel points to intersect the bottom chord and the main diagonal. The diagonals will either be horizontal or make angles with the horizontal that are twice the angle of the top chord.

In order to find the stresses in the various members due to dead and live loads, the forces resulting from these must first be evaluated. These forces will usually be equal except at the ends, where they will be of one-half values if there is no roof overhang. If the overhang is equal to

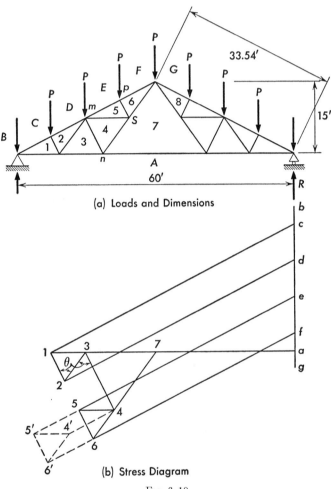

(a) Loads and Dimensions

(b) Stress Diagram

Fig. 6-10.

one-half the panel length, the two outside panel forces will have the same magnitude as the other forces.

Fig. 6-10b shows the construction of the stress diagram resulting from equal vertical loads at each panel point. The areas between forces and reactions are designated by letters a, b, c, d, $\cdots$, and those between members are identified by numbers 1, 2, 3, 4, $\cdots$. Due to symmetry, the two end reactions must be equal, and the force polygon for the external forces must be a straight line a, b, c, d, $\cdots$. If taken in succession, the first three truss joints (left end, first top-chord joint, first bottom-chord joint) will each have only two unknown stresses, and the diagram including the points *1*, *2*, and *3* can be readily constructed. Proceeding next to the adjacent joints m or n, it is seen that both contain three unknown stresses, and this condition apparently blocks further progress. A convenient way of completing the diagram is to skip temporarily the joints m and n, Fig. 6–10a, and go on to joint p. A value represented by f–6 is assumed for the stress in member F–6, and the diagram e–f–$6'$–$5'$ is drawn. Joint S is treated next. Because the resultant of 6–7 and 7–4 must lie on the main diagonal, the tentative position $4'$, corresponding to area *4*, can be determined by intersection of two lines parallel to 5–4 and 4–7. Finally, because the line connecting *3* and $4'$ in the stress diagram must be parallel to member 3–4, it is seen that point $4'$ must be moved to point *4* and that the assumed value of f–$6'$ must be replaced by f–6 in order to make the diagram consistent. The remaining portion of the diagram can now be readily constructed.

If the lengths cd, de, ef, and ag in the stress diagram are taken as unity, then by scaling the other lengths, it is possible to express all stresses as numerical coefficients times the panel load P. It is also possible to compute the various stresses from the diagram, and if the length of the top chord is 33.54 ft, then

$$S_{1-a} = 3.5P\frac{30}{15} = 7P$$

$$S_{1-c} = 3.5P\frac{33.54}{15} = 7.826P \tag{6-6}$$

$$S_{1-2} = P\,\frac{30}{33.54} = 0.894P$$

If the angle between *1*–*2* and *2*–*3* is θ, then

$$\frac{1}{2}S_{1-2} = S_{2-3}\cos\theta = S_{2-3}\frac{15}{33.54}$$

$$S_{2-3} = \frac{33.54}{30}S_{1-2} = \frac{33.54}{30}\times\frac{30}{33.54}P \tag{6-7}$$

$$S_{2-3} = P$$

The stress in member *6*–*7* must be three times the stress in member *2*–*3*; thus:

$$S_{6-7} = 3P$$

The stress in member *3*–*4* must be twice the stress in member *1*–*2*; thus:

$$S_{3-4} = 1.789P$$

The external wind forces acting upon the Fink truss in Fig. 6–10b are functions of the slope of the top chord. This angle of slope, whose tangent is ½, is 26°34′. Substituting in Eq. 6–3 gives a suction of 4.12 psf. On the leeward slope there will also be suction with an intensity of 9 psf (see Fig. 6–8).

These uniform loads, shown on Fig. 6–11, should be multiplied by panel length and truss spacing in order to be translated into panel forces. As indicated in Fig. 6–11b, the truss will be subjected to two sets of forces: P on the left top chord and P_1 on the right. It is convenient to treat each set separately.

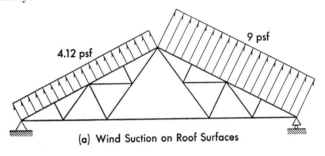

(a) Wind Suction on Roof Surfaces

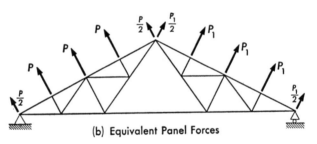

(b) Equivalent Panel Forces

Fig. 6–11.

Fig. 6–12a shows the truss subjected to one set of external forces. Also shown are some of the principal dimensions needed for the stress analysis. Thus the dimension x between points a and e is found to be $16.77 \div x = 30 \div 33.54$, and the distance from j to e is $60 - x$. In order to find the reaction at the right end, take moments about the left end.

$$R \times 60 = P \times 8.385\,(1 + 2 + 3 + 2); \qquad R = 1.118P$$

It can be readily seen that the stresses in all web members in the right half must be zero. By projecting the stresses and the reaction at j onto a vertical line,

$$1.118P - S_{hj}\frac{15}{33.54} = 0$$

$$S_{hj} = 2.5P$$

(6–8)

and by projecting on a line perpendicular to h–j,

$$1.118P + S_{ej}\frac{15}{30} = 0$$

$$S_{ej} = -2.236P$$

$$(6\text{–}9)$$

The stress in fh is found by taking moments of the right reaction, the external force at h, and the stress about joint e; thus:

$$(1.118P \times 41.25) - (\tfrac{1}{2}P \times 16.77) - (S_{fh} \times 8.385) = 0$$

$$S_{fh} = 4.5P$$

$$(6\text{–}10)$$

The stress in gh is evaluated by shifting the moment center to joint a.

$$(1.118P \times 60) - (\tfrac{1}{2}P \times 33.54) + (S_{gh} \times 15) = 0$$

$$S_{gh} = -3.354P$$

$$(6\text{–}11)$$

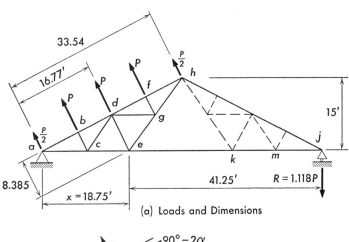

(a) Loads and Dimensions

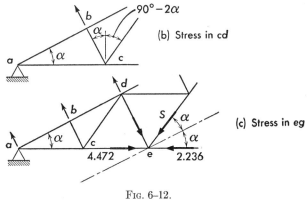

(b) Stress in cd

(c) Stress in eg

Fig. 6–12.

In order to find the stress in ac, a section is passed across this member and across ab. Moments of all members on the right of this section are then taken about joint h.

$$(1.118P \times 30) + (3P \times 16.77) + (S_{ac} \times 15) = 0$$

$$S_{ac} = -5.592P \qquad (6\text{--}12)$$

The stress in bottom chord ce is found by passing a section across members ce, cd, and bd. Moments about d gives

$$(1.118P \times 45) - (P \times 16.77) + (S_{ce} \times 7.5) = 0$$

$$S_{ce} = -4.472P \qquad (6\text{--}13)$$

The stress in ab can be found by the same section but using joint c instead for a moment center; thus:

$$-P(8.385 + 16.77 + \tfrac{1}{2} \cdot 25.155) + (1.118P \times 50.625)$$

$$- (S_{bd} \times 4.1925) = 0$$

$$S_{bd} = 4.5P \qquad (6\text{--}14)$$

The stresses in bc and fg are the same, and each is equal to P. From Fig. 6–12b it is seen that the stress in members cd and dg can be determined by projecting stresses at joints c on a vertical line; thus:

$$-P \cos \alpha = S_{cd} \sin 2\alpha$$

$$S_{cd} = \frac{-P}{2 \sin \alpha} \qquad (6\text{--}15)$$

$$S_{cd} = \frac{-P}{0.8944} = -1.118P$$

The stress in member de is found by projecting all stresses and forces at d onto this member; thus:

$$S_{de} = P + \left(2 \times 1.118P \, \frac{15}{33.54} \right) = 2P \qquad (6\text{--}16)$$

Fig. 6–12c shows that the stress in member eg must be the difference between stresses in members ce and ej; thus:

$$S_{eg} = -4.472 + 2.236 = -2.236P \qquad (6\text{--}17)$$

A summary of all stresses due to external wind forces on the left side is given in Fig. 6–13. These stresses should be added to those produced by external wind forces on the right, or leeward, side of the truss, as shown in Fig. 6–14.

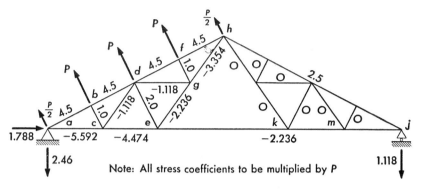

Fig. 6–13.

The advantages of treating each of the two sets of forces separately are readily realized from a comparison of Fig. 6–12 and Fig. 6–13. The two vertical reactions are the same except that they are interchanged. The horizontal reaction is the same; only its direction has been reversed. The stresses in the loaded top chord and in the web members under it are the same for both cases and need not be recomputed.

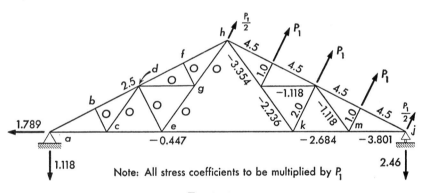

Fig. 6–14.

Finally the external forces P and P_1 should be evaluated. As a numerical application let it be assumed that the trusses are spaced 16 ft on center. From Fig. 6–11 it follows that the magnitudes of the panel loads will equal

$$P = 16 \times 8.385 \times 4.12 = 552.74 \text{ lb}$$
$$P_1 = 16 \times 8.385 \times 9 = 1207.44 \text{ lb}$$

(6–18)

The total wind load stresses have been evaluated and listed according to the above values in Table 6–2. Similarly the stress coefficients found in

TABLE 6–2

TOTAL STRESSES RESULTING FROM WIND

Top Chord	ah:	(4.500×553)	$+ (2.500 \times 1207)$	$= 5506$
Top Chord	hj:	2.500	$+ 4.500$	$= 6814$
Bottom Chord	ac:	-5.592	$- 0.447$	$= -3632$
Bottom Chord	ce:	-4.472	$- 0.447$	$= -3013$
Bottom Chord	ek:	-2.236	$- 0.447$	$= -1777$
Bottom Chord	km:	-2.236	$- 2.684$	$= -4476$
Bottom Chord	mj:	-2.236	$- 3.801$	$= -5836$

Fig. 6–10 can be used for determining the stresses due to dead load and live load. Assume that the vertical loads are as follows:

Weight of truss...............................	4.5 psf
Weight of roofing	10.5 psf
Live load	30.0 psf
	45.0 psf

the magnitude of the vertical panel force in Fig. 6–10 will be

$$P = 16 \times 7.5 \times 45 = 5400 \text{ lb} \qquad (6\text{–}19)$$

The maximum stress in the top chord will occur in the panel next to the support and will equal

$$5400 \times 7.826 = 42,260 \text{ lb} \qquad (6\text{–}20)$$

The maximum stress in the bottom chord will also occur in the end panel and will equal

$$5400 \times 7 = 37,800 \text{ lb} \qquad (6\text{–}21)$$

PROBLEMS

6–1. The roof trusses in the sketch are spaced 20 ft on center. Assume a wind velocity of 77.8 mph, and find the wind forces (pressures and suctions in pounds per square foot) on surfaces $ABCDE$.

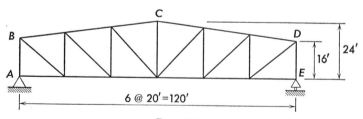

PROB. 6–1.

6–2. Find the panel loads in Problem 6–1 due to the wind forces.

6–3. Find stresses in all members due to the panel loads evaluated in Problem 6–2.

6–4. Determine the stresses in all members of the truss in Problem 6–1 due to vertical panel loads of 4 k on the top chord and 1 k on the bottom chord.

6–5. Find stresses due to panel loads in all members of the Fink truss shown in the illustration.

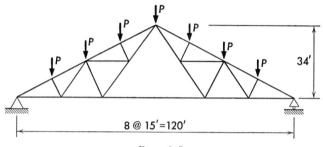

PROB. 6–5.

6–6. Find stresses due to panel loads in all members of the Pratt truss shown in the illustration.

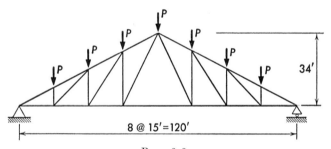

PROB. 6–6.

6–7. If S = stress and l = length of any member, then the quantity $\Sigma S \times l$ can be considered as proportional to the material required for the fabrication of a truss. Evaluate these quantities for the trusses in Problems 6–5 and 6–6, and compare for economy.

6–8. Find the ratio between the forces P_1 and P_2 if it is known that the stress in member AB is equal to zero.

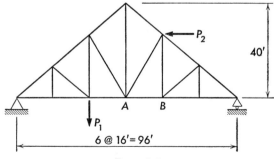

PROB. 6–8.

CHAPTER 7

THE INFLUENCE LINE

When a single unit load moves across a structure, its effect upon any function of the load for any position of the load is represented by a diagram, called *the influence line*. The function of the load may be a reaction, a bending moment, shear stress, deflection, or any other quantity, provided that its value is a function of the position of the unit load on the structure. The value of the function for any position of the unit load is measured by the ordinate to the influence line at the point where the load is placed.

Influence lines are important in analyses of structures subjected to the action of moving loads, such as bridges carrying railroad and highway traffic. In many cases they constitute the only practicable method of determining conditions for maximum and minimum loading.

7-1. Bending Moment. Influence lines for bending moments in beams are in many ways similar and often identical in appearance to moment diagrams, but their interpretation is very different. In order to bring out the similarities and differences between the two types of diagrams, consider the beam AB, Fig. 7-1, subjected to the action of a fixed unit load.

If the bending moments which occur at the various points of this beam are plotted directly above the points, the resulting diagram is a triangle known as the *moment diagram*.

Consider next the same beam AB in Fig. 7-2, which is subjected to the action of a moving unit load while an observer stationed at point M records the bending moments due to various positions of the traveling unit load. If these moments (all occurring at M) are plotted above the respective positions of the moving unit load, the resulting diagram is the influence line for the bending moment at M. It can be readily seen that the influence line is a triangle, having a maximum ordinate of $(ab) \div l$. The two triangles in Fig. 7-1 (the moment diagram) and Fig. 7-2 (the influence line) are identical, but the difference between them should be kept clearly in mind. In the case of the moment diagram the load is fixed, and the observer moves along the beam and records the bending moments at all points. In the case of the influence line the load moves from one end of the beam to the other, whereas the observer is fixed at one point and records the various values of the bending moment at this one point.

148

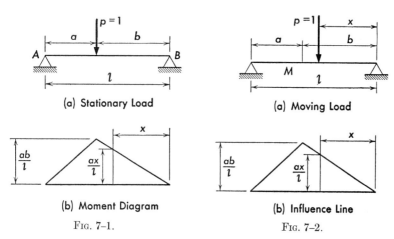

(a) Stationary Load   (a) Moving Load

(b) Moment Diagram   (b) Influence Line

FIG. 7–1.   FIG. 7–2.

Fig. 7–3 shows the influence line for the bending moment at M in a beam with an overhanging end. In this case the bending moment will change direction as the unit load passes over the support B. Between A and B the force will produce compression in the top of the beam at M; between B and C the moving load will effect tension in the top.

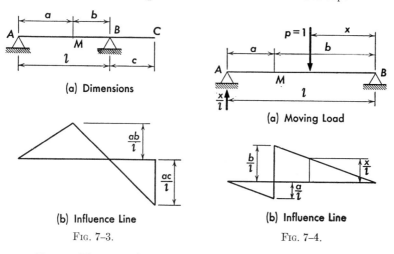

(a) Dimensions

(a) Moving Load

(b) Influence Line   (b) Influence Line

FIG. 7–3.   FIG. 7–4.

7–2. Shear. Fig. 7–4 shows a beam AB subjected to the action of a moving unit load. It is desired to find the variation in shear at the point M. If the distance from B to the moving load is called x, it is found that the reaction at A is equal to $x \div l$. As long as the force P occupies a position to the right of M, this reaction will equal the shear. The influence line between B and M will therefore be a straight line; thus:

$$V = \frac{x}{l} \tag{7–1}$$

If the load P is placed between A and M, the shear will equal the difference between this reaction and the force. Since the force is always greater than the reaction, the shear will be negative on this portion and numerically equal to

$$V = 1 - \frac{x}{l} \tag{7-2}$$

If the point M is chosen immediately adjacent to the support, the shear will be equal to the reaction, and the influence line will be a right triangle, as shown in Fig. 7–5.

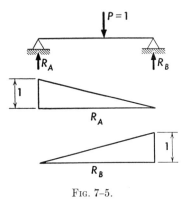

Fig. 7–5.

7–3. Influence Lines Between Panel Points. In a structure where the loads are transferred by members of a floor system to panel points, the influence line between consecutive load points is always a straight line.

Fig. 7–6 shows a girder on top of which rest a number of floor beams, which in turn support stringers running parallel to the girder. Thus the pressure exerted by a unit load is transmitted to the girder at points A, B, C. It is assumed that the stringers are each simply supported on the floor beams. Let y_1 and y_2 be the ordinates of the influence line when the load is placed at B and C, respectively. For intermediate positions the proportions of the load carried to the points B and C will be $x \div l$ and

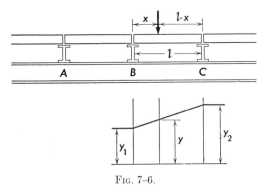

Fig. 7–6.

$(l - x) \div l$, respectively. The effect of the load in the intermediate position is therefore found by multiplying each end reaction by the corresponding value of the influence ordinate. Hence the effect will be

$$y = \frac{x}{l} y_2 + \frac{l - x}{l} y_1 \tag{7-3}$$

But this equation is linear in x; the influence line, which it represents, must be a straight line between the panel points B and C.

7–4. Parallel Chord Trusses. Fig. 7–7a shows a Pratt truss with parallel top and bottom chords. It is desired to find the influence lines for the bottom chord member cd and the diagonal Cd.

By passing a section through the bottom chord cd and either BC or CD, it is found that the stress in this member is equal to the bending moment at C of all forces (either to the right or to the left), divided by the lever

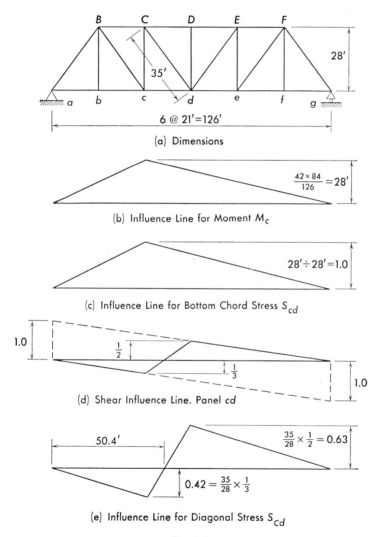

(a) Dimensions

(b) Influence Line for Moment M_c

$$\frac{42 \times 84}{126} = 28'$$

(c) Influence Line for Bottom Chord Stress S_{cd}

$$28' \div 28' = 1.0$$

(d) Shear Influence Line. Panel cd

$\frac{1}{2}$

$\frac{1}{3}$

1.0

1.0

(e) Influence Line for Diagonal Stress S_{cd}

50.4'

$$\frac{35}{28} \times \frac{1}{2} = 0.63$$

$$0.42 = \frac{35}{28} \times \frac{1}{3}$$

Fig. 7–7.

arm Cc. It follows that the influence line for the stress is the influence line for the moment at C (or c because all forces are vertical), divided by the depth of the truss. These two influence lines are shown in Fig. 7–7b and c, respectively.

The stress in the vertical member Cc will equal the shear in panel cd, and the influence line for this shear (Fig. 7–7d) will also be the influence line for the stress S_{Cc}. The stress in the diagonal Cd is also a function of the shear in panel cd and is equal to this shear divided by cosine of the angle between the diagonal and the vertical. The influence line for the stress in the diagonal will be as shown in Fig. 7–7e. Ordinates plotted above the base line indicate tension; those below, compression.

7–5. Curved Chord Trusses. Fig. 7–8 shows a Pratt truss with a curved top chord. Influence lines will be constructed for typical members.

In the case of the top chord member, BC, it is found that the stress will equal the moment about panel point c, divided by the perpendicular dis-

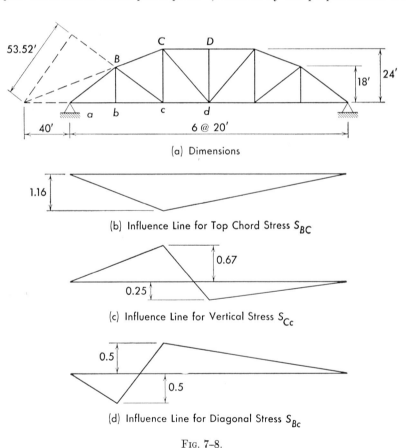

(a) Dimensions

(b) Influence Line for Top Chord Stress S_{BC}

(c) Influence Line for Vertical Stress S_{Cc}

(d) Influence Line for Diagonal Stress S_{Bc}

Fig. 7–8.

tance from this point to the member. The influence line for this member will be a triangle, Fig. 7–8b, having a maximum ordinate of

$$\frac{40 \times 80}{120 \times 23} = 1.16 \qquad (7\text{–}4)$$

The stress in the vertical member Cc is found by passing a section through this member and BC and cd and then taking moments about the

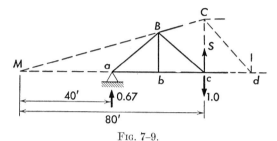

FIG. 7–9.

point of intersection of the two chord members. The two critical positions are the panel points c and d. If the unit load is placed at c, as shown in Fig. 7–9, the corresponding stress is

$$\frac{1 \times 80 - 0.67 \times 40}{80} = 0.67 \qquad (7\text{–}5)$$

and if the unit force is placed at d, the stress in the vertical will be compression and will equal

$$\frac{0.5 \times 40}{80} = 0.25 \qquad (7\text{–}6)$$

The stress in the diagonal member Bc can be found by passing a section through this member, top chord BC, and bottom chord bc. In order to find the stress, it is necessary first to determine the perpendicular distance from point M to Bc (Fig. 7–9) ; thus:

$$\frac{18}{\sqrt{18^2 + 20^2}}\, 80 = 53.52 \text{ ft} \qquad (7\text{–}7)$$

The critical points for the stress in diagonal Bc are the ends of the panel through which the section passes, namely, b and c. If the load is placed at b, the stress will be compression and will be equal to

$$\frac{1 \times 60 - 0.83 \times 40}{53.52} = 0.50 \qquad (7\text{–}8)$$

If the unit load is placed at c, the diagonal will be in tension equal to

$$\frac{0.67 \times 40}{53.52} = 0.50 \qquad (7\text{–}9)$$

The influence lines for the three members have been plotted in Fig. 7–8.

7-6. **Subdivided Trusses.** In order to achieve economy of materials, the slopes of the truss diagonals should be at approximately 45°. To obtain this slope, the panel length must be increased as the span (and consequently the depth) is increased, but long panel lengths will result in

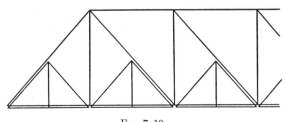

Fig. 7-10.

heavy and costly floor systems. The subdivided panel, as shown in Fig. 7-12, combines a large truss depth with a short panel and therefore is more economical. The subsequent discussion will show how influence lines can be constructed for a truss with subdivided panels.

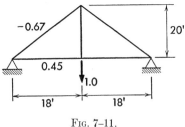

Fig. 7-11.

Fig. 7-10 explains how the subdivided truss can be considered as a main truss with six panels of 36 ft, upon which six smaller trusses are superposed. The stresses in the various members of the small truss, due to a unit load at its mid-span, are shown in Fig. 7-11.

Let it be desired to construct first the influence line for member ce in Fig. 7-12a. For the main truss this line is a triangle, having a maximum ordinate under point c equal to

$$\frac{(1/6) \times 180}{40} = 0.75 \tag{7-10}$$

For the subdivision truss, Fig. 7-11, the influence line is a triangle, having a base line corresponding to ce and a maximum ordinate under d equal to 0.45. The total ordinate under this point will be

$$(\tfrac{9}{10} \times 0.75) + 0.45 = 1.125 \tag{7-11}$$

The influence line for member CE is not affected by the subdivisions; it is shown in Fig. 7-11c. The line for the diagonal DE can also be obtained as a sum of two lines. For the main truss the influence line will consist of two parallel lines connected by the dotted line as shown in Fig. 7–11d. If the influence line in Fig. 7–11e is added, it will be found that the ordinate under point d will equal

$$0.67 - \tfrac{1}{2}(0.897 - 0.224) = 0.34 \qquad (7\text{--}12)$$

Finally the influence lines for the members Dc and Dd are constructed. They are shown in Fig. 7–12e and 7–12f.

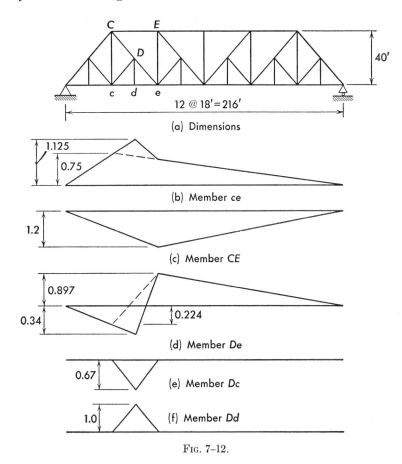

(a) Dimensions

(b) Member ce

(c) Member CE

(d) Member De

(e) Member Dc

(f) Member Dd

Fig. 7–12.

7–7. K-Trusses. This type of truss is being used increasingly for long-span bridges and for lateral bracing systems. In the following discussion typical influence lines will be constructed for a truss of the dimensions shown in Fig. 7–13a.

The influence line for bottom chord member cd is also the influence line for CD, the only difference being that the bottom chord is in tension while the top chord is in compression. The influence line for cd is shown in Fig. 7–13b. The maximum ordinate will occur under the moment

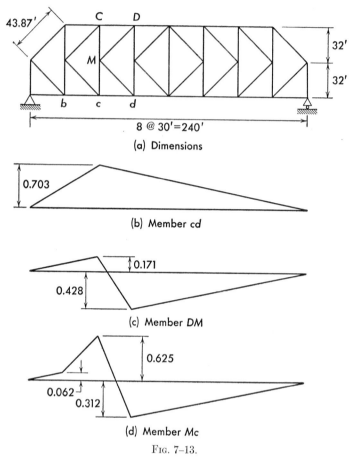

FIG. 7–13.

center C for this member, and the influence ordinates will be those for the moment influence line, divided by the lever arm (distance Cc); thus for the maximum ordinate:

$$\frac{60 \times 180}{240} \div 64 = 0.703 \tag{7–13}$$

The stress in the diagonal DM must be equal and opposite to the stress in the lower diagonal Md, and the sum of the two vertical components of these two stresses must be equal to the shear in panel cd. It follows that the influence line for member DM is the shear influence line for panel cd, divided by two times the cosine of angle CMD; thus:

$$2 \cos (CMD) = 2 \times 32 \div 43.87 = 1.46$$
$$0.25 \div 1.46 = 0.171 \qquad 0.625 \div 1.46 = 0.428 \tag{7–14}$$

The influence line is shown in Fig. 7–13c.

The stress in member Mc must be one-half the shear except when the unit load is placed directly under C, in which case it is found by subtracting one-half of the shear in panel bc from the unit load; thus:

$$1.00 - \tfrac{1}{2}0.75 = 0.625 \tag{7–15}$$

The influence line is shown in Fig. 7–13d.

7–8. Use of Influence Lines. The object of the influence line is to obtain an easily understood illustration of the effect of moving loads. By the use of influence lines it is possible to determine just what portion of a beam or a truss should be loaded in order to produce a maximum moment, shear, or stress in any particular part or member.

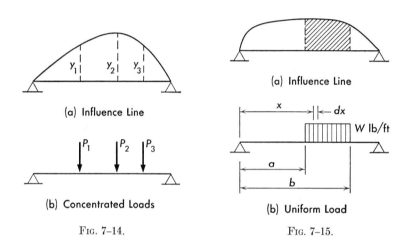

(a) Influence Line

(b) Concentrated Loads

Fig. 7–14.

(a) Influence Line

(b) Uniform Load

Fig. 7–15.

From Fig. 7–14 it is found that if the influence for a moment, shear, or stress is known, then the combined effect of a number of forces P_1, P_2, P_3, $\cdots$, will be

$$\Sigma Py = P_1 y_1 + P_2 y_2 + P_3 y_3 + \cdots \tag{7–16}$$

In the case of a uniformly distributed load covering a portion of a structure, as shown in Fig. 7–15, the total effect can be found by assuming the load to consist of an infinite number of infinitesimal forces, $w\,dx$. Integrating over the loaded portion gives

$$\int_a^b y \times w\,dx = w \int_a^b y\,dx = wA \tag{7–17}$$

where A is the area under that portion of the influence line that lies directly over the loaded portion. If this area is multiplied by the load intensity, the product will be the total effect of the uniformly distributed load.

As an example of the application of influence lines, consider the point M on a simply supported beam as shown in Fig. 7–16a. Let it be desired to find the maximum bending moment and the maximum shear which can be produced by a uniformly distributed live load. From Fig. 7–16b it is found that maximum moment will occur when the entire span is covered. Multiplying the area under the influence line by the load intensity gives

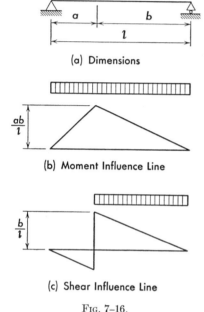

(a) Dimensions

(b) Moment Influence Line

(c) Shear Influence Line

Fig. 7–16.

$$M = \left(\frac{1}{2} \times \frac{ab}{l}\right) l \times w = \frac{1}{2} wab \tag{7-18}$$

In the case of maximum shear it can be seen from Fig. 7–16c that only a portion of the beam should be loaded, and the shear will be

$$V = \left(\frac{1}{2} \times \frac{b}{l}\right) b \times w = \frac{1}{2} \times \frac{b^2}{l} w \tag{7-19}$$

7–9. Numerical Example. Fig. 7–17 shows a truss supporting a conveyor belt and two runways. It is desired to find in all members the stresses due to live and dead loads indicated in the figure, as a preliminary to the design of the various parts of the truss.

Since the live load on the conveyor belt and the runways can occupy any portion of the bottom chord, it is necessary to construct the influence lines for the various members. As shown in Fig. 7–18, this can be done by placing a unit load at each of the five interior panel points and computing the stresses in the adjacent members. From Fig. 7–18 the influence lines for chord and web members can be plotted as indicated by Figs. 7–19, 7–20, 7–21, and 7–22. These figures also give the locations of points where (Figs. 7–21 and 7–22) the stress will change from tension to compression, and also show the areas (in feet) under the lines.

The influence lines can also be obtained directly from the moment and shear influence lines. In the case of the top chord, which will always be in compression, the maximum ordinate will be directly under the moment center and will equal the maximum moment divided by the lever arm.

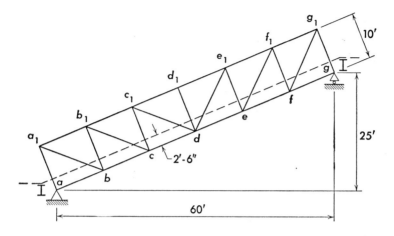

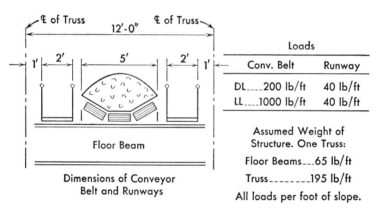

	Loads	
	Conv. Belt	Runway
DL____200 lb/ft		40 lb/ft
LL____1000 lb/ft		40 lb/ft

Floor Beam

Dimensions of Conveyor
Belt and Runways

Assumed Weight of
Structure. One Truss:

Floor Beams___65 lb/ft

Truss_____195 lb/ft

All loads per foot of slope.

Fig. 7–17.

Thus:

$$a_1b_1: \quad (10 \times 50 \div 60) \div 10 = 0.833$$

$$b_1c_1: \quad (20 \times 40 \div 60) \div 10 = 1.333 \qquad (7\text{--}20)$$

$$c_1d_1: \quad (30 \times 30 \div 60) \div 10 = 1.500$$

The stresses in the bottom chord will be in compression except for fg which, due to the slope, will be in tension. The bottom chord influence lines can also be constructed from the moment influence lines, but because the unit load is moving along the bottom chord and cannot be applied directly to the moment centers which lie on the top chord, these lines must be "shaved off" between panel points adjacent to the moment center. This will be illustrated for bottom chord member de. It is seen from Fig. 7–23

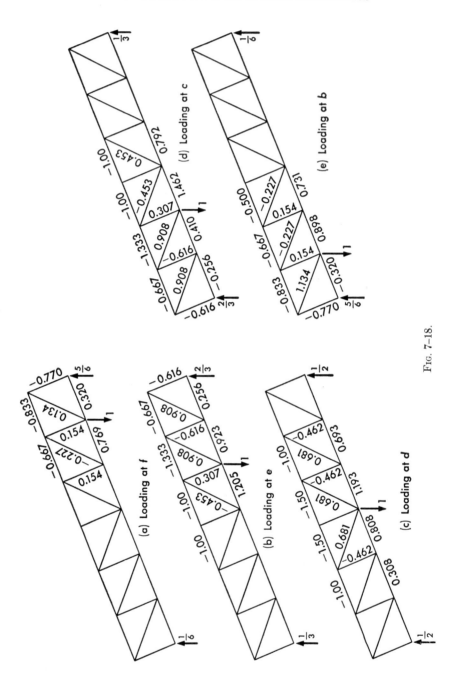

Fig. 7–18.

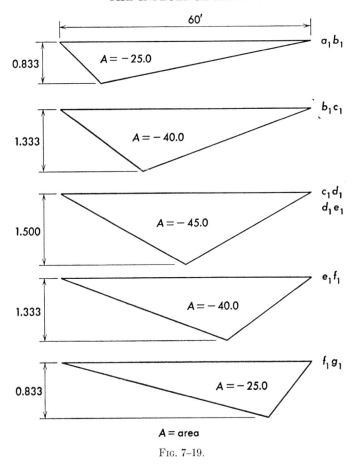

Fig. 7–19.

that the maximum ordinate for the stress, if the unit load could be placed at e_1, would be

$$\frac{36.15 \times 23.85}{60 \times 10} = 1.436 \qquad (7\text{--}21)$$

Because the unit load must be transmitted directly to panel points d and e, the influence line must be a single, straight line between these points; the corresponding ordinates are

$$30 \times (1.436 \div 36.15) = 1.194; \qquad 20 \times (1.436 \div 23.85) = 1.205 \quad (7\text{--}22)$$

In the case of the web members it should be recalled that these stresses can be found by passing appropriate sections and projecting onto lines perpendicular to the top chords. The influence lines for these members can be found by first determining the shear influence lines for the various panels in the truss, as shown in Fig. 7–24a. Next to be noted is that the

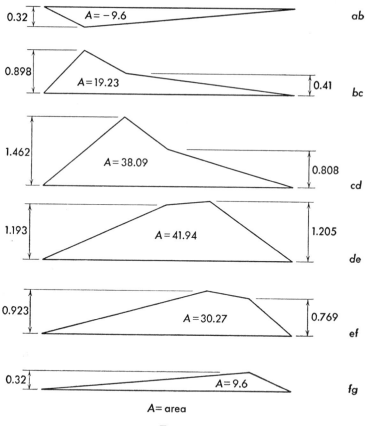

A= area

Fig. 7–20.

stresses in the verticals aa_1, bb_1, cc_1, $\cdots$ will equal the shears multiplied
by the cosine of the angle between the bottom chord and the horizontal.
This cosine is equal to $60 \div 65 = 0.923$. The result of this multiplication
is shown in Fig. 7–24b. For each panel point the quantity 0.923 is divided
up into two parts, and diagonally opposite points are connected. If
Fig. 7–22 is compared with Fig. 7–24b, it will be found that the influence
lines for the vertical web members are contained in Fig. 7–24b. The
influence lines for the diagonal web members can be found in a similar
manner.

The length of a diagonal is 14.74 ft. If S denotes the stress, then projecting onto a line perpendicular to the top and bottom chords gives

$$S \times \frac{10}{14.74} = \text{shear} \frac{60}{65}$$

$$S = 1.36 \times \text{shear}$$

(7–23)

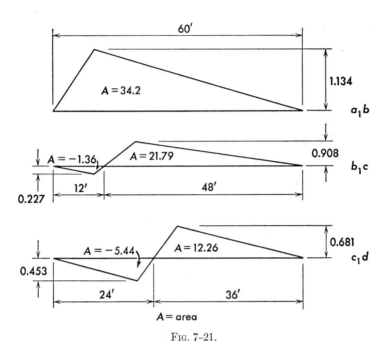

FIG. 7–21.

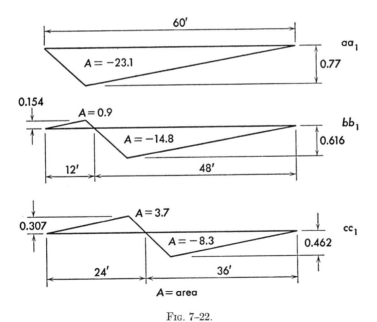

FIG. 7–22.

The result of this multiplication is shown in Fig. 7–24c, from which the influence lines for the diagonal web members can be taken directly (compare with Fig. 7–21).

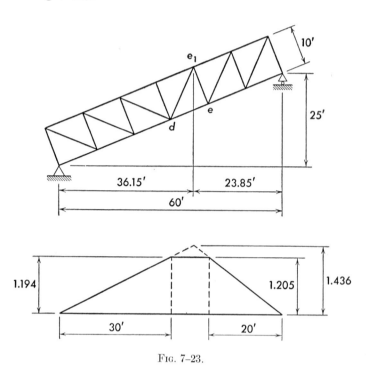

Fig. 7–23.

The dead and live loads can now be evaluated from Fig. 7–17; thus:

Floor beams	65 plf
Truss	195 plf
Conveyor belt	100 plf
Runway	40 plf
Total dead load	400 plf of slope
Conveyor belt	500 plf
Runway	40 plf
Total live load	540 plf of slope

Both load intensities should be converted to pounds per linear foot of horizontal projection by multiplication with 65 ÷ 60; thus:

Dead load	433 plf
Live load	585 plf

Finally all maximum stresses are found by applying dead and live loads to the influence lines. As an example consider the diagonal c_1d, the influence line of which is shown in Fig. 7–25. The dead load stress in this member is found by multiplying the difference between the areas under the influence line by the dead load intensity; thus:

$$(12.26 - 5.44)433 = 2960 \text{ lb} \tag{7-24}$$

which will be a tension stress. The live load can produce either compression or tension, depending on whether the load covers the lower or upper

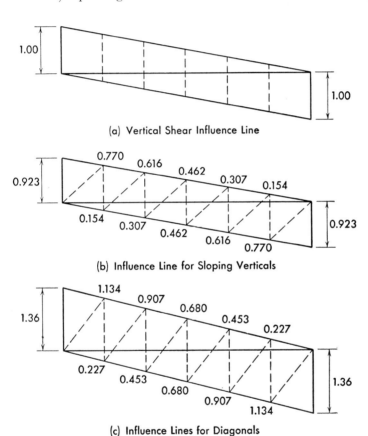

(a) Vertical Shear Influence Line

(b) Influence Line for Sloping Verticals

(c) Influence Lines for Diagonals

Fig. 7–24.

portion of the conveyor belt, as shown in Figs. 7–25c and 7–25d. The maximum tension due to live load is $12.26 \times 585 = 7180$ lb; this, added to the dead load stress, gives a total tension of 10,140 lb. The maximum

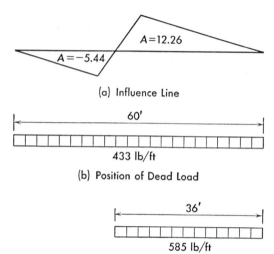

(a) Influence Line

60'

433 lb/ft

(b) Position of Dead Load

36'

585 lb/ft

(c) Position of Live Load for Maximum Tension

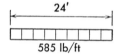

24'

585 lb/ft

(d) Position of Live Load for Maximum Compression

FIG. 7–25.

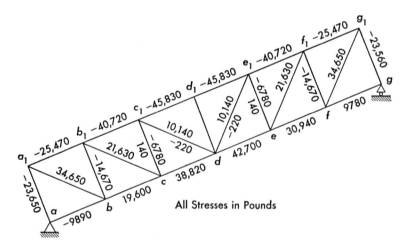

All Stresses in Pounds

FIG. 7–26.

compression due to live load is $5.44 \times 585 = 3180$ lb; this, added to the dead load stress, gives a net compression of 220 lb. A summary of all stresses is given in Fig. 7–26.

PROBLEMS

NOTE: All influence lines should show numerical values for ordinates at controlling points.

7–1. For the beam on two supports with overhangs (see illustration), draw the influence lines for (a) the two reactions; (b) shear at mid-span (20 ft from support); (c) bending moments over the two supports; and (d) bending moment at mid-span (point A).

7–2. For the structure shown in the sketch, assume a moving unit load acting vertically on horizontal member and horizontally on vertical member. Draw influence lines for (a) shear at points A and B, and (b) bending moments at points A and B.

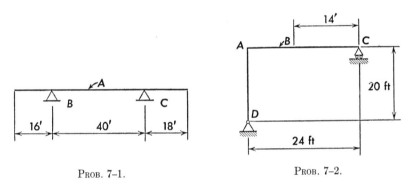

PROB. 7–1.   PROB. 7–2.

7–3. For the truss shown in the illustration draw influence lines for members BC, cd, Cc, and Cd, and find maximum stresses in them due to a live load of 800 plf.

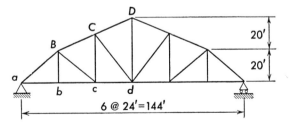

PROB. 7–3.

7–4. All web members of the truss in the sketch are 25 ft long. Draw influence lines for all members, and find maximum stresses due to a live load of 500 plf accompanied by a single force of 10 k.

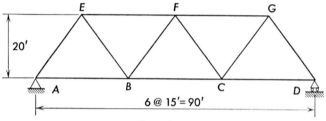

PROB. 7–4.

7–5. Draw influence lines for the three reactions shown in the figure, the shear at the interior hinge, and the bending moment at point A.

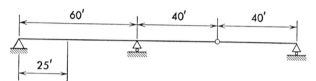

PROB. 7–5.

7–6. Draw influence lines for members Aa, ab, AB, and aB of the accompanying illustration.

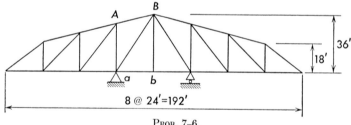

PROB. 7–6.

7–7. Draw influence lines for members BC, cd, mn, and mD in the sketch, and find maximum stresses due to a live load of 700 plf.

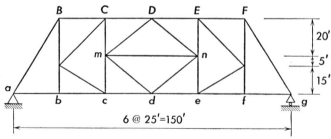

PROB. 7–7.

CHAPTER 8

MOVING LOADS

Bridges which serve highways and railroads are subjected to the action of not only their own weight (dead load) but also to that resulting from wheel loads (live load). The latter can occupy different positions, producing stresses which will vary according to these positions. In the case of a single load the critical positions can be spotted immediately because these will be the maximum ordinates of the influence line. In the case of several wheels, of various magnitude and spacing, moving across a bridge structure, the critical positions can be determined by trial or by the use of criteria to be explained in the discussion in this chapter.

8–1. Maximum Moment in Beam. Fig. 8–1 shows a beam over which a group of wheels is moving. It is desired to find the maximum bending moment which will occur under the wheel P during the passage of the

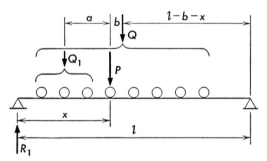

Fig. 8–1.

group. The resultant of all the forces in the group is Q, and the resultant of the wheel loads directly in front of P is Q_1. The distance from the left support to P is x. By taking moments about the right support, it is found that

$$R_1 = \frac{l - b - x}{l}\, Q \qquad (8\text{–}1)$$

The moment under P will equal to

$$M = Q\,\frac{l - b - x}{l}\, x - Q_1 a \qquad (8\text{–}2)$$

169

in which a and b are, as shown in Fig. 8–1, fixed distances from P to the resultant loads Q_1 and Q. This expression will become a maximum when its first derivative is zero. Hence

$$\frac{dM}{dx} = \frac{Q}{l}(l - b - 2x) = 0$$
$$l - b - 2x = 0 \qquad (8\text{–}3)$$
$$l - b - x = x$$

Eq. 8–3 states that in order to develop maximum bending moment under any given wheel of a group, the distance from one end of the beam to the wheel shall be equal to the distance from the other end of the beam to the resultant of all the wheel loads.

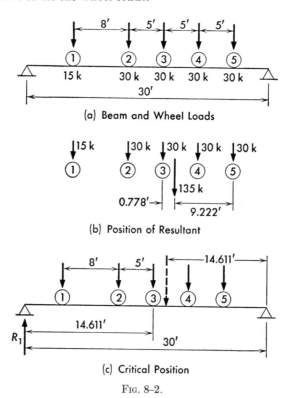

(a) Beam and Wheel Loads

(b) Position of Resultant

(c) Critical Position

Fig. 8–2.

Since each wheel will produce a maximum moment during the passage of the group, it is important to determine at once the wheel which will produce the absolute maximum. The maximum bending moment must occur *near* mid-span but not necessarily *at* mid-span. It follows that absolute maximum moment must occur under the load which is closest to the resultant of all the wheel loads.

As a numerical example let it be desired to find the maximum bending moments produced by the passage of the five wheels over the beam shown in Fig. 8–2a. The magnitude and position, with respect to the last wheel, of the resultant of the group are shown in Fig. 8–2b. It is evident from the foregoing that the absolute maximum moment will occur under wheel No. 3, and that the value of x according to Eq. 8–3 must equal

$$x = (30 - 0.778) \div 2 = 14.611 \tag{8–4}$$

The critical position is shown in Fig. 8–2c. The reaction at the left end will equal

$$R_1 = 135 \times 14.611 \div 30 = 65.75 \text{ k} \tag{8–5}$$

and the moment under wheel No. 3 will be

$$M = 65.75 \times 14.611 - 15 \times 13 - 30 \times 5 = 615.67 \text{ ft-k} \tag{8–6}$$

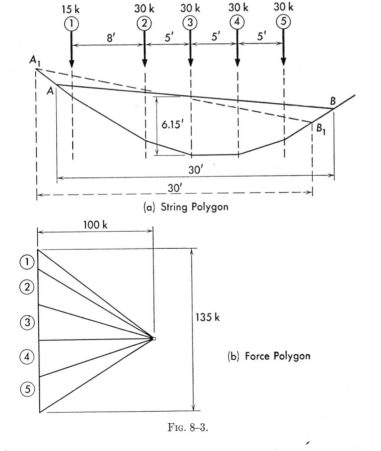

(a) String Polygon

(b) Force Polygon

FIG. 8–3.

8–2. Graphical Determination of Maximum Moment. As shown in this article, it is possible to determine the absolute maximum moment due to moving loads in a beam by a purely graphical method.

Fig. 8–3 shows the group of wheels in Fig. 8–2. It is desired to find the maximum bending moment which this group will produce when passing over a simply supported beam having a span of 30 ft.

The first step is to draw a force polygon, as shown in Fig. 8–3b. The final computation will be simplified if a round number is used for the polygon pole distance. In this case the pole distance has been made equal to 100 k, the same scale as was used for the five forces. Next a string polygon is drawn for the five forces, and this must now be superimposed on the beam in such manner that a maximum value is obtained for the vertical distances between the closing line and the other sides.

This can best be accomplished by drawing on a piece of transparent paper two vertical lines separated by a distance equal to the span of the beam (in this case 30 ft). Various positions are then tried out by placing the transparent paper over the string polygon and scaling off the intercepts. Thus the position AB in Fig. 8–3a will produce a maximum vertical distance under wheel No. 3, which, measured to the scale used for the horizontal distances, is 6.15 ft. The maximum bending moment, which equals the product of the length of the intercept and the pole distance, is 615 ft-k.

8–3. Maximum Reaction. Maximum reaction will always occur when one wheel is directly over the support. Thus, in Fig. 8–4,

$$R = \frac{Gm}{l} \tag{8–7}$$

where G = resultant of wheels on span

m = distance from G to other support

It follows that if several groups of wheels pass over a beam, the one which has a maximum of the product Gm will produce the largest reaction; and this reaction will always occur when a wheel is directly over the support.

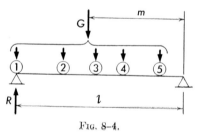

FIG. 8–4.

A floor beam or a pier will receive load from the wheel loads in two adjacent panels, as shown in Fig. 8–5. Maximum reaction will always occur under a wheel as the entire group passes over the two spans. It can be seen that for any one position of the group, the reaction R will equal

$$R = \frac{G_1 m_1}{l_1} + \frac{G_2 m_2}{l_2} \tag{8-8}$$

where G_1 = resultant of wheels on left span
$\quad G_2$ = resultant of wheels on right span

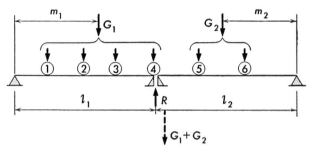

FIG. 8–5.

Suppose next that the entire group is moved a short distance toward the left; the reaction will then change by the following amount:

$$\Delta R = \left(\frac{G_2}{l_2} - \frac{G_1}{l_1}\right) \Delta x \tag{8-9}$$

Depending on the numerical values of the average load intensities ($G_2 \div l_2$ and $G_1 \div l_1$), this change will be either an increase or a decrease. If it is an increase, the maximum reaction will be reached by the first wheel of the subgroup G_2. If it is a decrease, the maximum reaction will occur under the last wheel of subgroup G_1. Thus the following criterion for the maximum floor beam reaction can be established:

The maximum reaction will occur under either one of the two wheels adjacent to the resultant of the entire group. If the average load intensity of the portion of the group on span l_1 is greater than the load intensity on span l_2, the wheel to the left of the resultant, $G_1 + G_2$, will produce the maximum. If the reverse is true, the wheel to the right of the resultant will be critical.

As a numerical example consider the group of wheels shown in Fig. 8–2b, and let it be desired to find the maximum floor beam reaction from two stringers of equal spans of 15 ft.

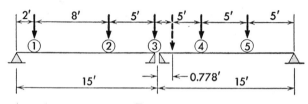

Fig. 8–6.

The resultant of this group lies between wheels Nos. 3 and 4. If, as indicated on Fig. 8–6, wheel No. 3 is placed over the center support, the two load intensities will be as follows:

$$
\begin{aligned}
(15 + 30 + 30) \div 15 = 5 \text{ klf} \\
(30 + 30) \div 15 = 4 \text{ klf}
\end{aligned}
\tag{8–10}
$$

It follows that this is the critical position of the group, and the maximum reaction is

$$
R = [\,(15 \times 2) + (30 \times 25) + (30 \times 15)\,] \div 15 = 82 \text{ k} \tag{8–11}
$$

As a second numerical example let it be desired to find the maximum reaction on two unequal spans of 19 ft and 15 ft, respectively, as shown in Fig. 8–7. If, as indicated in Fig. 8–7a, wheel No. 3 is placed over the support, the average load intensities are as follows:

$$
\begin{aligned}
\text{19-ft span:} \quad 75 \div 19 = 3.95 \text{ klf} \\
\text{15-ft span:} \quad 60 \div 15 = 4.00 \text{ klf}
\end{aligned}
\tag{8–12}
$$

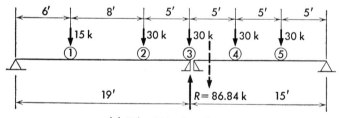

(a) Wheel No. 3 at Support

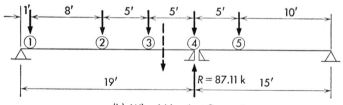

(b) Wheel No. 4 at Support

Fig. 8–7.

Hence, according to Eq. 8–9, a movement of the group toward the left will further increase the reaction, and the maximum must occur under wheel No. 4. If No. 4 is placed over the support, the average load intensities will be

$$
\begin{aligned}
\text{19-ft span:} \quad & 105 \div 19 = 5.53 \text{ klf} \\
\text{15-ft span:} \quad & 30 \div 15 = 2.00 \text{ klf}
\end{aligned}
\tag{8–13}
$$

These indicate that the position for maximum reaction has been reached. The reaction for this case is $R = 87.11$ k.

8–4. Maximum Shear. Fig. 8–8 shows the general case of a beam subjected to the passage of a group of wheels. It is desired to find the maxi-

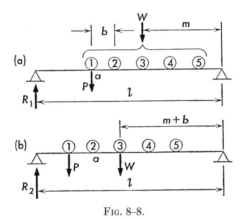

FIG. 8–8.

mum shear at point a. If the first wheel of the group is placed directly over a, the shear will equal the reaction at the left support; thus:

$$
V_1 = R_1 = \frac{Wm}{l}
\tag{8–14}
$$

If the group is moved toward the left, it is evident that another maximum shear will be reached when the second wheel arrives over point a. In this case the shear will equal the reaction at the left support, minus the first wheel load P, or

$$
V_2 = R_2 = \frac{W(m + b)}{l} - P
\tag{8–15}
$$

Subtracting Eqs. 8–15 and 8–14, it is found that V_2 will be greater than V_1 if

$$
W \frac{b}{l} > P
\tag{8–16}
$$

where b is the distance between the first and second wheel. This expression, Eq. 8–16, can be used for determining the wheel in a group which will produce maximum shear at a certain point, provided that, during the shifting of the group, no new wheel not previously on the span enters the span and no wheel in the group under consideration leaves the span.

As a numerical example, consider the group of wheels shown in Fig. 8–2b, which pass over a simply supported beam of 48-ft span. It is desired to find maximum shear at mid-span. If Eq. 8–16 is applied to the first wheel,

$$135 \times \frac{8}{48} = 22.5 > 15 \qquad (8\text{–}17)$$

it will be found that the second wheel will produce maximum shear everywhere in this beam. At mid-span this maximum shear is 36.25 k, according to Fig. 8–9b.

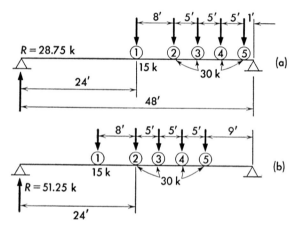

Fig. 8–9.

PROBLEMS

8–1. Find the maximum bending moment in the girder shown in the sketch, due to a dead load of 1000 plf and a live load consisting of two equal wheel loads of 25 k each.

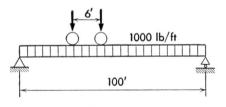

Prob. 8–1.

8–2. Find the length x of the overhang for the beam shown in the illustration if it is known that a passage of the two equal loads will produce the same maximum moment over the supports as they do in the interior of the span.

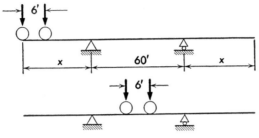

PROB. 8–2.

8–3. Find the maximum moment in the beam caused by the three wheel loads shown in the figure.

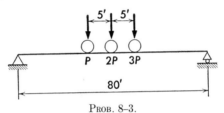

PROB. 8–3.

8–4. Find the distance x between the two wheels if it is known that a passage of the two wheels over the span will produce a maximum moment of 5184 ft-k in the beam. (See accompanying illustration.)

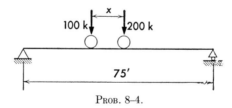

PROB. 8–4.

8–5. Find the span length l of the beam in the sketch if it is known that the transit of the two wheels across it will produce a maximum moment of 7031 ft-k.

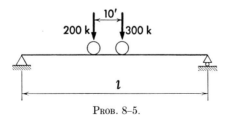

PROB. 8–5.

8–6. Find maximum moment in each of the two beams A and B due to the four moving loads of P, each at fixed distances apart. When a wheel leaves beam A at its left support, it will be carried directly by beam B.

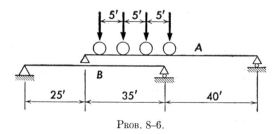

PROB. 8–6.

CHAPTER 9

RAILWAY BRIDGES

The function of a railway bridge is to carry traffic on rails over waterways, highways, or other rail lines. This traffic may be moved by steam, diesel, or electric power.

Railway bridges may receive their loads from the moving traffic either directly on their flanges or through a floor system consisting of stringers and floor beams. This load is a result of the forces on the wheels, and the impact (the increase in load) is due to the speed with which the wheels move over the track. This chapter discusses the determination of moments, shears, reactions, and stresses which must be evaluated before the various members and connections can be designed.

9–1. Common Types of Railway Bridges. Railway bridges may be classified according to the location of the tracks in relation to the main units and also in accordance with the make-up of these units. A bridge which carries the tracks upon or near the top chord or flange is called a *deck bridge*, whereas one on which the traffic passes between the girders or trusses is classed as a *through* bridge.

The track may transfer its load to the main elements either through gravel ballast and a trough (usually of reinforced concrete, as shown in Fig. 9–1a) or through a floor system consisting of longitudinal stringers and transverse floor beams, as shown in Fig. 9–1b and Fig. 9–2.

Very short spans (up to about 40 ft) can be constructed of rolled steel beams. The plate girder, consisting of a solid web, flange angles, and cover plates is usually economical up to well over 100 ft. For span lengths over 150 ft, the truss bridge is the common type, either as a deck or through bridge. A through bridge can be considered as a series of deck bridges: The stringers carry the deck loads to the floor beams, which in turn transmit them to the main units as concentrated loads.

In order to prevent the girders and trusses from overturning under load, it is necessary to provide them with bracing. Horizontal bracing is placed along the top and bottom chord in a truss bridge and along the top and bottom flange in a plate girder bridge. This bracing is usually supplemented by sway bracing in vertical planes at intervals. The sway bracing may be complete, as shown in Fig. 9–1a, or may be modified to clear traffic profile, as shown in Figs. 9–1b, 9–2, and 9–3.

In addition to resisting lateral forces due to wind and swaying of the moving load, the bracing has another important function. Since they are in compression, the top chords of through bridges will require more cross-sectional area than if the two trusses were not tied together, so as to produce shorter unsupported lengths.

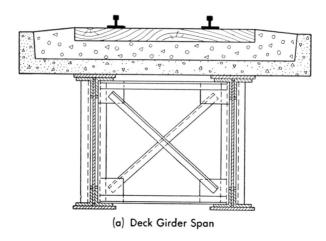

(a) Deck Girder Span

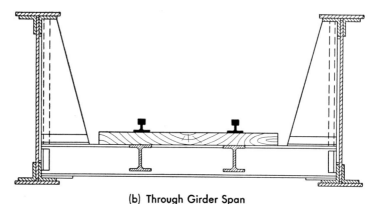

(b) Through Girder Span

FIG. 9–1.

9–2. **Loads.** The principal loads to be carried on a railway bridge are dead load, live load, and impact and wind pressure. Other loads to be considered include longitudinal forces resulting from starting and stopping of trains. If the track on the bridge is on a curve, centrifugal forces due to the moving train should also be included. After these loads, the dead load must be estimated. This includes the weight of track, ballast, floor system, trusses, and bracing.

9–3. **Live Loads.** Stresses in the various members of railway bridges can be evaluated from the forces which represent the actual concentrations of weights of locomotives and cars. Past experience in structural design of railway bridges has resulted in computations for definite loads, whether they be actual or assumed.

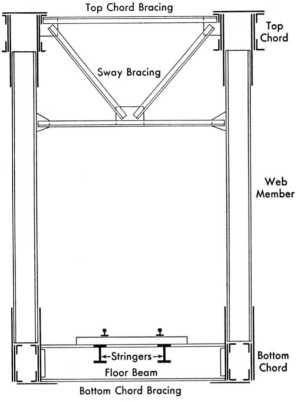

FIG. 9–2.

Until approximately 1940, rail traffic was hauled mainly by steam loco-motives, and the maximum weights could generally be represented by the axle loads shown as Cooper E72 in Fig. 9–4. This load arrangement, which simulates two steam locomotives followed by a row of cars, was first proposed in 1890 by Theodore Cooper. Its early applications were to much smaller loads, but as time went on, the heavier equipment caused a gradual increase in the axle loads. These changes were all in the same proportions, and therefore tables for shears and moments, based on smaller ratings, could be used for heavier loads by simply multiplying the values by a coefficient equal to the ratio between the ratings.

The complete dieselization of the railroads has caused a change in wheel spacing as well as a reduction in axle load. Consideration has been given to a substitution of the Cooper loading diagram as a basis for stress analysis in railway bridges. But loads other than conventional trains are

FIG. 9-3. Through-truss bridge under construction. (Courtesy, *The Military Engineer*.)

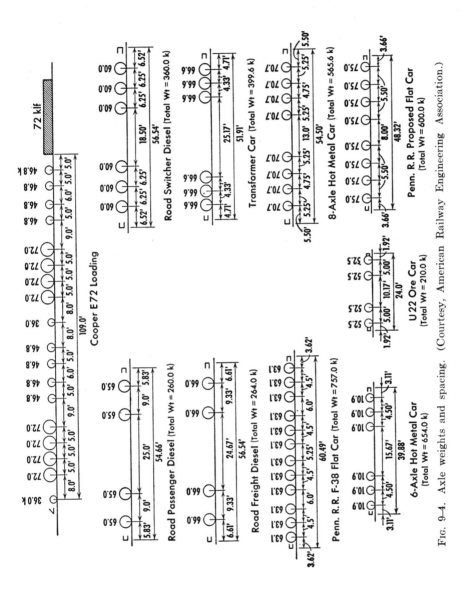

FIG. 9–4. Axle weights and spacing. (Courtesy, American Railway Engineering Association.)

still being hauled, as shown in Fig. 9–4. Furthermore the history of steam locomotives shows a steady increase of weight, and there is reason to expect that the trend of design in diesel locomotives will follow the same pattern.

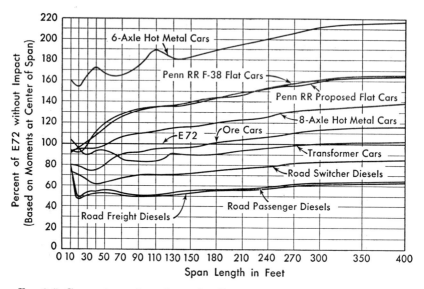

Fig. 9–5. Comparison of maximum bending moments–static loading. (Courtesy, American Railway Engineering Association.)

Fig. 9–5 shows comparisons of moments, and therefore also of stresses, resulting from the typical loadings of Fig. 9–4. It is evident that the Cooper E72 loading gives stresses which are on the safe side for all other loadings except those for very specialized equipment. Because the Cooper E72 loading was recommended in the latest specifications of the American Railway Engineering Association (1956) for design of bridges carrying rail traffic, it will be used in the discussion of stress problems in this chapter.

In order to reduce the computational work involved in using the Cooper loadings, the numerical values listed in Table 9–1 will be of considerable assistance. The table is based on a lower rating, that of E60, but can be readily used for any other higher or lower rating. The use of Table 9–1 will be illustrated by the following numerical example.

Let it be desired to find, for the simply supported beam shown in Fig. 9–6, the reactions and maximum moment due to the wheel loads of two locomotives of Cooper E72 rating, both in the positions indicated in the figure.

By consulting the table, it is found that the resultant of the 18 wheels is 426 k and that the moment of all the wheel forces about the last wheel

TABLE 9–1

COOPER'S E60 FOR ONE RAIL

DIST: Total distances from respective wheels (ft).

MOM: Moments of all loads to the left of a given wheel about that wheel

LOAD: Accumulated totals of all loads to and including given wheel (k).

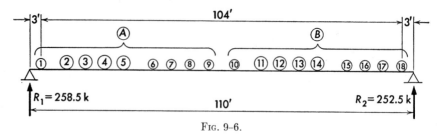

Fig. 9-6.

is 22,420 ft-k. The reaction at the left end must therefore equal

$$(22,420 + 426 \times 3) \div 110 = 215.44 \text{ k} \tag{9-1}$$

This value should be multiplied by the ratio $72 \div 60 = 1.2$ because the table is for a Cooper E60 rating, whereas the loading on the beam is for one rail supporting wheels of an E72 rating, or

$$R_1 = 1.2 \times 215.44 = 258.5 \text{ k} \tag{9-2}$$

The reactions at the right end will equal

$$R_2 = 1.2\,(426.00 - 215.44) = 252.5 \text{ k} \tag{9-3}$$

In order to find the maximum moment, the point of zero shear should first be located. Because the left reaction was 215 k for the E60 rating, the sum of all wheels is 213 k under wheel No. 9; it is seen that the shear will pass through zero under wheel No. 10. From Table 9–1, it is found that the moment of all the forces to the left of No. 10 is 6950 ft-k. Hence the bending moment under this wheel will equal

$$M = (258.5 \times 59) - (6950 \times 1.2) = 6911 \text{ ft-k} \tag{9-4}$$

9–4. Equivalent Loads. The use in stress analysis of the Cooper loading system is often inconvenient and is frequently time-consuming. For this reason it is, as a rule, expeditious to employ equivalent uniform loads, which will produce the same effects as the wheel concentrations (representing two locomotives) followed by the uniform load (representing cars).

Fig. 9–7 presents data and charts which will furnish all the information necessary for determining maximum live load moments and shears in beams and maximum live load stresses in trusses due to Cooper loadings. These data were originally presented by D. B. Steinman in 1923.* The use of equivalent uniform loads greatly simplifies the computational work for live load stresses.

As a numerical example consider again the beam in Fig. 9–6, and let it be desired to find the maximum reaction and the maximum bending moment which can be produced by a Cooper E72 loading.

* See "Locomotive Loadings for Railway Bridges," *Trans. ASCE,* 86, 606 (1923).

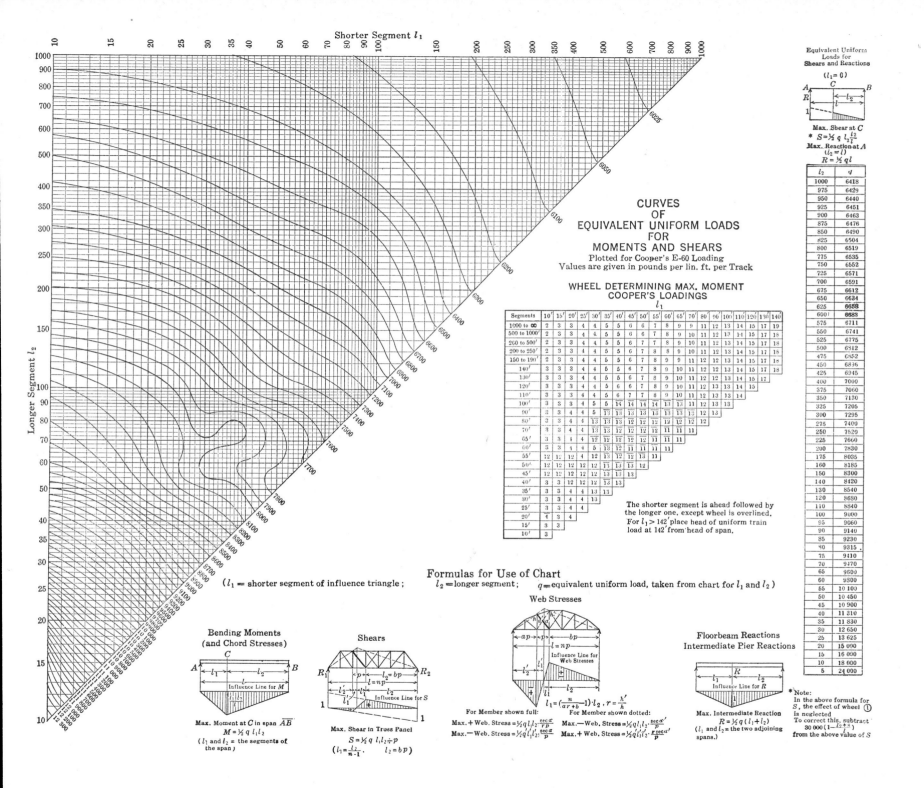

Fig. 9–7. Chart and tables for Cooper E60 railway loadings. (Courtesy, D. B. Steinman, Consulting Engineer.)

Fig. 9–8a shows the train with the first heavy wheel over the left support. According to Table 9–1 the reaction will equal

$$1.2[22{,}910 + (411 \times 9) + \tfrac{1}{2}(3 \times 9^2)] \div 110 = 291.6 \text{ k} \qquad (9\text{–}5)$$

Likewise if wheel No. 3 is placed over the left support, the reaction will equal

$$1.2[19{,}900 + (381 \times 14) + \tfrac{1}{2}(3 \times 14^2)] \div 110 = 278.5 \text{ k} \qquad (9\text{–}6)$$

This trial method should be avoided if the equivalent uniform load can be used. According to Fig. 9–7 the critical reaction will be produced by the load intensity of 8840 plf for the track or one-half of this amount for one rail. Hence the maximum reaction will be

$$R_1 = 1.2 \times \tfrac{1}{2} \cdot 4420 \times 110 = 291.7 \text{ k} \qquad (9\text{–}7)$$

The maximum bending moment has been evaluated in Fig. 9–9. According to Fig. 9–7 this will be produced by wheel No. 11 which, as shown in the preceding chapter, must be placed at a point where its distance from the right support will equal the distance from the left support

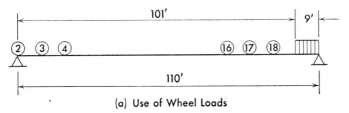

(a) Use of Wheel Loads

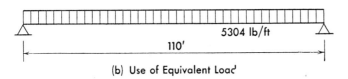

(b) Use of Equivalent Load

Fig. 9–8.

to the resultant of all the wheels. If wheel No. 11 is critical, it should be placed near the center of the span. From Table 9–1 it is found that it can be placed only near the center if the first wheel is omitted. According to the table the resultant of wheels Nos. 2 to 18, inclusive, is a distance from wheel No. 11:

$$\frac{20{,}860}{411} - 40 = 10.75 \text{ ft} \qquad (9\text{–}8)$$

and the distance from the right support to No. 11, and from the left support to the resultant, must equal (see Fig. 9–9)

$$(110 - 10.75) \div 2 = 49.625 \text{ ft} \qquad (9\text{--}9)$$

Table 9–1 can be used for finding the left reaction for the critical position; thus (for E60):

$$R_1 = [22,910 + (411 \times 4.625) + (\tfrac{1}{2} \cdot 3 \times 4.625^2)] \div 110$$
$$R_1 = 225.8 \text{ k} \qquad (9\text{--}10)$$

and for the bending moment under wheel No. 11; thus:

$$M = (225.8 \times 60.375) - 7810 = 5825 \text{ ft-k} \qquad (9\text{--}11)$$

The moment must be increased for the E72 rating; thus:

$$M = 1.2 \times 5825 = 6990 \text{ ft-k} \qquad (9\text{--}12)$$

In order to find the equivalent uniform load which will produce maximum bending moment, the triangular diagram in Fig. 9–7 is given values $l_1 = l_2 = 55$ ft. This yields a value of 7740 plf, or a moment of

$$M = \tfrac{1}{8} \times \tfrac{1}{2} \cdot 7740 \times 110^2 \times 1.2 = 7020 \text{ ft-k} \qquad (9\text{--}13)$$

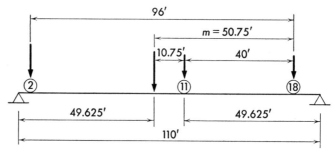

(a) Critical Position

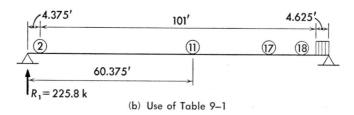

(b) Use of Table 9–1

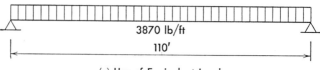

(c) Use of Equivalent Load

Fig. 9–9.

9–5. Impact. Live load in motion will produce higher stresses in truss members than the same load at rest. The increase in stress due to the dynamic effect is called *impact*. The impact allowance in percentage of live load is considerably higher for railway bridges than the corresponding allowance for highway bridges. It is known from mechanics that an instantaneously applied load will produce a stress which is twice the stress produced by the same load applied gradually. This 100 per cent increase can be considered as the absolute maximum of impact allowance, and depending on the length of the span, it is usually considerably less than this upper limit.

The American Railway Engineering Association recommends the following impact allowances:

A. To the axle loads there shall be added impact forces applied at the top of the rail and distributed thence to the supporting members, comprising:

1. The rolling effect:
   Vertical forces due to rolling of the train from side to side, acting downward on one rail and upward on the other, the forces on each rail being equal to 10 per cent of the axle loads.

2. The direct vertical effect:
   Downward forces, distributed equally to the two rails and acting normal to the top-of-rail plane, due, in the case of steam locomotives, to hammer blow, track irregularities, speed effect and car impact, and equalling the following percentages of the axle loads:

   a. For beam spans, stringers, girders, floor beams, posts of deck truss spans, carrying load from floor beam only and floor beam hangers.

$$\text{For } L, \text{ less than 100 ft} \quad 60 - \frac{L^2}{500}$$

$$\text{For } L, \text{ 100 ft or more} \quad \frac{1800}{L-40} + 10$$

   b. For truss spans $\quad \dfrac{4000}{L+25} + 15$

or due, in the case of rolling equipment without hammer blows (diesels, electric locomotives, tenders alone, etc.) to track irregularities, speed effect and car impact, and equalling the following percentages of axle loads:

$$\text{For } L, \text{ less than 80 ft} \quad 40 - \frac{3L^2}{1600}$$

$$\text{For } L, \text{ 80 ft or more} \quad \frac{600}{L-30} + 16$$

L = length, in ft, center to center of supports for stringers, transverse floor beams without stringers, longitudinal girders and trusses; or

L = length, in ft, of the longer adjacent supported stringer, longitudinal beam, girder or truss for impact in floorbeams, floorbeam hangers, subdiagonals of trusses, transverse girders, supports for longitudinal and transverse girders and viaduct columns.

B. For members receiving load from more than one track, the impact percentage shall be applied to the static load on the number of tracks shown below:

Load received from:

1. Two tracks:

   a. For L less than 175 ft. Full impact on two tracks.

   b. For L from 175 ft to 225 ft. Full impact on one track and a percentage of full impact on the other equal to: $450 - 2L$.

   c. For L greater than 225 ft. Full impact on one track and none on the other.

2. More than two tracks:

   For all values of L. Full impact on any two tracks.

In addition to the dynamic forces listed above, tractive forces that accompany acceleration or braking are often considered in the stress analyses of girder and trusses. The following recommendations are those of the American Railway Engineering Association.

The longitudinal force resulting from starting and stopping of trains shall be the larger of:

1. Force due to braking. Fifteen per cent of the live load without impact.
2. Force due to traction. Twenty-five per cent of the weight on the driving wheels, without impact.

The longitudinal force shall be taken on one track only and shall be assumed to act 6 ft above the top of the rail. For bridges where, by reason of continuity of members or frictional resistance much of the longitudinal force will be carried directly to the abutments (such as ballasted deck bridges of only three or four spans), only one-half of the longitudinal force shall be considered effective.

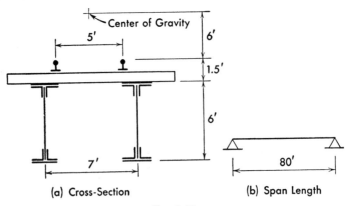

(a) Cross-Section   (b) Span Length

FIG. 9–10.

9-6. Numerical Examples. As a first example consider the deck girder bridge shown in Fig. 9–10. It is desired to determine reactions, shears, and moments due to a Cooper E72 loading and its resulting impact, in accordance with the specifications of the American Railway Engineering Association.

The equivalent uniform load which will produce maximum live load moment is found from Fig. 9–7 by taking both long and short segments equal to 40 ft. The impact percentages are evaluated for downward forces and rolling. The computations are as follows:

$$\text{Live Load Moment:} \quad \frac{1}{8}\,4050 \times 1.2 \times 80^2 = 3888 \text{ ft-k}$$

$$\text{Impact:} \quad 60 - \frac{6400}{500} = 47.2\%$$

$$(20 \times 5) \div 7 = 14.3\%$$

$$\overline{61.5\%} \qquad \underline{2391 \text{ ft-k}}$$

$$\text{Maximum Live Load Moment:} \qquad 6279 \text{ ft-k}$$

The maximum reaction is also determined by an equivalent uniform load from Fig. 9–7. The impact percentage is the same as for the moment.

Live Load Reaction: $\frac{1}{2} \cdot 9315 \times 80 \times 1.2 \times \frac{1}{2}$ = 223.5 k

Impact: 61.5% = 137.5 k

$$\overline{361 \text{ k}}$$

The maximum shear at mid-span is also found from Fig. 9–7; thus:

$$\text{Live Load Shear:} \quad \frac{1.2}{2}\,11{,}310 \times \frac{1}{2} \times 40 \times \frac{40}{80} = 67.9 \text{ k}$$

Impact: 61.5% = 41.7

$$\overline{109.6 \text{ k}}$$

The end reactions will be increased, due to the longitudinal forces resulting from starting and stopping of trains. The force due to braking should be taken as 15 per cent of the live load, without impact. Maximum live load for the girder can be found from Table 9–1 by noting that the distance from wheel No. 2 to wheel No. 15 is 80 ft, the same as the span length, and that the sum of the wheel loads (Nos. 2 to 15, inclusive) is 352.5 k. Therefore, due to braking,

$$F = 0.15 \times 352.5 \times 1.2 = 64 \text{ k} \tag{9–14}$$

The longitudinal force due to traction should be taken as 25 per cent on the driving wheels, without impact; thus:

$$F = 0.25 \times 8 \times 36 = 72 \text{ k} \tag{9–15}$$

Fig. 9–11 shows the largest of the two possible longitudinal forces applied 6 ft above the top of the rails. It is readily verified that at the left support

$$V = \frac{72 \times 13.5}{80} = 12.15 \text{ k}$$

and

$$H = 72 \text{ k}$$

(9–16)

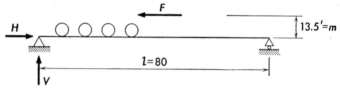

Fig. 9–11.

It is interesting to note that if the force F is assumed uniformly distributed along the entire length of the beam, then there will be no bend-

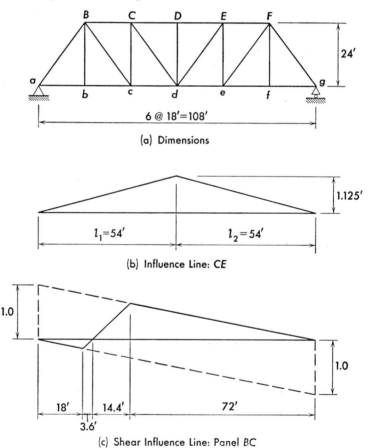

(a) Dimensions

(b) Influence Line: CE

(c) Shear Influence Line: Panel BC

Fig. 9–12.

ing moments anywhere in the beam; thus at a distance x from the left support,

$$M = Vx - F\frac{x}{l}m = Vx - Vx = 0 \qquad (9\text{-}17)$$

As a second numerical example consider the truss span shown in Fig. 9–12. It is desired to find stresses in typical members due to a railway live load represented by an E60 Cooper rating. The two bridge trusses support a single track.

Consider first the top chord member CD, which has joint d for its moment center. The equivalent uniform load is found from Fig. 9–7 by locating in the triangular diagram the point which corresponds to the two segments $l_1 = l_2 = 54$ ft in the influence line for this member. The point in the diagram represents an equivalent load of 7750 plf for the two trusses. The stress is

$$S = \frac{(\frac{1}{8})3875 \times 108^2}{24} = 235 \text{ k} \qquad (9\text{-}18)$$

Next consider the diagonal Bc, whose influence line is shown in Fig. 9–12c. Maximum stress in this member will be tension, and the two segments of the right portion of the influence line are $l_1 = 14.4$ ft and $l_2 = 72$ ft. The corresponding point is located in the interior of the triangular diagram and represents an equivalent load of 8420 plf. The stress in diagonal Bc will equal

$$S = \frac{(\frac{1}{2})4210 \times 14.4 \times 72}{18} \times \frac{30}{24} = 151 \text{ k} \qquad (9\text{-}19)$$

It is of interest to check these stresses obtained from equivalent uniform loads, by direct application of the concentrated wheel loads. From Fig. 9–7 it is found that, for a span length of 108 ft, a maximum moment

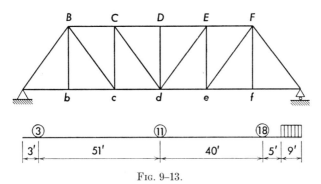

Fig. 9–13.

will be produced by wheel No. 11. Fig. 9–13 shows this wheel to be directly over the maximum ordinate of the influence line for the top chord member CE. According to Table 9–1 the reaction for this position will equal

$$R = [19{,}900 + (381 \times 9) + \tfrac{1}{2}(3 \times 9^2)] \div 108 = 217 \text{ k} \qquad (9\text{--}20)$$

and the corresponding stress (also with the aid of Table 9–1) will be

$$S = (217 \times 54 - 6130) \div 24 = 233 \text{ k} \qquad (9\text{--}21)$$

A comparison of Eqs. 9–18 and 9–20 indicates a difference of 2 per cent. In order to produce maximum stress in the diagonal Bc, maximum shear

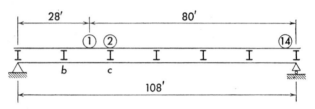

Fig. 9–14.

must occur in panel bc. Fig. 9–14 shows the critical position of the wheels. Table 9–1 is used for finding the reaction; thus:

$$R = (13{,}090 + 348) \div 108 = 124.4 \text{ k} \qquad (9\text{--}22)$$

From this should be subtracted the shear produced in the simple beam bc.

$$V = 124.4 - \frac{15 \times 8}{18} = 120 \text{ k} \qquad (9\text{--}23)$$

The corresponding stress in Bc is

$$S = 120\frac{30}{24} = 150 \text{ k} \qquad (9\text{--}24)$$

which compares very favorably with Eq. 9–19.

Figure 9–15 shows how traction stresses can be evaluated for the truss of the dimensions given in Fig. 9–12a. According to the specifications of the American Railway Engineering Association, the horizontal force due

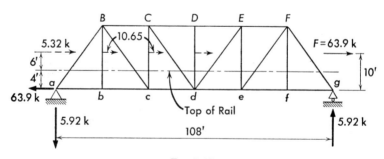

Fig. 9–15.

to braking is 15 per cent of the wheel loads; thus: $426 \times 0.15 = 64$ k. Due to starting of the train, the horizontal force should be 25 per cent of

Fig. 9–16. Hot-metal ladle cars crossing bascule bridge. (Courtesy, Hazelet and Erdal, Consulting Engineers.)

the load on the driving wheels; thus: $8 \times 30 \times 0.25 = 60$ k. The larger of these two forces should be applied 6 ft above the top of the rail, and the reactions are then evaluated by taking moments about one end. If the total horizontal force is distributed uniformly, each vertical will take one-sixth the total load. Typical stresses can be found as follows:

$$BC: \quad \frac{5.92 \times 36 - 15.97 \times 10}{24} = 2.22 \text{ k}$$

$$Bc: \quad 5.92 \frac{30}{24} = 7.4 \text{ k} \qquad\qquad (9\text{--}25)$$

$$bc: \quad \frac{5.92 \times 90 + 47.93 \times 14}{24} = 50.2 \text{ k}$$

PROBLEMS

9–1. The railroad girder bridge in the accompanying illustration carries an E66 rail loading. It is desired to find and compare the quantities that are found

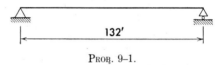

132′

Prob. 9–1.

by directly applied wheel loads and equivalent uniform loads: (a) maximum reaction, (b) maximum shear at mid-span, (c) maximum shear at quarter-point, (d) maximum moment at mid-span, and (e) maximum moment at quarter-point.

9–2. Assume that the two deck girders in Problem 9–1 are 8 ft on center and 10 ft deep; the top of the rails is 20 in. above the girder tops. Find impact allowances for the five quantities listed.

9–3. The skew bridge in the sketch is similar to the one shown in Fig. 9–10 (crossties rest directly on girder flange). The trapezoidal diagram indicated can

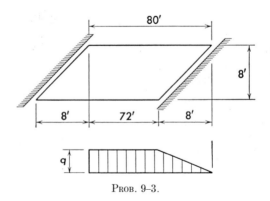

Prob. 9–3.

be used as equivalent load for the far girder, where q is the intensity which would apply for a rectangular bridge. Find the two maximum reactions by use of the equivalent loads and by direct application of E72 wheel loads.

9–4. Two parallel trusses, 17 ft on center, support a single-track railway. Find the stresses in all members due to: (a) dead load of 2 klf of bridge, (b) E72 railway loading, (c) impact according to AREA, (d) longitudinal force due to braking, and (e) longitudinal force caused by traction.

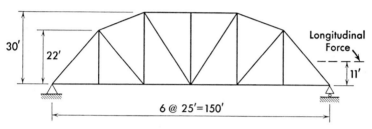

PROB. 9–4.

9–5. This problem deals with a railway bascule bridge (see Fig. 9–16) carrying hot-metal ladle cars between blast furnaces and open hearth ovens. The dimensions of the truss and the spacing of wheels and their loads are shown in

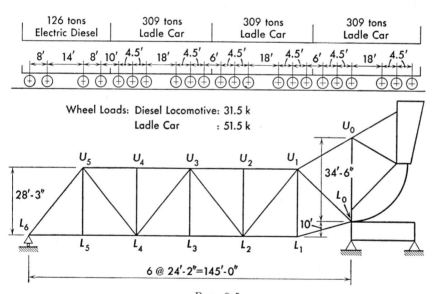

PROB. 9–5.

the accompanying illustration. It is desired to find the following quantities due to the passage of three ladle cars, either pulled or pushed by a diesel electric locomotive: (a) maximum reaction at L_6, (b) maximum stress in U_3–U_5, and (c) maximum stress in L_2–L_4.

CHAPTER 10

HIGHWAY BRIDGES

The volume of traffic which moves over the highways is considerably greater than that of the railways, and therefore the number of highway bridges is increasing at a very high rate.

Highway bridges usually receive their loads from the moving traffic through a floor slab, which may either be of reinforced concrete or consist of open steel gratings. In contrast to railway bridges, the traffic on highway bridges is not transversely fixed and can occupy any position on the floor slab.

This chapter will discuss the determination of moments, shears, reactions, and stresses which must precede the design of the various members.

10–1. Common Types of Highway Bridges. Similar to railway bridges, highway bridges are usually classified according to the location of the roadway in relation to the main units and also in accordance with the make-up of these units. Thus a highway bridge which supports the roadway upon the top chord joints of the trusses or the top flanges of plate girders is also called a *deck bridge,* and one on which the pavement slab is placed between the girders or trusses is classified as a *through* bridge.

The bracing systems in highway bridges are also similar to those in railway bridges. Horizontal bracing is placed along top and bottom chord in a truss bridge and along the top and bottom chord in a plate girder bridge. The bracing is usually supplemented with sway bracing in vertical planes incorporating panel points in truss bridges and stiffener angles in girder bridges. The function of the bracing system is twofold: to resist lateral forces, due to wind, traction, and braking, and to reduce the unsupported lengths of members of main trusses and girders.

10–2. Loads. The loads which are considered in the design of highway bridges are: dead load, live load, impact, and wind loads. In addition longitudinal forces resulting from starting and stopping of vehicles are considered, and if the highway is on a curve, centrifugal forces should be included.

Practically all highway bridges in the United States have been designed for loads specified by the American Association of State Highway Officials (AASHO). In Art. 10–3 reference will be made to the 1957 specifications of AASHO.

10–3. Live Load. Highway bridges must carry many different types of loads, such as automobiles, tractors, oil tanks, and motor trucks. Of these the motor truck, with its relatively heavy wheel concentrations, constitutes the most severe load on the floor system of a highway bridge.

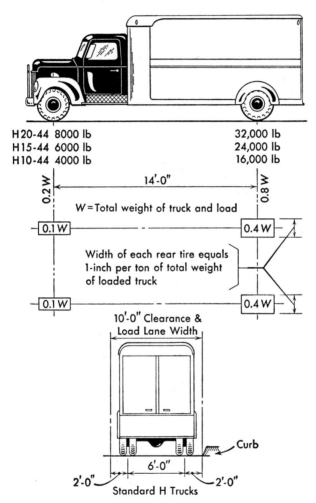

Fig. 10–1. Standard truck loading. (Courtesy, American Association of State Highway Officials.)

The American Association of State Highway Officials recommends that live loads on highway bridges should consist of standard trucks. Two types of trucks are specified and designated as H-loading and HS-loading.

Fig. 10–1 shows the H-loading, which consists of a two-axle truck having its total weight W distributed as 20 per cent and 80 per cent between the front and rear axle, respectively. There are three classes of this loading: H20, H15, and H10. Loadings H15 and H10 are 75 per cent and 50 per cent, respectively, of loading H20.

Fig. 10–2 shows the HS-loading, which consists of a tractor truck with a semi-trailer. There are two classes of this loading: H20–S16 and H15–S12; the latter is 75 per cent of the former. Both the H-loadings

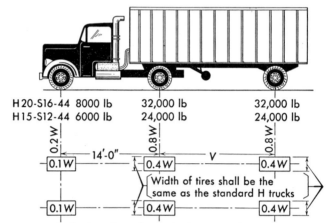

W = Combined weight on the first two axles which is the same as for the corresponding H truck

V = Variable spacing - 14 feet to 30 feet inclusive. Spacing to be used is that which produces maximum stresses

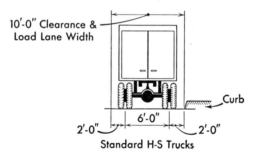

Fɪɢ. 10–2. Standard trailer loading. (Courtesy, American Association of State Highway Officials.)

and the HS-loadings are followed by numbers which indicate the year the loading was specified. Thus the designation H20–S16–44 indicates a 20-ton truck and a 16-ton trailer, as adopted in 1944.

The standard trucks are assumed to occupy traffic lanes having a width of 10 ft each. On the roadway the traffic lanes can be assumed to occupy any position that will produce maximum stress but which will not result in overlapping of adjacent lanes.

In the design of a highway bridge it would be time-consuming to find the stresses which would be produced by every possible combination and arrangement of various truck loadings. In order to expedite the design, it is convenient to use a conventional load which will produce stresses at least as large as those that will result from the passage of the specified truck loading. The American Association of State Highway Officials meets this necessity by the use of equivalent-loading systems. These equivalent loads are shown in Fig. 10–3. For the computation of moments

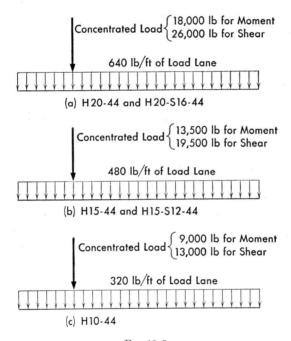

Fig. 10–3.

and shears, different concentrated loads should be used as indicated. The lighter concentrated loads should be used when the stresses are primarily bending stresses or top and bottom chord stresses, and the heavier concentrated loads should be used when the stresses are primarily shearing stresses or stresses in web members.

10–4. Impact. As is the case with railway bridges, the effects of highway loadings upon a bridge structure are augmented by the dynamic forces caused by the motion of the traffic, unless the live load is considered to be a static load. Live load stresses produced by H- and HS-loadings are therefore increased. According to the specifications of the American Association of State Highway Officials, this allowance or increment is expressed as a fraction of the live load stress and can be determined by the formula:

$$I = \frac{50}{L + 125} \qquad (10\text{–}1)$$

where I = impact fraction (maximum 0.3).

L = length in feet of the portion of the span which is loaded in order to produce the maximum stress in the member.

For uniformity of application, the loaded length L should be as follows: For roadway floors, use the design span length. For transverse members, such as floor beams, use the span length of member, center to center of supports. For computing truck load moments, use the span length except for cantilever arms, for which use 30 per cent of the length.

10–5. Other Loads. Highway bridges are usually designed for longitudinal forces in the direction of the centerline of the bridge. The AASHO recommends that provision be made for the effect of longitudinal forces: 5 per cent of the live load in all traffic lanes carrying traffic in the same direction. All lanes should be assumed to be loaded for bridges likely to become one directional in the future. The load should be the lane load plus the concentrated load (see Fig. 10–3) for moment, but without impact, and with reduction for multiple-loaded lanes (as explained below). The center of gravity of the longitudinal force should be assumed to be located 4 ft above the floor slab. The longitudinal force due to friction at expansion bearings should also be provided for in the design.

The reductions in load intensity, as recommended by AASHO, are as follows:

One or two lanes	100 per cent
Three lanes	90 per cent
Four lanes or more	75 per cent

The wind load forces are usually determined as the pressure per square foot of exposed area. The exposed area is considered as the sum of the areas of all members, including the floor system and railing, as seen in elevation at 90° to the longitudinal axis of the structure. According to AASHO, a moving uniformly distributed wind load of the following intensities should be applied horizontally at right angles to the longitudinal axis of the bridge:

For trusses and arches	75 psf
For girders and beams	50 psf

The total force should not be less than 300 plf in the plane of the loaded chord and 150 plf in the plane of the unloaded chord on truss spans and not less than 300 plf on girder spans.

10–6. Numerical Examples. It can be readily seen that the wheel loads in Fig. 10–1 will produce higher shears and bending moments than the equivalent loading systems in Fig. 10–3 on only short spans, whereas on longer spans, the reverse will be true. Let it be desired to find the span lengths where the equivalent loads will catch up with the truck loads.

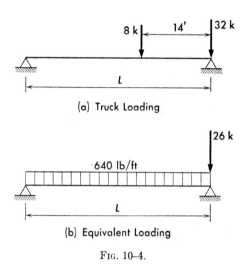

(a) Truck Loading

(b) Equivalent Loading

Fig. 10–4.

Fig. 10–4 shows the critical positions for maximum reactions on a simply supported beam of span length L. Equating the two reactions gives

$$32 + 8 \frac{L - 14}{L} = \frac{1}{2} 0.64L + 26$$

$$L^2 - 43.75L + 350 = 0 \qquad (10–2)$$

$$L = 33.21 \text{ ft}$$

Fig. 10–5a shows a simply supported beam carrying the standard truck load in order to produce maximum bending moment. By taking moments about the left support, the reaction R can be found; thus:

$$R = \frac{1}{L} (40L - 40x - 112)$$

and the bending moment under the rear axle will equal

$$M = Rx = \frac{x}{L} (40L - 40x - 112) \qquad (10–3)$$

In order to find the position of the truck which will produce maximum bending moment, Eq. 10–3 is differentiated and equated to zero; thus:

$$40L - 80x - 112 = 0$$

$$x = \frac{1}{2}L - 1.4$$

(10–4)

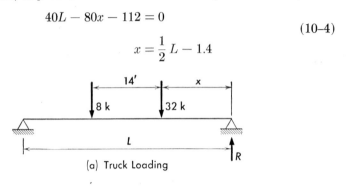

(a) Truck Loading

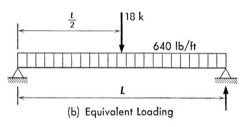

(b) Equivalent Loading

Fig. 10–5.

Substituting Eq. 10–4 in Eq. 10–3 gives the maximum bending moment during the passage of the truck:

$$M_{\max} = \frac{10L^2 - 56L + 78.4}{L}$$

(10–5)

Equating this moment to the maximum bending moment in Fig. 10–5b gives

$$\frac{1}{L}(10 L^2 - 56L + 78.4) = \frac{1}{8}0.64L^2 + \frac{1}{4}18L$$

$$L^3 - 68.75L^2 + 700L - 980 = 0$$

(10–6)

$$L = 57.25 \text{ ft}$$

Although an H20–44 loading was used in the above example, both Eq. 10–2 and Eq. 10–6 are also applicable to H15–44 and H10–44 loadings. In the case of the HS-loadings (Fig. 10–2), the standard trailer governs for much longer spans. The transition takes place at $L = 127.25$ ft for the reaction and at $L = 145.50$ ft for the bending moment.

10–7. **Typical Analysis.** Fig. 10–6 shows a Pratt truss which will be used for a highway through bridge that will carry two lanes of H20 traffic.

It is desired to find maximum live load stresses and impact allowances for the members BC, B_1C_1, and B_1C and CC_1.

The influence lines for these four members can be constructed in the usual manner and are shown in Fig. 10–6b, c, d, and e together with

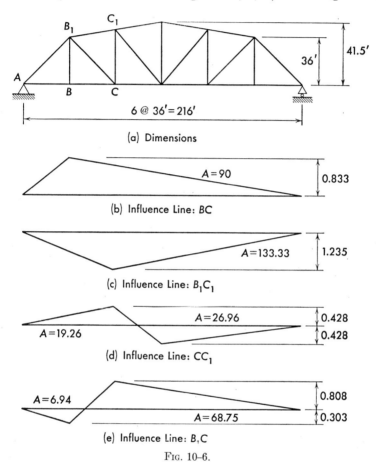

(a) Dimensions

(b) Influence Line: BC

(c) Influence Line: B_1C_1

(d) Influence Line: CC_1

(e) Influence Line: B_1C

Fig. 10–6.

maximum ordinates and areas enclosed by the lines. Using the equivalent loadings in Fig. 10–3 gives for maximum stresses:

BC: $(18 \times 0.833) + (90 \times 0.64) = 72.60$ tension

B_1C_1: $(18 \times 1.235) + (133.33 \times 0.64) = 107.56$ compression

CC_1: $(26 \times 0.428) + (19.26 \times 0.64) = 23.45$ tension
                     $(26 \times 0.428) + (26.96 \times 0.64) = 28.38$ compression

B_1C: $(26 \times 0.303) + (6.94 \times 0.64) = 12.32$ compression
                     $(26 \times 0.808) + (68.75 \times 0.64) = 65.00$ tension

All the stresses are in kilopounds (kips). It should be noted that the concentrated load of 18 k is used for the chord stresses and that 26 k is used for the web stresses. The impact allowances can be evaluated from Eq. 10–1:

$$BC \text{ and } B_1C_1: \quad \frac{50}{216 + 125} = 0.147$$

$$CC_1: \quad \frac{50}{126 + 125} = 0.200; \quad \frac{50}{90 + 125} = 0.233$$

$$B_1C: \quad \frac{50}{170 + 125} = 0.169; \quad \frac{50}{46 + 125} = 0.292$$

The total live load and impact stresses for the four members will be

$$BC: \quad 1.147 \times 72.6 = 83.27$$
$$B_1C_1: \quad 1.147 \times 107.56 = 123.37$$
$$CC_1: \quad 1.200 \times 28.38 = 34.06$$
$$1.233 \times 23.45 = 28.91$$
$$B_1C: \quad 1.292 \times 12.32 = 15.92$$
$$1.169 \times 65 = 75.99$$

The top and bottom chords of the main trusses will also act as chords of the lateral trusses which make up the bracing system of the bridge, as shown in Fig. 10–7. The floor beams, which support stringers and roadway slab, also function as verticals in the lateral trusses. In order to allow the traffic to pass between the two trusses, it is necessary to interrupt the top chord bracing in the end panels. The lateral forces which are present at the top of these panels are transmitted to the supports by the portal frames of the end panels.

The forces which are resisted by the lateral bracing trusses are the result of the action of wind on the structure and on the traffic on the bridge. The pressure of the wind, the roadway slab, and the traffic on the structure is delivered to the joints of the lateral trusses by the various members of the main trusses, which act as beams. The determination of the magnitude of the horizontal load on the lateral trusses requires a knowledge of the exposed area of the main truss members, floor system, and trucks as well as the amount of pressure to be expected from the wind, as explained elsewhere in this chapter. It will be assumed that the lateral pressures are 150 plf and 300 plf for top and bottom chords, respectively, as indicated in Fig. 10–7. Maximum stresses in chord and web members of the bottom lateral bracing truss will be determined for this pressure.

Two different arrangements of web members are considered. Fig. 10–8a shows crossing diagonals in each panel. If these diagonals are considered to resist tension only, it is seen that for wind blowing in the direction shown by the forces, those web members indicated by full lines will

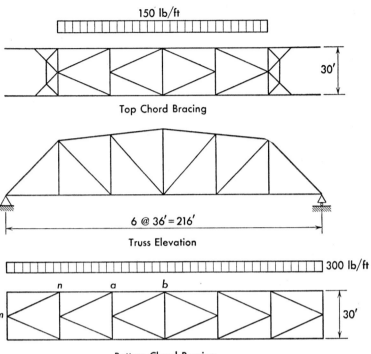

150 lb/ft

Top Chord Bracing

30'

6 @ 36' = 216'

Truss Elevation

300 lb/ft

m   n   a   b

30'

Bottom Chord Bracing

Fɪɢ. 10–7.

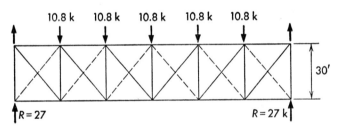

10.8 k   10.8 k   10.8 k   10.8 k   10.8 k

30'

R = 27   R = 27 k

(a) Bracing with Counters

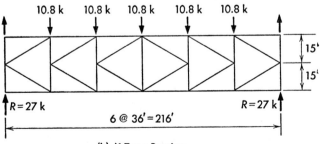

10.8 k   10.8 k   10.8 k   10.8 k   10.8 k

15'

15'

R = 27 k   R = 27 k

6 @ 36' = 216'

(b) K-Type Bracing

Fɪɢ. 10–8.

be active, while those shown by dotted lines will not transfer stress. If the wind blows in the opposite direction, the dotted diagonals will resist the shears in tension and the full diagonals will become stressless. The other arrangement of web members is a K-system in which any pair of diagonals will have equal and opposite stresses; one will be in tension, the other in compression.

If the uniformly distributed load of Fig. 10–7 is converted into concentrated panel loads of 10.8 k each, it will be seen that for the system of counters the maximum chord stresses are

$$\frac{27 \times 108 - 10.8(72 + 36)}{30} = 58.32\text{-k compression}$$

$$\frac{27 \times 72 - 10.8 \times 36}{30} = 51.83\text{-k tension} \tag{10–7}$$

and the maximum stress in the end diagonal is

$$27 \times \frac{46.86}{30} = 42.17\text{-k tension} \tag{10–8}$$

If the K-type bracing is used (Fig. 10–8b), the maximum stresses in the chords will be 51.83 k, and the maximum stresses in the web members will be

$$27\frac{39}{30} = 35.10\text{-k tension and compression} \tag{10–9}$$

10–8. Rhomboid Truss. Fig. 10–9a shows a truss, known as the *Rhomboid truss*, resting on three supports. It is desired to find the maximum center reaction due to an H20 highway loading.

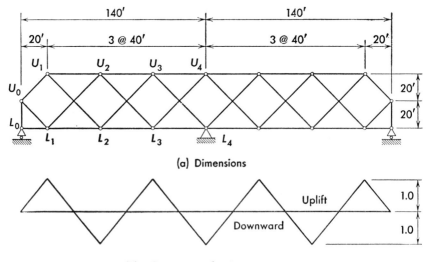

(a) Dimensions

(b) Influence Line for Center Reaction

Fig. 10–9.

Although this truss rests on three supports, it is statically determinate. The three supports furnish four unknowns, the number of members is 32, and the number of joints is 18. Because each joint will provide two equations, the total number of unknowns will equal the total number of available equations; thus:

$$2j = m + 4; \qquad 36 = 32 + 4$$

The influence line for the center reaction can therefore be found by statics alone. In order to find the center reaction, it will be expeditious to treat the symmetrical cases as indicated by Fig. 10–10c. Because the

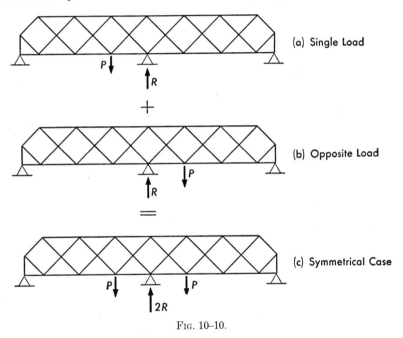

(a) Single Load

(b) Opposite Load

(c) Symmetrical Case

Fig. 10–10.

truss is symmetrical, it is seen that the reaction due to a single load at any panel point is always one-half the reaction due to a pair of loads placed at equal distances from the center.

Fig. 10–11 shows the truss subjected to the action of two forces placed at L_3 and L_5. Starting at joint U_4, it is found that the stresses in the two diagonals connecting to this joint must be equal and of the same sign (both tension or both compression). Because there is no external force acting at this joint, projecting the four stresses on a vertical line indicates that the two diagonals U_4L_3 and U_4L_5 must have stresses equal to zero. The two members have therefore been shown by dotted lines in the illustration. Proceeding next to joint L_3, it is found that the stress in L_3U_2 must have a vertical component equal to P. In considering joint U_2, it becomes apparent that the stress in U_2L_1 must have a stress equal and opposite to U_2L_3. Likewise the stress in L_1U_0 must be equal and opposite to L_1U_2; that of U_0U_1 is the same but with opposite sign. The reaction at the left-end support must be equal to $2P$ and of course equal to the reaction at the right-end support. With both end reactions known, the center reaction is found by equating the three reactions to the two outside forces.

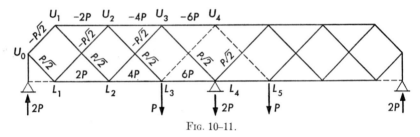

Fig. 10–11.

A similar procedure is followed in Fig. 10–12 where two equal forces, P, have been applied at L_2 and L_6. Starting at joint U_4, it is seen that the stresses in all members, shown by dotted lines, must be equal to zero, and those shown in solid lines must be as indicated. In this case the two end reactions are zero, and the center reaction is upward and equal to the sum of the two outside forces.

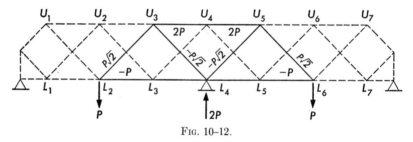

Fig. 10–12.

In Fig. 10–13 two equal loads are placed at L_1 and L_7, and the Principle of Static Equilibrium is applied successively to all joints starting at U_4. In this case the three reactions are identical to those in Fig. 10–11.

If the influence line for the center reaction is plotted as in Fig. 10–9b, it will be found that the Rhomboid truss has the peculiar characteristic

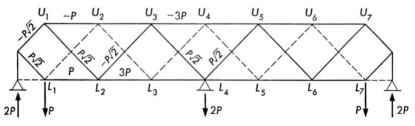

Fig. 10–13.

of having its center reaction, due to a single load, numerically equal to that load and acting alternately up or down, depending upon the panel point at which it is located.

The H20 loading which will produce maximum downward reaction at the center support is shown in Fig. 10–14b. It consists of three portions

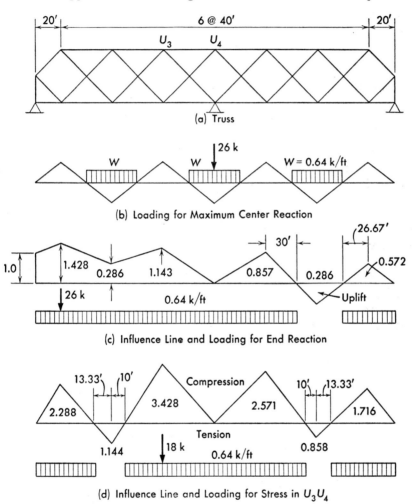

(a) Truss

(b) Loading for Maximum Center Reaction

(c) Influence Line and Loading for End Reaction

(d) Influence Line and Loading for Stress in U_3U_4

Fig. 10–14.

of equivalent uniform load and the concentrated load at the support. Since each of the three triangles has an area of 20 ft (the area under an influence line is measured by a linear dimension), the maximum reaction will be

$$R_{max} = (3 \times 20 \times 0.64) + 26 = 64 \text{ k}$$

To this should be added the impact allowance which, according to Eq. 10–1, is

$$\frac{50}{120 + 125} \times 64 = 0.204 \times 64 = 13 \text{ k}$$

Contrary to continuous beams on three supports, the Rhomboid truss will develop greater reactions at the ends than at its center. Fig. 10–14c shows the influence line for the left-end reaction and also the loading (H20 equivalent) which will produce maximum downward pressure. The magnitude of this reaction is

$$R_{\max} = (26 \times 1.428) + 0.64 (24.28 + 34.28 + 28.56 + 22.86$$
$$+ 17.14 + 12.86 + 13.35)$$
$$R_{\max} = 135 \text{ k} \tag{10–10}$$

The figures in the parentheses represent the areas under the straight lines of the influence line. The impact allowance for the end reaction should be based on the total loaded length of 256.67 ft and will equal

$$I = \frac{50}{256.67 + 125} = 0.131 \tag{10–11}$$

which will give a total reaction (live load plus impact) of

$$1.131 \times 138 = 153 \text{ k} \tag{10–12}$$

Also shown in Fig. 10–14d is the influence line for the stress in top chord member U_3U_4. This line can be readily derived from the influence line for the end reaction if it is noted that for a unit load anywhere on the

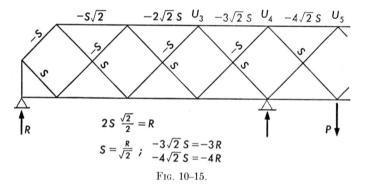

Fig. 10–15.

left span, the stress will equal four times the right-end reaction; and if the unit load is anywhere on the right span, the stress will equal three times the left-end reaction. This statement has been verified in Fig. 10–15.

In evaluating the maximum stress in U_3U_4, the equivalent uniform load of 640 plf should be used in connection with a concentrated load of

18,000 lb because a chord stress is representative of a moment, whereas a reaction is representative of a shear. The live load stress in U_3U_4, produced by the loading shown in Fig. 10–14d, will be found to be 255 k, and the impact allowance will be 14 per cent, or 36 k.

PROBLEMS

10–1. Find maximum bending moments and maximum shears due to H20 highway loading at end, fourth point, third point, and mid-span.

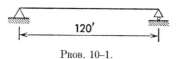

Prob. 10–1.

10–2. Find maximum bending moment and maximum shears due to a dead load of 1200 plf and a live load of H20 at the following sections: (a) mid-span of suspended girder, (b) support of main girder, and (c) mid-span of main girder.

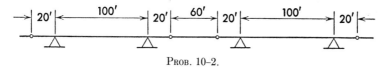

Prob. 10–2.

10–3. Find maximum stresses due to a dead load of 1000 plf and an H15 live load in all members of the truss shown in the illustration.

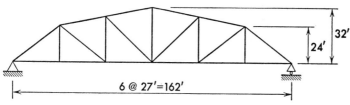

Prob. 10–3.

10–4. Find impact stresses in all members of the truss in Problem 10–3.

10–5. The deck truss shown in the sketch will be designed for a dead load of 1500 plf, a live load of H20, and AASHO impact. Find maximum stresses in all members.

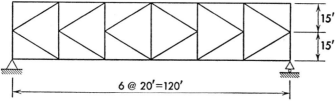

Prob. 10–5.

10–6. Show that the truss (the Wichert truss) illustrated is statically determinate. Draw the influence line for the stress in members *mn* and find the maximum stress in it due to an H20 live load.

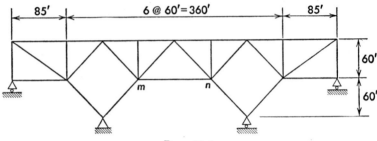

PROB. 10–6.

10–7. For the truss in Problem 10–5 find the additional stresses which would result from the action of a longitudinal force acting 8 ft above the centerline of the top chord and which would equal 5 per cent of the live load on one lane (103 k).

CHAPTER 11

THREE-HINGED ARCHES

An arch is a structural unit sustained by supports capable of developing horizontal as well as vertical reaction components. Furthermore it is a structure of such shape that its horizontal components are developed under load and constitute thrusts rather than pulls.

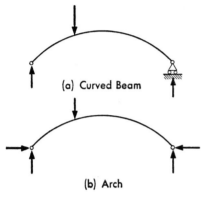

(a) Curved Beam

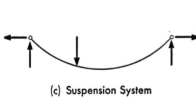

(b) Arch

It follows from this definition that the structure shown in Fig. 11–1a is not an arch. Because the right end is supported on rollers, no horizontal reaction components can be developed for vertical loads. This structure is therefore a curved beam.

A true arch is shown in Fig. 11–1b. Here, both supports are immovable, and horizontal reaction components in addition to vertical

(c) Suspension System

Fig. 11–1.

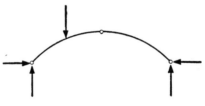

Fig. 11–2.

components will occur at each end. Since the vertical components are the same as those in Fig. 11–1a, the bending moments everywhere in the arch are smaller than those in a curved beam.

Although the structure shown in Fig. 11–1c rests on immovable supports, it does not meet the requirements for an arch. The horizontal reaction components are pulls, whereas this structure is a suspension system.

The structure shown in Fig. 11–1b is called *a two-hinged arch* and is statically indeterminate. If a third hinge were to be introduced somewhere between the two end hinges (Fig. 11–2), the structure would become statically determinate. In addition to the three equations of statics, a

215

fourth relationship can be established to express absence of any moment at the intermediate hinge. Then the four unknown reaction components can be found from these four equations.

11-1. The Arch as a String Polygon. The object of arch design is to produce a structural unit which will be (preferably) uniformly compressed or completely in compression, or failing this, a structure in which the bending moments are the smallest possible to attain. If the loads were always the same in magnitude and location, this would be quite easy to accomplish because any structure shaped to conform to given loads in an equilibrium polygon would have all its parts stressed in uniform compression.

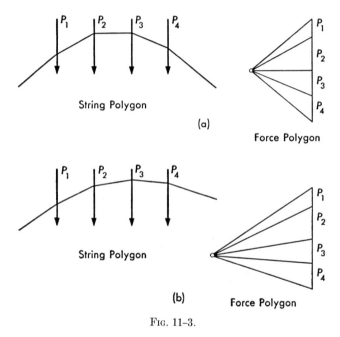

Fig. 11-3.

Fig. 11-3 shows string polygons constructed to a set of given loads P_1, P_2, P_3, P_4 $\cdots$. Depending on the pole distance, it will be seen that the compression in the various parts will be comparatively small (as shown in Fig. 11-3a) or large (as shown in Fig. 11-3b). It will also be found that the arch axis for a number of concentrated loads consists of a series of straight lines.

11-2. The Parabolic Arch. Fig. 11-4 shows a uniformly distributed load of intensity w, covering a length l. It is desired to find the arch axis for this load. If a pole distance h is selected for the force polygon, it will be seen that the total force is made up of an infinite number of infinitesimal forces, $w\,dx$, representing small concentrated forces. If lines are drawn parallel to the rays of the force polygon, these lines will be tangents to the equilibrium curve. The equation for the involute of these

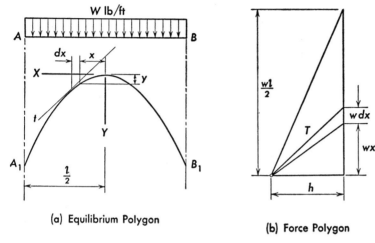

(a) Equilibrium Polygon

(b) Force Polygon

Fig. 11–4.

lines will now be found. The slope of the ray T and the tangent t must be equal; therefore

$$\frac{dy}{dx} = \frac{wx}{h} \tag{11–1}$$

Integrating

$$y = \frac{w}{2h}\,x^2 \tag{11–2}$$

which represents a second degree parabola.

It is evident that an infinite number of parabolas can be drawn for this uniform load. In fact any parabola or portion of a second-degree parabola lying between the lines AA_1 and BB_1 will represent an arch for this uniform load.

11–3. Properties of the Parabola. Because the second-degree parabola is so important, a few of its properties will be discussed in the following paragraphs.

In Fig. 11–5 let the span length of a parabolic arch be represented by l and the rise by f. If the origin of the coordinate system is placed at the crown, it will be seen that the equation for the parabola is

$$y = \frac{4f}{l^2}\,x^2 \tag{11–3}$$

If the origin of the coordinate system is placed at the springing, as shown in Fig. 11–5b, then the equation for the same parabola will be

$$y = \frac{4f}{l^2} x(l - x) \tag{11-4}$$

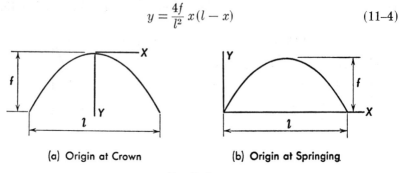

(a) Origin at Crown   (b) Origin at Springing

Fig. 11–5.

Points on a parabola can be constructed very easily when rise and span are given. Let it be desired to construct points on a parabola having a vertex A and going through B, as indicated in Fig. 11–6. The distances AB and BC are divided into the same number of subdivisions. Parallel lines are drawn through the subdivisions on AB, and the subdivisions on BC are connected to the vertex A by another set of lines. Points of intersection between corresponding lines will lie on the parabola.

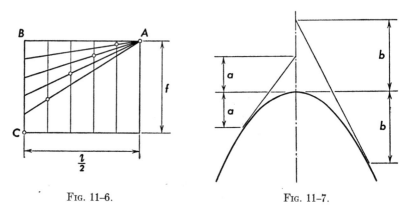

Fig. 11–6.   Fig. 11–7.

Another important property of the parabola is shown in Fig. 11–7. The projection on the axis of a point on a parabola and the intersection of the tangent at this point with the axis are equal distances from the vertex.

11–4. Thrust in a Parabolic Arch. It has been shown that no bending moments will exist in a parabolic arch subjected to the action of a vertical, uniformly distributed load. Without bending moments, shear will also be zero everywhere, and only thrusts will occur on the various sections.

Fig. 11–8 shows one-half of a parabolic arch treated as a free body. The thrust at the crown will equal the horizontal component of the reaction at the springing H. Equality of moments gives

$$H = \frac{wl^2}{8f} \tag{11-5}$$

The thrust will increase from crown to springing, where it will equal

$$T = \frac{wl}{2} \sqrt{1 + \left(\frac{l}{4f}\right)^2} \tag{11-6}$$

11–5. Rise-Span Ratio. It has been shown in the foregoing discussion that any parabola, such as the one in Fig. 11–8, will be an arch, due to a uniformly distributed load. The question that immediately arises is: "Which ratio of rise to span is the most economical?" If the rise is small, the total length of the arch will also be small, but the thrust will be large and will therefore necessitate a large cross-section. If the rise is large, a long arch will result, but this longer arch will be subjected to a smaller thrust. The most economical ratio of rise to span is the one which requires the least amount of material.

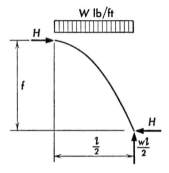

Fig. 11–8.

Before the parabolic arch is more thoroughly investigated, the principle to be applied to it will first be used to find the economical proportions of a simple truss. Fig. 11–9 shows a symmetrical, simply supported truss subjected to the action of a concentrated load P at mid-span. It is desired to find the most economical value of the angle α.

The total volume V of material in the truss is equal to the sum of the products of lengths and cross-sectional area. If the allowable working stress s is the same for both tension and compression, then

$$V = LA = L\frac{S}{s} \sim LS \tag{11-7}$$

Substituting the values from Fig. 11–9,

$$V = 2\,\frac{Pl}{4 \sin \alpha \cos \alpha} + 2\,\frac{Pl}{4 \tan \alpha} + \frac{Pl \tan \alpha}{2}$$

$$V = \frac{2\,Pl}{\sin 2\alpha} \tag{11-8}$$

Differentiating with respect to α and equating to zero give

$$\frac{dV}{d\alpha} = -4Pl\,\frac{\cos 2\alpha}{\sin^2 2\alpha} = 0; \qquad \alpha = 45° \tag{11-9}$$

In the event the allowable stress in compression is smaller than that in tension, it is necessary to divide the various terms in Eq. 11–8 by their respective unit stresses. For the truss shown in Fig. 11–9, it will be found that the most economical slope of the top chord is always 45°, regardless of the ratio between allowable stresses in tension and compression.

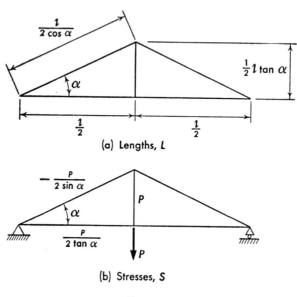

(a) Lengths, L

(b) Stresses, S

Fig. 11–9.

Fig. 11–10 shows a parabolic arch subjected to the action of a uniformly distributed load. It is desired to find the ratio between rise f and span l which will result in the minimum amount of material.

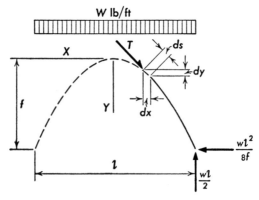

Fig. 11–10.

If the origin of the coordinate system is placed at the crown, it will be seen that the equation for the arch axis and its first derivative will be

$$y = \frac{4f}{l^2} x^2; \qquad \frac{dy}{dx} = \frac{8fx}{l^2} \qquad (11\text{-}10)$$

If the thrust T is projected on a horizontal line, it will be seen that

$$T = \frac{wl^2}{8f} \cdot \frac{ds}{dx} \qquad (11\text{-}11)$$

The volume of material, V, for the arch is equal to

$$\begin{aligned}
V &= 2 \int_0^{l/2} T\, ds = 2 \int_0^{l/2} \frac{wl^2}{8f} \times \frac{(ds)^2}{dx} \\
&= \int_0^{l/2} \frac{wl^2}{4f} \left[1 + \left(\frac{dy}{dx}\right)^2\right] dx \\
&= \frac{wl^2}{4f} \int_0^{l/2} \left[1 + 64\,\frac{f^2 x^2}{l^4}\right] dx \\
&= \frac{wl^2}{4f}\left[\frac{l}{2} + \frac{8f^2}{3l}\right] = \frac{wl^2}{16}\left[\frac{l}{f} + \frac{16}{3} \times \frac{f}{l}\right]
\end{aligned} \qquad (11\text{-}12)$$

Differentiating and placing the derivative equal to zero gives

$$\frac{dV}{df} = \frac{wl^2}{16}\left[-\frac{l}{f^2} + \frac{16}{3l}\right] = 0 \qquad (11\text{-}13)$$

$$f = 0.433l$$

Thus the most economical rise to span ratio is about 43 per cent.

11-6. Graphical Analysis. The determination of reactions, moments, and shears in a three-hinged arch can be made by either algebraic computations or graphical construction. The following discussion is an account of the graphical method.

Let it first be assumed, as shown in Fig. 11–11, that the arch is subjected to the action of a single force. In this case it is known that the reaction at B must pass through the top hinge. It is also known that the

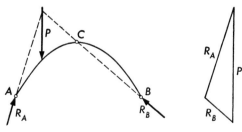

Fig. 11–11.

two reactions and the given force must pass through the same point, which is the intersection of the line BC and the force P. The direction of the left reaction is therefore also known, and a force polygon is readily constructed from which the magnitudes of the two reactions can be determined.

If, as shown in Fig. 11–12, several forces are acting on the arch but all are on the same side of the top hinge, the reactions can be determined by first finding the resultant of the given forces and then proceeding in the manner indicated by Fig. 11–11.

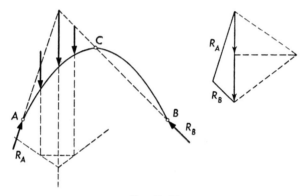

FIG. 11–12.

Next consider the general case of a three-hinged arch subjected to the action of a system of forces acting on both sides of the top hinge, as shown in Fig. 11–13a. This system can be replaced conveniently by the equivalent two systems shown in Fig. 11–13b, and each of these can be treated by the method indicated in Fig. 11–12, and the results added.

The equivalent force systems are A and B. System A is made up of all forces on one side of the top hinge, and system B of the forces on the other side. It is evident that the final reactions can be found by vector additions of the reactions for each of the two systems. The procedure is given in the following paragraph.

A force polygon is constructed for all the forces, rays are drawn to a pole point, and a string polygon is constructed for the given location of the forces. By intersection of the proper sides in this string polygon, the resultants of each of the two systems A and B are found. From the positions of these resultants the directions of reactions at each of the two end hinges can next be found. With the directions known, the magnitudes are found from the force polygon. They are labeled according to force system (A or B) and hinge location (1 or 2). The final reaction R_1 is found by adding the two vectors A_1 and B_1, final reaction R_2, by addition of the vectors A_2 and B_2.

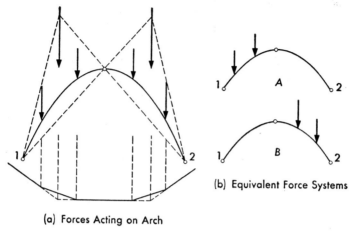

(a) Forces Acting on Arch

(b) Equivalent Force Systems

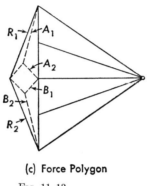

(c) Force Polygon

FIG. 11–13.

11–7. Evaluation of Moments. The reactions on a three-hinged arch are readily found by supplementing the equations of statics with an equation which expresses absence of bending moment at the top hinge. As a numerical example consider that the arch shown in Fig. 11–14 is subjected

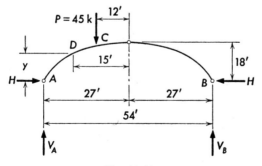

FIG. 11–14.

to a vertical force of 45 k. The vertical component of the left reaction is found by taking moments about the other end; thus:

$$V_A = 45 \frac{39}{54} = 32.5 \text{ k} \tag{11-14}$$

The horizontal component H is next found by taking moments of all forces on one side of the top hinge and equating to zero. For forces on the right

$$H \times 18 = 12.5 \times 27; \qquad H = 18.75 \text{ k} \tag{11-15}$$

or for the forces on the left,

$$(-H \times 18) + (32.5 \times 27) - (45 \times 12) = 0$$
$$H = 18.75 \text{ k} \tag{11-16}$$

In order to find the bending moment at an arbitrary point D, its ordinate y must first be computed. Assuming a second-degree parabola,

$$y = \frac{4f}{l^2} x(l - x) = \frac{4 \times 18}{54 \times 54} (12 \times 42) = 12.44 \text{ ft} \tag{11-17}$$

The bending moment at D will equal

$$M_D = 32.5 \times 12 - 18.75 \times 12.44 = 157 \text{ ft-k} \tag{11-18}$$

If a three-hinged arch is subjected to the action of a single force, the moment diagram for the entire arch can be obtained rapidly and accurately, as indicated in the following discussion. By referring to Fig. 11–15,

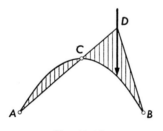

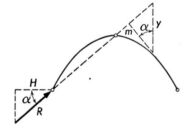

FIG. 11–15.   FIG. 11–16.

it will be shown that the lengths of the vertical intercepts between the arch axis and line $ACDB$, multiplied by the magnitude H of the horizontal reaction component, will equal the bending moments in the arch produced by P.

The derivation of this theorem is made with reference to Fig. 11–16. It will be seen that the horizontal component H and the lever arm m can both be expressed in terms of the same angle, α; thus:

$$H = R \cos \alpha; \qquad m = y \cos \alpha \tag{11-19}$$

The bending moment at any point is equal to

$$M = R \times m = \frac{H}{\cos \alpha} \times y \cos \alpha = H \times y \qquad (11\text{--}20)$$

11–8. Influence Lines. It will be recalled that an influence line is a diagram, the ordinates of which indicate at a stationary point the effect (shear, moment, stress, etc.) due to a unit load moving on the structure in such manner as to occupy all possible positions.

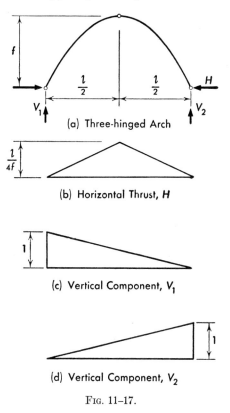

(a) Three-hinged Arch

(b) Horizontal Thrust, **H**

(c) Vertical Component, **V₁**

(d) Vertical Component, **V₂**

Fig. 11–17.

The influence lines for the reaction components for a three-hinged arch are shown in Fig. 11–17. One can see that the expressions for the vertical components are identical to those of a simply supported beam; hence the influence lines for V_1 and V_2 are the same as for a beam of the same span.

In the case of the horizontal component H, it is found that a unit load placed a distance x from the left end will produce a thrust of

$$H = \frac{x}{2f}$$

which shows that the thrust influence line is a triangle, having its maximum ordinate equal to

$$H = \frac{l}{4f} \tag{11-21}$$

The influence line for the moment at a point in a three-hinged arch can be readily found to be the difference between two influence lines, namely:

1. Influence line for the moment that would exist for a simply supported beam of the span, and
2. Influence line for the moment that would be the result of the horizontal component H, produced by the moving unit load.

Fig. 11–18 shows the three-hinged arch for which the moment influence line for point A is desired. For an arbitrary position of the unit load, it will be found that a total of five forces are acting on the arch:

1. The unit load and the two vertical reaction components.
2. The two (equal and opposite) horizontal components.

It is known that the influence line for the first set of forces is a triangle with a maximum ordinate equal to

$$M_s = \frac{ab}{l} \tag{11-22}$$

The influence line for the moment due to the horizontal components H must be the influence line in Fig. 11–17b multiplied by the vertical distance from H to point A. According to Eq. 11–4, this distance is

$$y = \frac{4f}{l^2} ab \tag{11-23}$$

The maximum ordinate for the influence line for the moment due to the horizontal component is found by multiplication of Eq. 11–21 and Eq. 11–23; thus:

$$\frac{l}{4f} \times \frac{4f}{l^2} ab = \frac{ab}{l} \tag{11-24}$$

which has the same numerical value as Eq. 11–22. The maximum ordinates of the two triangles, to be subtracted, are the same; one occurs under the top hinge and the other under the section under consideration. The final moments at A are represented by the lengths of the intercepts between the two lines, as shown in Fig. 11–18e. It should be noted that this figure applies only to three-hinged arches shaped according to second-degree parabolas. For any other shape the two maximum ordinates in Fig. 11–18c and d will not be equal.

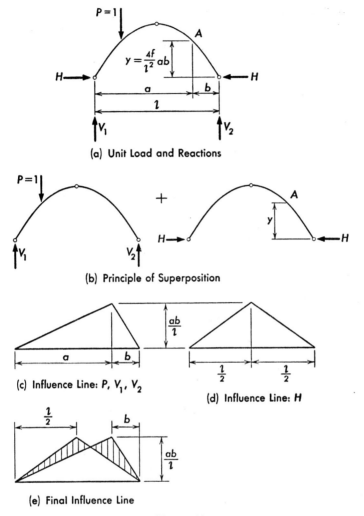

(a) Unit Load and Reactions

(b) Principle of Superposition

(c) Influence Line: P, V_1, V_2

(d) Influence Line: H

(e) Final Influence Line

Fig. 11–18.

The influence line for the thrust on an arbitrary section will next be derived. Consider the section at N of the three-hinged arch in Fig. 11–19a. If a unit load is placed at any point of the arch (including N), this section will be subjected to moment, shear, and thrust. With the reactions known, it is possible to find the thrust by projecting onto it all forces either to the left or to the right. Fig. 11–19b shows the case of the unit load occupying a position to the right of the section. If all forces to the left of the section are projected onto the tangent to the arch axis at N, it will be found that

$$T = H \cos \alpha + V_1 \sin \alpha \tag{11-25}$$

If the unit load occupies a position to the left of the section, projection of all forces to the right of the section on the tangent to the arch axis at N gives

$$T = H \cos \alpha - V_2 \sin \alpha \tag{11-26}$$

The influence lines for H, V_1, and V_2 have been plotted in Fig. 11–17; if they are combined in accordance with Eqs. 11–25 and 11–26, the resulting diagram will be the one shown in Fig. 11–19d. The thrust influence

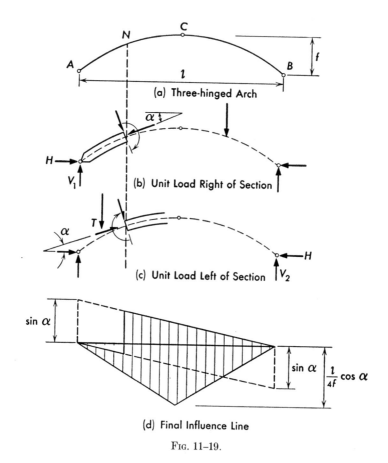

Fig. 11–19.

line is independent of the shape of the arch axis, and the axial force is always a compressive force.

Both moment and thrust influence lines are usually plotted from horizontal base lines, as shown in Fig. 11–20. General expressions are given for maximum ordinates. It should be noted that the expressions for the thrust influence line apply to any shape of the arch axis, whereas those

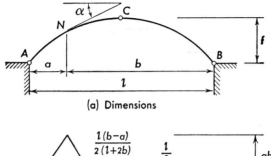

(a) Dimensions

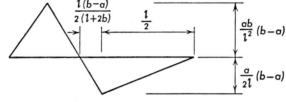

(b) Moment Influence Line

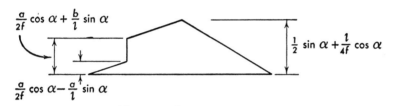

(c) Thrust Influence Line

Fig. 11–20.

for the moment influence line are correct only if the arch axis is a second-degree parabola.

11–9. Numerical Example. Fig. 11–21 shows a parabolic three-hinged arch. It is desired to construct the influence lines for thrusts and moments at points A, B, C, and D and also for the thrust at crown and springing.

The vertical distances from the horizontal base line to the various points on the arch axis can be evaluated by Eq. 11–23; thus:

$$y = \frac{4 \times 50}{200^2} x(200 - x) = x\left(1 - \frac{x}{200}\right) \tag{11–27}$$

The angle α between the tangent and the horizontal at the various points is determined by differentiation of Eq. 11–27; thus:

$$\tan \alpha = 1 - \frac{x}{100} \tag{11–28}$$

Table 11–1 lists the values for ordinates and trigonometric functions of α for the various points. The influence lines for the moments are shown in

TABLE 11–1

NUMERICAL VALUES FOR THREE-HINGED ARCH

Point	x	y	$\tan \alpha$	$\cos \alpha$	$\sin \alpha$
Springing	0	0	1.0000	0.7071	0.7071
A	20	18	0.8000	0.7809	0.6247
B	40	32	0.6000	0.8576	0.5145
C	60	42	0.4000	0.9285	0.3712
D	80	48	0.2000	0.9804	0.1968

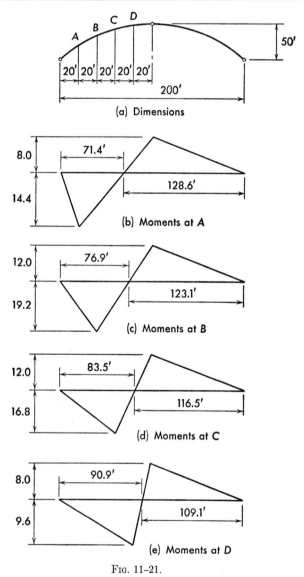

(a) Dimensions

(b) Moments at A

(c) Moments at B

(d) Moments at C

(e) Moments at D

FIG. 11–21.

Fig. 11–21. The maximum ordinates and horizontal distances have been computed from the general expressions in Fig. 11–20b. Thus, for the influence line in Fig. 11–21b, the maximum ordinates are

$$\frac{20 \times 180}{40,000}(180 - 20) = 14.4 \quad \text{and} \quad \frac{20}{400}(180 - 20) = 8 \quad (11\text{–}29)$$

The influence lines for the thrust at the various points are plotted in Fig. 11–22. The ordinates have been computed from the general expres-

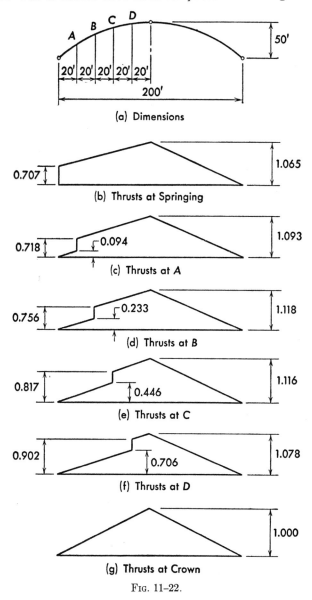

(a) Dimensions

(b) Thrusts at Springing

(c) Thrusts at A

(d) Thrusts at B

(e) Thrusts at C

(f) Thrusts at D

(g) Thrusts at Crown

Fig. 11–22.

sions in Fig. 11–20c; thus for the influence line in Fig. 11–22c, the maximum ordinates are

$$\left(\frac{1}{2} \times 0.6247\right) + \left(\frac{200}{4 \times 50} 0.7809\right) = 1.093$$

$$\left(\frac{20}{2 \times 50} \times 0.7809\right) - \left(\frac{20}{200} \times 0.6247\right) = 0.0937 \qquad (11\text{–}30)$$

$$\left(\frac{20}{2 \times 50} \times 0.7809\right) + \left(\frac{180}{200} \times 0.6247\right) = 0.7184$$

Next let it be assumed that the arch is subjected to loading corresponding to H20 load as prescribed by the American Association of Highway Officials. The load is shown in Fig. 11–23. It is desired to find maximum moments and thrusts due to this load.

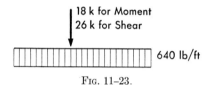

FIG. 11–23.

Consider the influence line for the moments at A (Fig. 11–21b). The two triangular areas are each equal to 514 sq ft. The maximum bending moment at A will therefore be equal to

$$514 \times 640 + 14.4 \times 18{,}000 = 588{,}000 \text{ ft-lb} \qquad (11\text{–}31)$$

Likewise, for the maximum bending moments at the other points, it is found that

$$B: \quad (738 \times 640) + (19.2 \times 18{,}000) = 816{,}000 \text{ ft-lb}$$

$$C: \quad (701 \times 640) + (16.8 \times 18{,}000) = 751{,}000 \text{ ft-lb} \qquad (11\text{–}32)$$

$$D: \quad (436 \times 640) + (9.6 \times 18{,}000) = 452{,}000 \text{ ft-lb}$$

Because the thrusts are functions of the end shears, it is customary to use the concentrated load of 26 k for evaluation of axial forces. The maximum thrusts are therefore

$$\text{Springing:} \quad (142 \times 640) + (1.065 \times 26{,}000) = 118{,}500 \text{ lb}$$

$$A: \quad (128 \times 640) + (1.093 \times 26{,}000) = 110{,}400 \text{ lb}$$

$$B: \quad (117 \times 640) + (1.118 \times 26{,}000) = 103{,}700 \text{ lb}$$

$$C: \quad (108 \times 640) + (1.116 \times 26{,}000) = 97{,}900 \text{ lb} \qquad (11\text{–}33)$$

$$D: \quad (102 \times 640) + (1.078 \times 26{,}000) = 93{,}500 \text{ lb}$$

$$\text{Crown:} \quad (100 \times 640) + (1.000 \times 26{,}000) = 90{,}000 \text{ lb}$$

PROBLEMS

11-1. A tower (see illustration) consisting of three members is subjected to a horizontal force P. For a given height h, find the angle α that will give minimum amount of material for this frame. Assume the allowable stress in compression to be three-quarters of the allowable stress in tension.

11-2. Find the angle α that will result in maximum economy of material for the arch shown in the sketch.

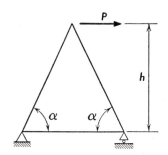

PROB. 11-1.

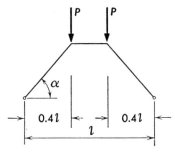

PROB. 11-2.

11-3. Find the most economical angle α for the cantilever truss shown in the illustration, if the allowable stress in tension is 20 ksi and that in compression is 16 ksi.

11-4. It is known that, at the left support of the three-hinged arch shown in the illustration, the vertical and horizontal components of the reaction are 617 k and 475 k, respectively. Find the forces P_1 and P_2.

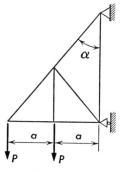

PROB. 11-3.

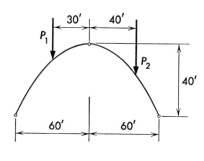

PROB. 11-4.

11-5. Find the equation in terms of l (span length) and f (rise) if the arch axes (no bending moments allowed) correspond to the loads indicated below and those in the accompanying figure. The crown should be made the origin for the coordinate system, and the Y-axis should be downward: (a) triangular load, (b) stepped uniform load, and (c) trapezoidal load.

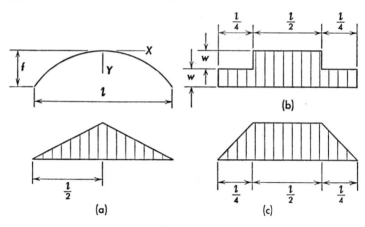

PROB. 11–5.

11–6. A symmetrical three-hinged arch of the dimensions shown is shaped as a circular arc. Find the influence lines for bending moment and thrust at the quarter-points (43.3 ft from the ends).

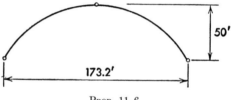

PROB. 11–6.

11–7. In Problem 11–4 remove the forces P_1 and P_2, and find the maximum bending moment and maximum thrust at the quarter-points (30 ft from the ends) due to a moving live load of 1 klf. The arch axis is a second-degree parabola.

CHAPTER 12

THREE-DIMENSIONAL FRAMES

Nearly all structures are space structures. In most cases it is possible to resolve these space structures into component parts which are coplanar and to treat them separately. The ordinary highway or railway bridge is an example of such treatment. It is truly a three-dimensional frame; however, for convenience and simplification, one is able to treat separately each of the main trusses, the upper and lower lateral bracing, and the portals and sway bracing. In many structures simplification is impossible because of the complex interaction of the elements, or it is not preferred because treatment as a space structure would be actually easier than treating each of the component parts. Derricks, cranes, framed pedestals, framed domes, and tower structures are examples of space structures so treated in this chapter.

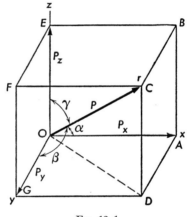

Fig. 12–1.

12–1. Review of Space Statics (Concurrent Forces). Fig. 12–1 shows a space vector located within a frame formed by three mutually perpendicular axes. The projections of the force P on each of the axes are designated P_x, P_y, and P_z. Since the frame of which P is a diagonal is a rectangular parallelepiped, the angles α, β, and γ are included in the three right triangles AOC, GOC, and EOC. Thus the expressions for the components can be written as

$$P_x = P \cos \alpha; \qquad P_y = P \cos \beta; \qquad P_z = P \cos \gamma \qquad (12\text{–}1)$$

The cosines used to describe these components are called the *direction cosines* of the force P. In addition, if the coordinates x, y, and z are known, the direction cosines of the force can be defined in terms of the sides of the parallelepiped and the length of its diagonal; thus:

$$P_x = P \frac{x}{r}; \qquad P_y = P \frac{y}{r}; \qquad P_z = P \frac{z}{r} \qquad (12\text{–}2)$$

where $r = \sqrt{x^2 + y^2 + z^2}$.

235

Also, the resultant P may be described in terms of its components; thus:

$$P_x^2 + P_y^2 + P_z^2 = P^2(\cos^2 \alpha + \cos^2 \beta + \cos^2 \gamma)$$

but

$$(\cos^2 \alpha + \cos^2 \beta + \cos^2 \gamma) = 1$$

so that

$$P = \sqrt{P_x^2 + P_y^2 + P_z^2} \qquad (12\text{-}3)$$

In order to find the resultant of several concurrent forces, the components of each force must first be found. The sum of all components along each of the axes is designated ΣF_x, ΣF_y, or ΣF_z. Then the resultant of the forces can be described by:

$$R = \sqrt{\Sigma \overline{F}_x^2 + \Sigma \overline{F}_y^2 + \Sigma \overline{F}_z^2} \qquad (12\text{-}4)$$

and the direction of the resultant can be defined by the direction cosines:

$$\cos \theta_x = \frac{F_x}{R}; \qquad \cos \theta_y = \frac{F_y}{R}; \qquad \cos \theta_z = \frac{F_z}{R} \qquad (12\text{-}5)$$

For the case of a force system in equilibrium, the resultant acting on the body must be equal to zero. This condition is described by the well-known equations of equilibrium:

$$\Sigma F_x = 0; \qquad \Sigma F_y = 0; \qquad \Sigma F_z = 0 \qquad (12\text{-}6)$$

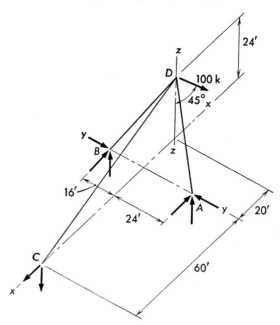

FIG. 12-2.

Fig. 12–3. One of the world's largest tower derrick boats being used to erect steel for towers of the suspension bridge over the Delaware River between South Philadelphia and Gloucester City, N. J. Its capacity is 115 tons. (Courtesy, Bethlehem Steel Company.)

Fig. 12–4. The shear leg. *Pacific Atlas,* owned by Ben C. Gerwick, Inc., of San Francisco, shown placing a 100-ton precast spandrel tie beam on the Richmond-San Rafael Bridge. The *Atlas* is capable of 160-ton lifts. (Courtesy, Ben C. Gerwick, Inc.)

As an example of how to apply Eqs. 12–6, consider the shear leg derrick shown in Fig. 12–2. The schematic diagram is typical of many cranes and derricks found in practice, especially in the construction phases of various structures. Other similar types are shown in Figs. 12–3 and 12–4.

In the case at hand, three two-force members meet at a joint D where a load is applied at an angle of 45° from the vertical in the xz-plane. Joint D represents a concurrent force system in equilibrium. There are three unknown forces and three equations of equilibrium, and thus a solution is possible by a simultaneous solution of Eqs. 12–6.

The lengths of the members are computed first:

$$CD = \sqrt{80^2 + 24^2} = 83.5 \text{ ft}$$
$$AD = \sqrt{24^2 + 24^2 + 20^2} = 39.4 \text{ ft}$$
$$BD = \sqrt{16^2 + 24^2 + 20^2} = 35.2 \text{ ft}$$

It is evident that the cable CD is in tension and that the shear legs AD and BD are in compression. Nevertheless all the members will be initially assumed to be in tension. Then compression stresses in members will be indicated by the resulting minus sign in the answers of the equations.

$$\Sigma F_x = \frac{80}{83.5}\,DC + \frac{20}{39.4}\,AD + \frac{20}{35.2}\,BD - \frac{100}{\sqrt{2}} = 0$$

$$\Sigma F_y = \frac{24}{39.4}\,AD - \frac{16}{35.2}\,BD \qquad\qquad = 0$$

$$\Sigma F_z = \frac{24}{83.5}\,DC + \frac{24}{39.4}\,AD + \frac{24}{35.2}\,BD + \frac{100}{\sqrt{2}} = 0$$

The simultaneous solution of these equations yields

$AD = -80.5$-k compression; $\qquad BD = -107.85$-k compression

$CD = 180.4$-k tension

12–2. Moments of Forces in Space. In a coplanar force system a moment is sometimes described as the tendency of a force to rotate about an axis. Thus a moment is defined in Art. 1–1 as the magnitude of the force multiplied by the perpendicular distance between the force and the axis about which the moment is desired.

This concept of a moment is, however, inadequate for space statics because three axes are involved, and a force may have moments about all three. Fig. 12–5 shows the arbitrary force P located in the xyz coordinate frame. The xy-plane shows $A'B'$, the projection of P. OC is the perpendicular distance from $A'B'$ to the z-axis. The moment of $A'B'$ about the z-axis is in the ordinary sense; i.e., for coplanar forces, $A'B' \times OC$. It will be noted that this is also the area of the shaded triangle $A'B'O$ in the xy-plane, as shown in Fig. 12–5. This is the extended concept of a moment, which is very valuable in space statics. Suppose,

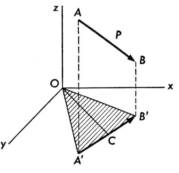

FIG. 12–5.

for instance, that the force P is parallel to the z-axis; then the component $A'B'$ disappears and the area $A'B'O$ approaches zero, as does the moment. From this condition one may establish the rule: *A force has no moment about a parallel axis.* As a corollary it can be established: *If a force system is in equilibrium, the projection of the resultant in any plane is zero, and consequently the area of the describing triangle and the moment about any axis equals zero.* This is expressed by the additional equations of equilibrium:

$$\Sigma M_x = 0; \qquad \Sigma M_y = 0; \qquad \Sigma M_z = 0 \qquad\qquad (12\text{–}7)$$

These equations can be used for an alternate solution for the shear leg derrick problem of Fig. 12–2. Considering the three concurrent forces at D, the tension in the cable CD can be found directly. Moments of the forces are taken about the yy-axis. The stresses are initially assumed to be in tension, as before.

$$\Sigma M_{yy} = \frac{100}{\sqrt{2}} \cdot 20 + \frac{100}{\sqrt{2}} \cdot 24 - \frac{24}{83.5} \, 80 \times \frac{3}{4} \, CD = 0$$

$$CD = 180.4\text{-k tension}$$

The other stresses can be found in a similar fashion:

$$\Sigma M_{x'x'} = \left(\frac{100}{\sqrt{2}} \cdot 16 \right) + \left(180.4 \times \frac{24}{83.5} \times 16 \right) + \frac{24}{39.4} \, AD \times 40 = 0$$

$$AD = -80.5 \text{ compression}$$

$$\left(\frac{24}{39.4} \times 80.5 \right) - \frac{16}{35.2} \, BD = 0$$

$$BD = -107.9\text{-k compression}$$

Actually any combination of Eqs. 12–5 and 12–7 can be used in obtaining a solution. For a concurrent force system, therefore, there are at least six equations that can be written. Of course there are only three independent equations for concurrent force systems, and the analyst should pick the most convenient summation of forces and moments for ease of solution.

12–3. Simple Space Trusses. A simple space truss may be considered to be a series of points (joints) rigidly constrained in space against movement in any direction. In order to understand how a simple space truss is constructed, consider the constraint of a single point D in space. In Fig. 12–6 bars AD and BD are first established, and these prevent movement in the plane ABD. This would be sufficient to constrain the point if the structure were coplanar. However, in this case, the point can move perpendicular to plane ABD. The addition of another member, CD, Fig. 12–6b, constrains the point D from movement in any direction. The point is now completely constrained by a minimum number of forces. If a load were placed on joint D, the same relationship would exist as for the shear leg derrick of Art. 12–1, and the three equations of statics would be sufficient to provide a solution. The addition of still another bar to constrain the point would result in a statically indeterminate structure. The tripod shown is the simplest space truss possible.

The addition of more bars to other points of the system will constrain more points in space and extend the truss. The pyramid shown in Fig. 12–6c is constructed by this process. Joint E is constrained by extending bars from B, C, and from the now constrained joint D. Likewise joint F is constrained by DF, EF, and CF, and in turn, G is constrained by DG, EG, and FG.

Note that for each point constrained, three bars are required. A relationship can thus be established for the joint-bar relationship:

$$3j = m \qquad\qquad (12\text{--}8)$$

where j is the number of joints and m the number of members. Since there are three independent equations of statics for each joint and three

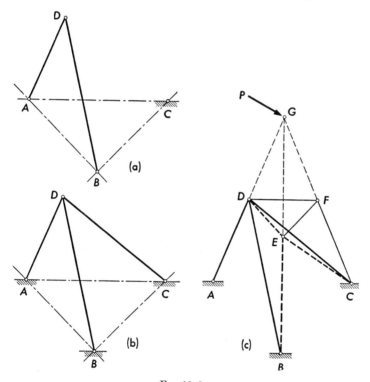

Fig. 12–6.

unknown stresses for each joint, Eq. 12–8 will express the statical determinacy of the system. If $m > 3j$, the system is statically indeterminate, and if $m < 3j$, the structure is unstable, since one or more joints are not completely constrained. Even if Eq. 12–8 were satisfied, there would be no assurance that the structure would be stable or statically determinate, since the equation is a necessary but not sufficient requisite for this condition. The successive order of the constraint of the joint should be studied in conjunction with the equation as it applied to the pyramid. This process is similar to that discussed in Art. 5–2 for plane trusses. Because of the complexity of some space structures, it is easy to select accidentally an unstable structure or "critical form" of a structure without knowing it. (See Art. 12–19.) If it can be shown that Eq. 12–8 is satisfied and that each joint is restrained by three additional bars in some definitive order, then one will be assured that the truss is determinate, stable, and has a unique solution.

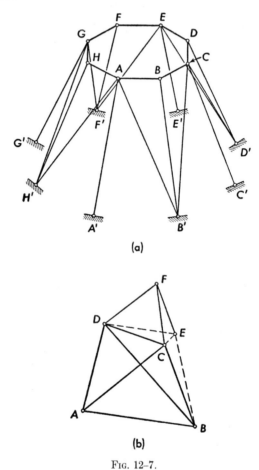

Fig. 12-7.

Another example of a simple truss is shown in Fig. 12–7a. In this case more than three support points are used. Since 3×8 joints $= 24$ members, Eq. 12–8 is satisfied. Joint A is restrained by bars AH', AA', and AB'. Likewise, joints C, E, and G are restrained by three bars extending from three points in the base plane. The joints B, D, F, and H are dependent upon other joints. Joint B is restrained by bars BB', AB from the now constrained joint A, and BC from the now constrained joint C. The other joints are also restrained by a bar to a point in the base plane; two other bars, to previously restrained joints. The structure is statically determinate, stable, and has a unique solution, according to this analysis.

A self-contained truss such as an aircraft frame poses a slightly different problem. The construction must be started with the simplest self-contained unit, a tetrahedron such as $ABCD$ in Fig. 12–7b, which consists of six members and four joints. The three extra members and three extra joints take the place of the base supports. By adding three members, another joint may be incorporated into the system. Thus E is constrained by BE, CE, and DE, and joint F is in turn constrained by CF, DF, and EF. The relationship between members and joints becomes

$$m = 3j - 6$$

Similar arguments can be presented for the stability of the truss so that if $m < 3j - 6$, the structure is unstable; if $m > 3j - 6$, the structure is statically indeterminate. A critical form can exist even if the equation has been satisfied.

12–4. Special Theorems of Space Statics. Certain rules can be deduced from the equations of statics which may make solutions easier and more rapid. For example, even the novice analyst soon recognizes that when two members of a three-member joint in coplanar structures are collinear, the third member must have zero stress if there is no load at the joint. Likewise certain similar rules for equally recognizable conditions exist in space structures. The student should use the following rules whenever possible to simplify his solutions. They should be justified by the equations of statics and thoroughly understood before use.

1. At a space joint where all bars except one lie in the same plane, the stress component normal to the plane of the bar not in the plane is equal to the component normal to the same plane of the load applied at the joint.
2. Likewise, in the same situation, if the joint has no applied load, the stress in the bar not in the plane must be equal to zero.
3. As a further consequence, if three noncoplanar bars meet at a joint, and there is no applied load at the joint, all the bars must have zero stress, provided that two of the bars are not collinear. In fact, if at a joint consisting of any number of noncoplanar bars, all bars except two can be shown to have zero stress, then the remaining two bars must also have zero stress, provided they are not collinear.

12–5. Constraint of an Object in Space. Consider the parallelepiped of Fig. 12–8a, which is acted upon by the arbitrary general force P. It is to be constrained, i.e., held rigid in space, by a group of forces. Recall that three *nonconcurrent* forces are needed to constrain an object in a coplanar force system. Visualize the projection of forces on the $B'BC$

plane of Fig. 12–8a. Three forces are needed for constraint, and B_z, C_z, and B_x are provided. Likewise, projection of forces on the ABB' plane shows that A_z, B_z, and B_y will provide the proper relationship, whereas projection upon the ABC plane provides B_y, C_y, and B_x. Each of the mutually perpendicular planes has projected forces which will provide equilibrium.

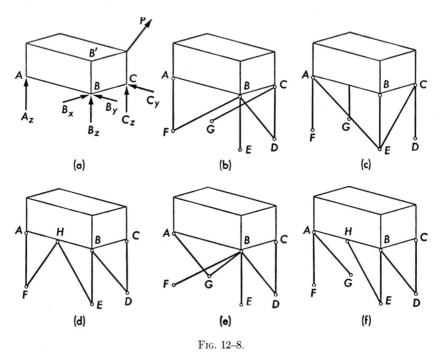

Fig. 12–8.

Further visual examination will show the body to be rigidly restrained against moments or forces in any direction, and it will be noted that six forces are the minimum number necessary to restrain the body against movement. There are six equations of statics available for the summation of forces in each of three directions and for the summations of moments about three different axes. The directions of force summation and the direction of the moment axes are usually taken as mutually perpendicular, but this is not mandatory. In fact in many cases it may be convenient to use nonorthogonal sets of axes. The well-known equations of statics are

$$\Sigma F_x = 0 \qquad \Sigma M_{xx} = 0$$
$$\Sigma F_y = 0 \qquad \Sigma M_{yy} = 0 \qquad (12\text{–}9)$$
$$\Sigma F_z = 0 \qquad \Sigma M_{zz} = 0$$

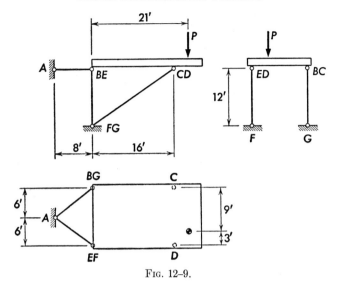

Fig. 12–9.

The use of Eqs. 12–9 is illustrated by the analysis of the structure in Fig. 12–9. The structure is a slab attached to foundation points by six bars as shown and is loaded by the vertical load P. Find the stresses in the bars in terms of P.

$$\Sigma F_{BE} = \frac{3}{5} AB - \frac{3}{5} AE = 0$$

$$AB = AE$$

$$\Sigma M_{FG} = \left(2 \times \frac{4}{5} AE \times 12\right) - 21P = 0$$

$$AE = \frac{35}{32} P \text{ tension}$$

$$\Sigma M_{BG} = \left(\frac{4}{5} \times \frac{35}{32} P \times 12\right) + \left(\frac{4}{5} DF \times 12\right) = 0$$

$$DF = -\frac{35}{32} P \text{ compression}$$

$$\text{(12–10)}$$

$$\Sigma F_{BC} = \frac{4}{5}\left(\frac{35}{32} P + \frac{35}{32} P\right) + \frac{4}{5}\left(-\frac{35}{32} P + CG\right) = 0$$

$$CG = -\frac{35}{32} P \text{ compression}$$

$$\Sigma M_{BC} = 9P - \left(\frac{3}{5} \times \frac{35}{32} P \times 12\right) + 12EF = 0$$

$$EF = \frac{3}{32} P \text{ compression}$$

$$\Sigma F_{BG} = -\left(2 \times \frac{3}{5} \times \frac{35}{32} P\right) - \frac{3}{32} P + BG + P = 0$$

$$BG = \frac{13}{32} P \text{ tension} \quad \text{(12–11)}$$

As further examples of space constraint, consider the objects of Fig. 12–8b to f. Fig. 12–8b is statically determinate and properly restrained, since resolution of the bar forces provides only three forces in each of three mutually perpendicular planes. Fig. 12–8c is found to be unstable, since one may visually note the four perpendicular bars; however, in addition, the projection of the bar forces on the ABC plane yields only components of bars AE and CE in this plane, and therefore the structure is unstable.

Examination of Fig. 12–8e shows a slightly more difficult problem. A cursory examination may indicate that the projection of bar forces on the ABC plane will result in enough forces to satisfactorily constrain the body; however, further examination will show that since more than three bars meet at B, this point is constrained by a statically indeterminate force system which prevents a solution. Fig. 12–8f illustrates another system which meets all constraint conditions. It can be solved for bar stresses by Eqs. 12–9.

12–6. Types of Reactions. Since there may be only six exterior reactions for a rigid body while still maintaining statical determinacy, special devices well known to engineers must be used to limit the number of reaction forces. There are three types of connections to be made: three-force component connections, two-force component connections, and one-force connections. The three-force connection can be provided by a ball-and-socket connection, an ideal case not often encountered in practice. A practical substitute could be a bolt through a plate or any of a number of other similar crude approximations. A two-force connection can be created by a roller restrained against side movement or by a bolt moving in a slotted plate. A one-force member can be just two greased plates which slide over one another or a bolt in a loose-fitting hole. In any case the component of force is zero in the direction in which movement is allowed.

Such devices not only permit statical analysis of the structure but also allow it to expand and contract with temperature changes and thus to prevent internal stress or thrust in undesirable directions, such as a perpendicular to a masonry wall.

12–7. Numerical Example: Solution of Space Truss. One of the difficulties in solving for the stresses in a space truss is the process of keeping track of progress made toward the solution. In the first place it is most difficult to picture the three-dimensional structure in a two-dimensional drawing, especially in determining the axis of moments and the forces which are to be included in the various summations for space structures. Secondly, there are usually numerous bars, trigonometric functions, and stress components which need to be recorded. The engineer must develop a neat, methodical bookkeeping system to use during the solution. The following example illustrates one such method.

Fig. 12–10a, b, and c illustrates a cantilever truss structure which will be analyzed for bar stresses. All methods of analysis will be utilized. Table 12–1 will be used to keep track of the analysis during the process.

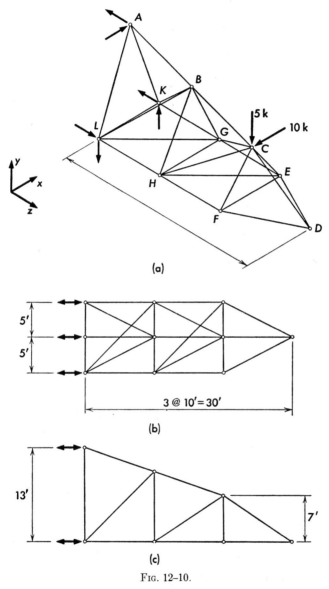

(a)

(b)

(c)

Fig. 12–10.

The truss is attached to the wall by three connections, A, L, and K, which provide six constraining exterior forces. The truss itself is a simple space truss, which may be treated as a rigid body attached to the wall by six constraining forces.

TABLE 12-1

Bar	Projections			Length	Cosines			Components			Stress
	x	y	z		cos x	cos y	cos z	x	y	z	
AB	0	3	10	10.43	0	0.287	0.956	0	2.31	7.69	8.04
AK	5	13	0	13.95	0.357	0.932	0	5.45	14.21	0	-15.25
AL	5	13	0	13.95	0.357	0.932	0	4.54	11.90	0	12.72
BC	0	3	10	10.43	0	0.287	0.956	0	1.51	5.0	5.24
BG	5	10	0	11.18	0.448	0.896	0	2.62	5.25	0	-5.86
BH	5	10	0	11.18	0.448	0.896	0	4.36	8.74	0	9.76
BK	5	10	0	15.0	0.333	0.667	0.667	2.85	5.71	5.71	8.56
BL	5	10	0	15.0	0.333	0.667	0.667	4.20	8.40	8.40	-12.60
CG	5	7	10	13.19	0.379	0.531	0.758	3.75	5.25	7.50	9.89
CH	5	7	10	13.19	0.379	0.531	0.758	6.24	8.74	12.45	-16.45
GH	10	0	0	10.0	1.0	0	0	1.84	0	0	1.84
GK	0	0	10	10.0	0	0	1.0	0	0	10.44	10.44
GL	10	0	10	14.14	0.707	0	0.707	2.94	0	2.94	-4.16
KL	10	0	0	10.0	1.0	0	0	2.60	0	0	2.60
HL	0	0	10	10.0	0	0	1.0	12.59	0	0	-12.59

The first step is to find the exterior reactions. Six equations of statics are written as follows:

SOLUTION FOR EXTERIOR REACTIONS:

$$\Sigma M_{LK} = 0; \quad 5 \times 20 = 13A_z$$
$$A_z = 7.69 \text{ k}$$

$$\Sigma F_x = 0; \quad A_x - 10 = 0$$
$$A_x = 10.0 \text{ k}$$

$$\Sigma M_{L \text{ vert}} = 0; \quad (7.69 \times 5) - (10 \times 20) + 10K_z = 0$$
$$K_z = 16.15 \text{ k}$$
$$\Sigma M_{K \text{ vert}} = 0; \quad (10 \times 20) - 10L_z + (5 \times 7.69) = 0 \tag{12–12}$$
$$L_z = 23.85 \text{ k}$$

$$\Sigma M_{LF} = (10 \times 13) - 10K_y - (10 \times 7) + (5 \times 5) = 0$$
$$K_y = 8.5 \text{ k}$$

$$\Sigma M_{KE} = (10 \times 7) + (5 \times 5) - (10 \times 13) + 10L_y = 0$$
$$L_y = 3.5 \text{ k}$$

The solution will be made easier if the bars with zero stress are eliminated first. By applying the rules given in Art. 12–4, one finds that all bars joining at D have zero stress, and as a result all bars joining at F and E also have zero stress. The structure is thus simplified considerably. Only the remaining members are entered in the Table 12–1. Noting the zero stress members at this point saves considerable work in computing cosines, lengths, and other values incidental to the stress calculations.

To illustrate the method of moments, bar stresses in AB will be found from a free body created by passing a plane through all members between panels ALK and BHG. By taking moments about the LK-axis, the stress can be found directly.

JOINT A:

$$\Sigma M_{LK} = 5 \times 20 = 0.956AB \times 13$$
$$AB = 8.04 \text{ k} \tag{12–13}$$

Likewise, stress in BC is found.

JOINT C:

$$\Sigma M_{GH} = 5 \times 10 = 0.956BC \times 10$$
$$BC = 5.24 \text{ k} \tag{12–13a}$$

The solution can now proceed by the method of joints, as shown hereafter.

JOINT C:

$$-1.51 + 5.0 + 0.553CG + 0.533CH = 0$$
$$10.0 - 0.379CG + 0.379CH = 0$$
$$CG = 9.89\text{-k tension}$$
$$CH = -16.45\text{-k compression}$$

(12–14)

JOINT A:

$$\Sigma F_y = 2.31 + 0.932AL + 0.932AK = 0$$
$$\Sigma F_x = -10.00 + 0.357AL - 0.357AK = 0$$
$$AL = 12.72 \text{ k}$$
$$AK = -15.25 \text{ k}$$

(12–15)

JOINT K:

$$\Sigma F_y = -14.21 + 0.667BK + 8.5 = 0$$
$$BK = 8.56 \text{ k}$$
$$\Sigma F_x = KL - 5.45 + 2.85 = 0$$
$$KL = 2.60 \text{ k}$$
$$\Sigma F_z = 16.15 - 5.71 - GK = 0$$
$$GK = 10.44 \text{ k}$$

(12–16)

JOINT L:

$$\Sigma F_y = -3.5 + 11.90 + 0.667BL = 0$$
$$BL = -12.60 \text{ k}$$
$$\Sigma F_x = 4.54 - 4.20 + 2.60 + 0.707GL = 0$$
$$GL = -4.16 \text{ k}$$
$$\Sigma F_z = HL - 2.94 - 8.40 + 23.85 = 0$$
$$HL = -12.59 \text{ k}$$

(12–17)

JOINT G:

$$\Sigma F_x = GH - 2.64 + 3.74 - 2.94 = 0$$
$$GH = 1.84 \text{ k}$$
$$0.896BG + 5.25 = 0$$
$$BG = -5.86 \text{ k}$$

(12–18)

JOINT H:

$$0.896BH - 8.74 = 0$$

$$BH = 9.76 \text{ k}$$

$$GH + 4.37 - 6.23 = 0$$

$$\qquad (12\text{–}19)$$

$$GH = 1.86 \text{ k} \qquad (Check)$$

The problem illustrates the interchange of methods possible throughout the solution. An experienced analyst will change his methods, his directions of force, summation axes, and moment axes at his convenience. Oftentimes the X, Y, Z component system must be discarded and a newly oriented set of axes chosen for each joint as the work progresses. In each case a different type of tabulation must be created to suit the particular problem.

12–8. Compound Space Trusses. Fig. 12–11a shows a truss which may be shown to satisfy Eq. 12–8 and thus is statically determinate.

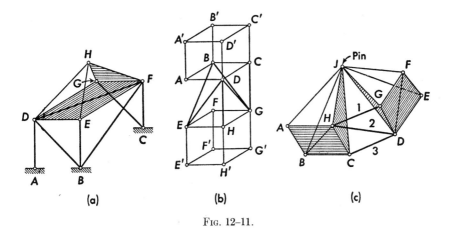

Fig. 12–11.

Upon examination it will be noted that the portion of the truss $DEFGH$ forms an independent simple truss. This simple truss is connected by six bars to the foundation points ABC. Therefore, during the solution for bar forces, the simple truss may be regarded as a rigid object, restrained in space by a system of bars as described in Art. 12–6. The solution for the stresses in these supporting members can be made by use of Eqs. 12–9, after which the bar forces in the simple truss can be found by the method of joints or by the use of Eq. 12–6.

Such trusses are called *compound* trusses, and they are common engineering structures. Fig. 12–11b and c indicate other schematic forms.

Oftentimes two simple trusses (internal and web bars not shown), such as $ABCD$ and $EFGH$ in Fig. 12–11b, are joined together by a series of six bars to form a compound truss. This could be the case, for example, in an aircraft structure. Or the structure may be further compounded by extending support bars from $E'F'G'H'$ to foundation points.

Fig. 12–11c shows another compound truss. In this case two trusses are joined together by only three bars and a pin. A space pin (joint) provides three components of force to yield the six forces for proper constraint. In either of these structures the bar stresses can be found by applying the six equations of statics to find the stresses in the compounding bars, and then the stresses in the other trusses can be found by independent methods.

12–9. Complex Space Trusses. Complex space trusses encompass most of the forms useful in structural engineering practice because they include the envelope forms. Envelope forms are those that provide an internal region of usable space. Domes, dirigible frames, most aircraft trusses, and towers without internal cross-members are usually of the complex type.

In order to understand the solution of complex trusses, one must understand how they are evolved. Consider the truss shown in Fig. 12–12a. It is a simple space truss formed by first constraining joint D by bars AD, BD, and CD. Joint E is next constrained by DE, AE, and CE, and joint F is constrained by the additional bars EF, CF, and BF. The structure satisfies the relationship $m = 3j$ and therefore is statically determinate. Fig. 12–12b illustrates the same structure with one exception—bar DC has been removed and DF substituted. Of course the relationship $m = 3j$ is still satisfied, and the structure must be statically determinate. It is immediately apparent that each of the joints, D, E, and F, connects four bars which prevent a solution at a joint by use of the three equations of statics for a concurrent force system. Nevertheless enough equations are available for a solution, since there are nine equations—three for each joint—and nine bars. Therefore the nine equations must be solved simultaneously in order to find the bar stresses. There is no direct solution possible for the stress in an individual bar by either the method of moments or the method of joints.

It can be seen that the simultaneous solution would become exceedingly laborious as more joints were added to the system. The illustrated structure is the least complicated complex truss, and each additional joint adds three equations to the system. Obviously other methods are needed to solve such problems, and most of the remaining articles of this chapter will deal with more rapid or special methods to solve the complex truss problem. It may be noted that the more common usage of digital computers, for which more centers are being established around the country, will make possible the rapid solutions of large systems of simultaneous equations at nominal cost.

As a further example of a complex truss, consider Figs. 12–12c and d. Fig. 12–12c illustrates a simple self-contained space truss which can be solved directly by the method of joints. It also satisfies the $m = 3j - 6$ relationship. By changing member CF to BE, Fig. 12–12d, a complex structure is created, with the same problems of solution as previously described. In this case $3 \times 6 = 18$ simultaneous equations would be involved.

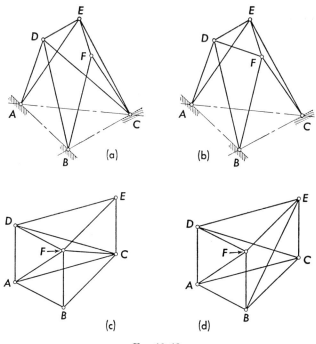

Fig. 12–12.

For complex trusses it must be shown that a critical form does not exist, to be assured that a unique solution is possible (see Art. 12–19).

12–10. Space Frames with Four or More Vertical Reactions. Many engineering structures have more than six external reactions and thus have more reactions than can be found by use of the six equations of statics as described in Art. 12–5. Many bridges are examples of this feature, since they usually have four vertical reactions and three additional reactions in a horizontal plane for a total of seven.

Fig. 12–13 shows another structure—a four-sided pyramid—which also has seven external reactions. At first glance this structure appears to be statically indeterminate; however, when one applies Eq. 12–8, one finds that the structure must be statically determinate because

$$3 \times 5 \text{ joints} = 8 \text{ members} + 7 \text{ reactions}$$

where each reaction is counted as a bar. The problem can be solved by looking for another condition to use in conjunction with the external equations of statics. Of course the obvious conditions in this case are the internal statics equations. In order to enter the frame, it is assumed that one of the vertical reactions is known, say, $C_z = R$. Then the other external reactions are found in terms of R; thus:

$$M_{zA} = (10 \times 6) - (5 \times 4) - 10B_x = 0$$

$$B_x = 4.0 \text{ k}$$

$$F_x = 4 - 10 + D_x = 0$$

$$D_x = 6.0 \text{ k} \tag{12-20}$$

$$F_y = 5 - A_y = 0$$

$$A_y = 5 \text{ k}$$

and if $C_z = R$,

$$M_{AB} = 12R + 12D_z - (10 \times 10) - (6 \times 4) = 0$$

$$D_z = 10.33 - R$$

$$M_{AD} = 10R - 10B_z - (6 \times 6) - (5 \times 10) = 0$$

$$B_z = R - 8.60 \tag{12-21}$$

$$F_z = R - (R - 8.60) + (10.33 - R) - 6 - A_z = 0$$

$$A_z = 12.93 - R$$

The lengths of the edge members of the pyramid are shown in Fig. 12–13c. Next the stress in member CD can be calculated from both joints D and C and the results equated.

From joint D: $\quad DE = (10.33 - R) \cdot \dfrac{14.14}{10}$

From joint C: $\quad CE = R \cdot \dfrac{13.42}{10} \tag{12-22}$

Member CD: $\quad \dfrac{13.42}{10} R \cdot \dfrac{4}{13.42} = \dfrac{(14.60 - 1.414R)}{14.14} \cdot 6$

$$R = 6.19 \text{ k}$$

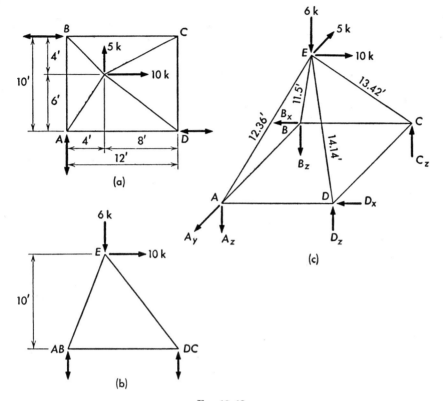

Fig. 12–13.

Once the assumed value R is found, one may proceed by the method of joints to find that the other reactions and stresses are as follows:

$$A_z = 12.93 - 6.19 = 6.74$$
$$B_z = 6.19 - 8.60 = -2.41 \qquad (12\text{--}23)$$
$$D_z = 10.33 - 6.19 = 4.14$$

Joint A:

$$\frac{10}{12.36} AE = 12.93 - 6.19 \qquad\qquad AE = 8.35 \text{ tension}$$

$$AB = \left(8.35 \times \frac{6}{12.36}\right) - 5.0 \qquad AB = 0.96 \text{ tension} \quad (12\text{--}24)$$

$$AD = 8.35 \times \frac{4}{12.36} \qquad\qquad AD = 2.70 \text{ compression}$$

JOINT C:

$$CE = 6.19 \times \frac{13.42}{10} \qquad CE = 8.31 \text{ compression}$$

$$CD = 8.31 \times \frac{4}{13.42} \qquad CD = 2.48 \text{ tension} \qquad (12\text{–}25)$$

$$BC = 8.31 \times \frac{8}{13.42} \qquad BC = 4.96 \text{ tension}$$

JOINT B:

$$BE = \frac{11.5}{10} \times 2.41 \qquad BE = 2.76 \text{ compression} \qquad (12\text{–}26)$$

JOINT D:

$$DE = \frac{14.14}{10} \times 4.14 \qquad DE = 5.84 \text{ compression} \qquad (12\text{–}27)$$

12–11. Solution by Symmetry. The analyst should look for condition of symmetry in every structure, since it simplifies the solution extensively

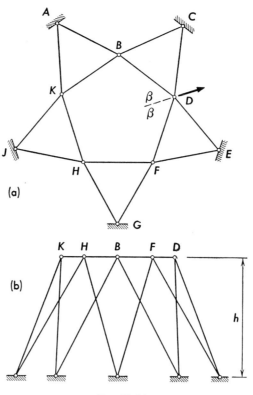

(a)

(b)

FIG. 12–14.

in most cases. This may consist of general symmetry of the truss, symmetry of a joint, and/or symmetry of loads. Fig. 12–14a illustrates a pedestal consisting of an equilateral pentagon top ring supported by symmetrical legs. It is loaded at D with the load P. The frame is statically determinate, since 5 joints $\times$ 3 = 15 members. Each joint has four members, and therefore the structure is complex. One method of solution is the writing of the 15 equations of statics for the five joints and solving them simultaneously—a great deal of time-consuming work. Upon further examination it will be found that each joint is itself symmetrical. By summing forces perpendicular to the plane of the two supporting members AB and BC, it is found that $S_{BD} = -S_{KB}$.

Progressing from joint to joint around the top of the pedestal, one finds that

$$S_{BD} = -S_{KB} = S_{HK} = -S_{FH} = S_{FD} \tag{12–28}$$

so that $S_{BD} = S_{FD}$. This yields the condition necessary for finding one of the bar stresses which will permit solution without simultaneous solution. Taking joint D as a free body, and letting h be the vertical height of the pedestal,

$$2S_{BD} \cos \beta = P$$

$$S_{BD} = \frac{P}{2 \cos \beta} \tag{12–29}$$

The remainder of the bar stresses can be found by application of the equations of statics at each joint in rotation.

Another example is illustrated in Fig. 12–15a, where a pedestal is loaded symmetrically by four loads, P, at the upper ring. The vertical rib $CC'C''$ is isolated and shown in the plane it describes in Fig. 12–15b.

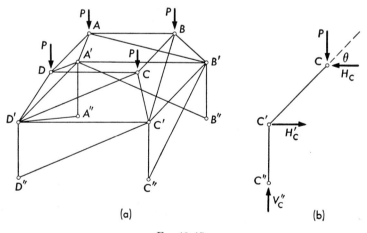

(a)   (b)

Fig. 12–15.

Obviously this free body can only be in equilibrium if the forces H are in the plane of the rib. In each case this can be true only if the web members CD' and BC' are zero, since a stress in these would pull the resultant out of the plane $CC'C''$. It may therefore be concluded that the stresses in all the diagonals are zero. As a result, the stresses in all vertical members in the lower tier are equal to P, and the ribs in the upper tier have the stress $S = P/\sin \theta$, while $H_C = H_{C'} = P/\tan \theta$. The forces H are the resultants of stress in the ring members CD, CB, $C'D'$, and $C'B'$, and therefore, by summation of forces in the horizontal plane at a typical upper ring joint $CB = -P \sin \alpha/\tan \theta$ and $CD = -P \cos \alpha/\tan \theta$ where α is the angle between plane $CC'C''$ and a vertical plane through C and D. Likewise, at a lower ring joint $C'B' = -CB$ and $C'D' = -CD$.

12–12. Solution by Substitute Member.* The substitute member method has been a convenient one in some cases, such as the Fink roof

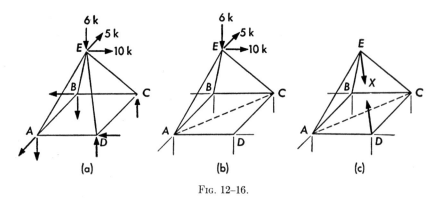

Fig. 12–16.

truss in coplanar structures. It is also convenient to use in solving some space trusses. Fig. 12–16 illustrates how the method can be extended. For illustration the same truss used in Art. 12–10 will be solved by this method.

The first step is illustrated in Fig. 12–16b. Member DE is removed and AC is substituted in order to maintain stability and satisfy the relationship $m = 3j$. The removed member is selected so that a joint exists after removal, such as E, where the equations of statics can be used to find the bar stresses directly. The stress in the substitute member AC is designated S. Secondly, a load X is applied along the line of action of DE, as shown in Fig. 12–16c. The original state in Fig. 12–16a demands that the stress in the substitute AC equals zero. This may be expressed by a simple

---

* L. Henneberg, *Statik der Sparrensysteme* (Darmstadt, 1886).

equation. Let u be the stress in AC due to a unit load along DE, and then the stress in AC due to X will be uX. Then

$$S_{AC} = S + uX = 0 \qquad (12\text{--}30)$$

and the unknown stress in DE is

$$X = \frac{-S}{u} \qquad (12\text{--}31)$$

The numerical solution is completed. By referring to Fig. 12–16b again, and using joint E as a free body,

$$\Sigma M_{AB} = (6 \times 4) + (10 \times 10) + \left(\frac{8}{13.42} \times 10 S_{CE}\right)$$

$$+ \left(\frac{10}{13.42} \times 4 S_{CE}\right) = 0 \qquad (12\text{--}32)$$

$$S_{CE} = -13.88\text{-k compression}$$

Joint C:

$$\Sigma F = \frac{4}{13.42} S_{CE} + \frac{10}{15.62} S_{AC} = 0$$

$$S_{AC} = 6.45\text{-k tension} \qquad (12\text{--}33)$$

Now, applying the unit load along DE in Fig. 12–16c, the stress in AC is found:

Joint E:

$$\frac{8}{14.14} + \frac{8}{13.42} S_{CE} = 0; \qquad S_{CE} = 0.95 \text{ k} \qquad (12\text{--}34)$$

Joint D:

$$\frac{6}{14.14} S_{DE} + S_{CD} = 0; \qquad S_{CD} = -0.424 \text{ k} \qquad (12\text{--}35)$$

Joint C:

$$\frac{10}{15.62} S_{AC} - 0.424 - 0.95 \times \frac{4}{13.42} = 0; \qquad S_{AC} = 1.103 \text{ k} \quad (12\text{--}36)$$

Substitution in Eq. 12–31 yields

$$S_{DE} = \frac{6.45}{1.103} = 5.85\text{-k compression} \qquad (12\text{--}37)$$

This is the value obtained by the method in Art. 12–10. Once one of the stresses is obtained, the solution for stresses in the other members can be completed in the normal manner.

In this method the question arises as to which bar should be replaced by a substitute member. There are usually several possibilities for the substitution, as, in this case, any of the members meeting at E could be removed. The substitute member should be placed so that the stability of the truss is restored and so that the least numerical work will ensue. Some study may be necessary in order to find the most time-saving method in the more complex structures. In the example it would be also possible to remove one of the reactions and substitute an internal bar (for example, C_z removed in favor of AC or BD). The reverse is also possible; internal members can be removed in favor of external reactions, as is shown in Art. 12–13.

12–13. Solution by Multiple Substitute Members. Fig. 12–17 illustrates another complex structure which may be solved by the substitute

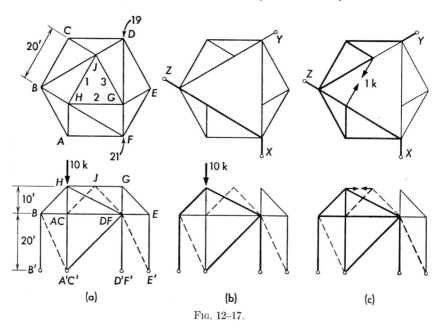

Fig. 12–17.

member method. In this case removal of three members is necessary. The removal of JH and GH are two of the obvious choices, since only three members will be left. This permits entry into the truss with the equations of statics at joint E. Further examination shows that removal of JG is also necessary for the solution to proceed to joint J or G without simultaneous solution of the equations of statics at the joints. Instead of internal members, external reactions (bars) in the horizontal plane will be added to make joints B, D, and F rigid against movement after removal of other members.

As before, the condition to be met is that the added members x, y, and z must have zero stress when the proper stresses exist in members 1, 2, and 3, the removed members. Each of the stresses X, Y, and Z will be interdependent upon the stresses S_1, S_2, and S_3, so that a set of three simultaneous equations must still be solved.

Let S be the stress in the members of the simplified structure, Fig. 12–17b, and let u designate the stress in members due to unit loads along lines of action 1, 2, or 3. The first subscript will designate the member stressed; the second, the application point of the unit stress. The simultaneous equations expressing the zero stress in the substitute members are:

$$X = S_x + u_{x,1}S_1 + u_{x,2}S_2 + u_{x,3}S_3 = 0$$

$$Y = S_y + u_{y,1}S_1 + u_{y,2}S_2 + u_{y,3}S_3 = 0 \qquad (12\text{–}38)$$

$$Z = S_z + u_{z,1}S_1 + u_{z,2}S_2 + u_{z,3}S_3 = 0$$

For a more complex structure more equations may be written; thus, for n substitute members, there will be n simultaneous equations. Note that for the case at hand, the reduction in number of simultaneous equations will be from 9 joints $\times$ 3 = 27 equations to only 3 equations.

The numerical solution is as follows: The precise details of the stresses at each joint are omitted, and the results are listed in Table 12–2. The lengths of the members are listed in column 2. The stresses S are noted in column 3 for the simplified structure with substitute members subjected to the applied loading. The heavy lines in Fig. 12–17b indicate the stressed members for this case. Fig. 12–17c illustrates the application of a unit load to member 2 and the members stressed under such load. The stresses for this condition are noted in column 4. The stresses for the unit loads on lines 1 and 3 can be obtained from the symmetry of the structure by cyclic interchange of the joint-lettering system. These stresses are noted in columns 5 and 6. The equations for the solution of S_1, S_2, and S_3 are

$$X = -38.5 - 0.384S_1 - 2.505S_2 - 0.433S_3 = 0$$

$$Y = -0.433S_1 - 0.384S_2 - 2.505S_3 = 0 \qquad (12\text{–}39)$$

$$Z = -70.3 - 2.505S_1 - 0.433S_2 - 0.384S_3 = 0$$

from which

$$S_1 = -27.0\text{-k compression}$$

$$S_2 = -12.38\text{-k compression}$$

$$S_3 = 6.56\text{-k tension}$$

TABLE 12-2

Bar	L	S	u_4	u_2	u_3	S_1u_4	S_2u_2	S_3u_3	Total
AA'	20.0	0	1.000	0.500	0	−27.0	−6.19	0	−33.19
AF	20.0	0	0.665	−0.333	0	−17.98	4.13	0	−13.85
AH	15.3	0	1.53	0.765	0	−41.2	−9.56	0	−50.76
BB'	20.0	−45.9	−1.842	0.250	−1.000	49.7	−3.09	−6.56	−5.65
BA	20.0	0	1.333	−0.50	0	−35.85	6.19	0	−29.66
BH	15.3	−102	−1.022	0	0	27.50	0	0	−74.50
BJ	25.2	0	−1.26	0	−0.837	33.90	0	−2.22	31.68
BC	20.0	0	−0.333	0	0.665	9.00	0	4.36	13.36
BC'	28.28	0	0.940	0.354	0.940	−25.40	−4.38	6.16	−23.62
CJ	15.3	0	0.765	0	1.530	−20.65	0	10.04	−10.61
CD	20.0	0	−0.500	0	−1.333	13.50	0	−8.75	4.75
CC'	20.0	0	0.500	0	1.000	−13.50	0	6.56	−6.94
DJ	15.3	0	0	0	−1.022	0	0	−6.71	−6.71
DG	25.2	0	0	−0.837	−1.260	0	10.34	−8.26	2.08
DE	20.0	0	0	0.665	−0.333	0	−8.11	−2.15	−10.26
DE'	28.28	0	0.354	0.940	0.940	−9.52	−11.63	6.16	−14.99
DD'	20.0	0	0.250	−1.000	−1.842	−6.75	12.38	−12.09	−6.46
EE'	20.0	0	0	1.000	0.500	0	−12.38	3.28	−9.10
EG	15.3	0	0	1.530	0.765	0	−18.93	5.02	−13.91
EF	20.0	0	0	−1.333	−0.500	0	16.62	−3.28	13.34
FF'	20.0	−100	−1.000	−1.842	0.250	27.0	22.80	1.84	−48.36
FG	15.3	0	0	−1.022	0	0	12.68	0	12.68
FH	25.2	−84.0	−0.837	−1.260	0	22.61	15.60	0	45.79
FA'	28.28	94.3	0.940	0.940	0.354	−25.40	−11.63	2.32	59.59
GH	20.0	0	0	1.000	0	0	−12.38	0	−12.38
HJ	20.0	0	1.0	0	0	−27.0	0	0	−27.0
JG	20.0	0	0	0	1.0	0	0	6.56	6.56
x	0	−38.5	−0.384	−2.505	−0.433	10.4	31.0	−2.9	0
y	0	0	−0.433	−0.384	−2.505	11.7	4.8	−16.5	0
z	0	−70.3	−2.505	−0.433	−0.384	67.6	5.3	−2.52	0

The stresses in each member of the truss can be found by adding the effects of each of these stresses; thus:

$$S_{BB'} = -45.9 + 1.842\,(27.0) - 0.250\,(12.38) - 1.0\,(6.56)$$
$$= -5.65 \text{ k}$$

(12–40)

12–14. Solution by Subdivision into Plane Trusses. It is an accepted fact among engineers that bridges can be divided into coplanar parts—the main trusses, the wind bracing, and the portals—for separate analysis.

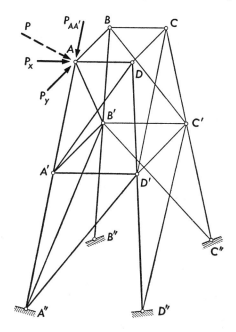

Fig. 12–18.

Towers, too, are often analyzed by treating each side separately. It will be valuable to reconsider at this point how such division is possible. Consider the double-tiered tower shown in Fig. 12–18, with the arbitrary load P applied at the upper corner A. The tower is a complex envelope structure with at least four members meeting at each joint. The components of the force are also shown resolved along the column line AA'' and in the plane of the two trusses $AA'B'B$ and $A'AD'D$. By application of the special rules of Art. 12–4, one can mark the members of zero stress. At joints B and D, members AB and CD frame into a joint where no external loads are applied and where the other members at the joint are coplanar. Thus CD and BC must have a zero stress. One proceeds with this analysis throughout the truss to find that only the heavily outlined portion of the truss is stressed. Of course this is consistent with the ordinary assumption that trusses receive only forces in their plane. The members at the joining line, in this case $AA'A''$, are parts of both trusses. The stress in AA' will be the sum of stresses in truss $AA'B'B$ due to P_y; in truss $AA'D'D$, due to P_x; and column stresses in AA' due to $P_{AA'}$.

The plane system is extended advantageously to more complex structures in the next article.

Despite the foregoing analysis, the loads cannot always be resolved along planes. In cases such as that illustrated in Fig. 12–19, where the tower shape is held rigid by a tank or other structure and the whole structure deflects as a unit, another method must be used.* As shown in Fig. 12–19a, the octagonal top ring moves as a unit a distance Δ to the right, owing to wind loads P at A and H. Assume that the force taken by each plane is dependent upon its deflection; thus, W_n will be dependent upon $\Delta \sin \beta$. Let $W_n = C \sin \beta_n$, where C, a constant to be determined, incorporates Δ. From the summation of forces,

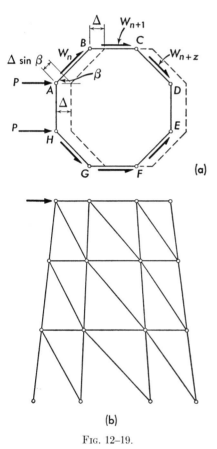

Fig. 12–19.

$$H = 2P = W_n \sin \beta_n = C\Sigma \sin^2 \beta_n \qquad (12\text{–}41)$$

But $\Sigma \sin^2 \beta_n = n$, where $2n$ equals the number of sides of the polygon, so that

$$2P = Cn \qquad \text{or} \qquad C = \frac{2P}{n}$$

and thus

$$W_n = C \sin \beta_n = \frac{2P}{n} \cdot \sin \beta_n \qquad (12\text{–}42)$$

<hr />

* Müller-Breslau, "Beitrag zur Theorie der Kuppel- und Turmdächer und verwandter Konstrucktionen," *Zeitschrift des Vereins deutscher Ingenieure*, Heft **44** (1898).

For the octagonal truss shown, $2n = 8$, $n = 4$, and

$$W_n \ (45° \text{ sides}) = \frac{2P}{4} \sin 45° = \frac{P}{4}\sqrt{2}$$

and   (12–43)

$$W_n \ (\text{sides parallel to loads}) = \frac{P}{2}$$

Sides perpendicular to the loads carry no loads. The individual trusses can be solved as coplanar structures, Fig. 12–19b, with the loads W_n applied in its plane. Columns that are common to two planes will have two stresses which must be added.

12–15. Solution by Plate Analogy.* One of the characteristics of a coplanar truss is that it is rigid against distortion in its plane but is assumed to be flexible perpendicular to its plane. This fact can be used as the basis of an analogy which simplifies the solution of certain space frameworks. Consider the solution of the complex envelope frame of Fig. 12–12d. Each of the sides and the top of the truss may be assumed to be plates, as shown in Fig. 12–20.

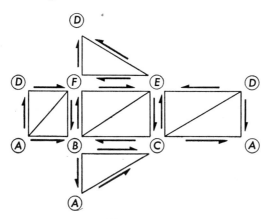

Fig. 12–20.

As an example, consider the forces acting upon a general plate free body from a space frame. On each of the edges of the trapezoid a force will exist. The equilibrium condition of the plate may be expressed by three equations of statics for a force system in a plane; i.e.,

$$\Sigma F_x = 0$$

$$\Sigma F_y = 0 \qquad\qquad (12–44)$$

$$\Sigma M_0 = 0$$

* Based on a method presented by F. Stüssi, *Baustatik* (Zürich, 1948).

The plate $ABFD$ is joined to other similar plates in the system such as $FBCE$. At the joint BF or edge of the two plates, equal and opposite forces exist. Likewise for this plate, three independent equations of statics exist. For some plates, of course, there will be free edges (no edge force). In addition, there may be external forces on the plates from reactions and loads. Thus, for a system of p plates, there are $3p$ independent equations. Therefore for p plates, r unknown external reactions, and f edge forces, the following relationship must exist in order for the system to be statically determinate:

$$3p = r + f \qquad (12\text{--}45)$$

If the system contains triangular plates, such as ABC, Fig. 12–20, with one edge free, then only two forces exist on the edges and two equations are sufficient to describe the conditions of statics. As a result Eq. 12–45 must be modified. If p' is the number of triangular plates with one free edge, then the equation becomes

$$3p + 2p' = r + f \qquad (12\text{--}46)$$

Once the edge forces are known on any plate $ABCD$, then it is an easy step to find the stresses in the diagonal AC. In fact an advantage of the method is that the solution for the edge forces is completely independent of the conformation of the interior members. Once the web members are found, the solution may continue in a normal fashion with Eqs. 12–6.

The method will be illustrated by the solution for the stresses in the pedestal of Fig. 12–21a. The web members are shown only in $DCHE$ and consist of tension rods which cross each other in each plane. One of the

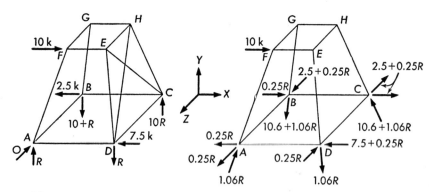

(a) Reactions on Pedestal   (b) Reactions Resolved Along Plane Edges

$$AB = BC = CD = DA = 30'$$
$$EF = FG = GH = HE = 15'$$
Vert. Dist. $ABCD$ and $EFGH = 30'$

Fig. 12–21.

problems connected with the solution by ordinary methods is to determine which of the tension rods is acting. One must be slack in each plane or the frame will be statically indeterminate. By the plate analogy the edge forces may be solved without determining which rod is acting. A further complication is the fact that there are four vertical reactions. From Eq. 12–45 we find 3×5 plates $= 7$ reactions $+ 8$ edge forces, and therefore the structure is statically determinate. Because all the reactions cannot be found from the external equations of statics, the vertical reaction at A is assumed to be of known value R, and the remainder of the reactions are found in terms of R. These reactions are shown in Fig. 12–21a. The next step is to resolve each of the reactions into the plane of the plates as shown in Fig. 12–21b. Next the structure is broken down into its plate components, and the plate forces are placed upon the plate free bodies, as shown in Fig. 12–22a. In the case of a force $1.06R$ at A, which coincides with the edge AF, the force may be placed upon either plate $AFED$ or $AFGB$. As noted in Fig. 12–22a the load of 10 k is arbitrarily placed on the top plate $EFGH$ instead of plate $AFED$. The force system on plate $EFGH$ can be simplified immediately by taking moments about F to show that $GH = HE$, and consequently $GF = HE$ and $FE = 10 - HE$ from the summation of forces in the vertical and horizontal directions.

The equations of statics can be written for the plates and solved simultaneously as follows (see Fig. 12–22b).

PLATE I

1. $\Sigma F_H = 0$, $0.236AF +$ $0.236ED$ $- 0.250R -$ $HE + 2.5 = 0$
2. $\Sigma F_V = 0$, $0.97AF -$ $0.97ED$ $+ 1.03R$ $= 0$
3. $\Sigma_M = 0$, $19.4ED$ $- 20.6HE + 206 = 0$

$$(12\text{–}47)$$

PLATE II

4. $\Sigma F_H = 0$, $+ 0.236ED + 0.236HC + 0.250R +$ $HE + 2.5 = 0$
5. $\Sigma F_V = 0$, $+ 0.97ED -$ $0.97HC - 1.03R +$ HE $= 0$
6. $\Sigma_M = 0$, $+ 19.4HC$ $+ 20.6HE$ $= 0$

$$(12\text{–}48)$$

Solving: From 1 and 4

$$AF = HC$$

and 2 and 5 are the same. From 6,

$$HE = -0.942HC$$

From 3, $ED = -10.6 - HC$

From 5, $R = -10.0 - 1.887HC$

From 2, $AF = -1.75$ k

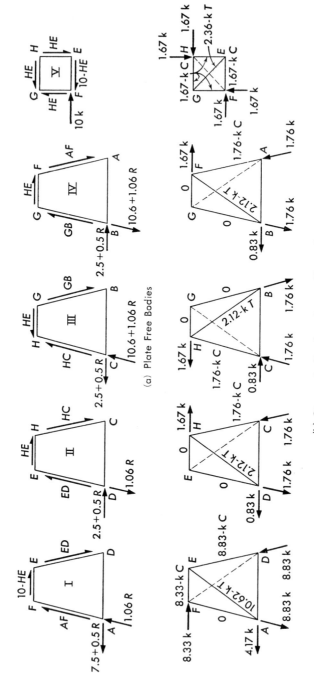

(a) Plate Free Bodies

(b) Stresses in Members Due to Planar Forces

Fig. 12–22.

From 4,
$$HC = -\frac{2.50}{1.414} = -1.77$$

$$R = -10.0 + 3.33 = -6.67 \text{ k}$$

$$ED = -10.6 + 1.77 = -8.83 \text{ k}$$

$$HE = 0.942 \times 1.77 = +1.67 \text{ k}$$

PLATE III

7. $\Sigma F_V = 0$, $-1.72 - 0.97GB - 6.87 + 10.3 = 0$

$$GB = 1.76 \text{ k}$$

(12–49)

The forces from the solution are shown on the plate free-body diagrams in Fig. 12–22b. By solution of each separate plate truss, it can be determined which of the tension members is acting. Those that are inactive in each plate are shown by a dashed line. Note that in solving for the stresses in the members, the plate forces are moved along their line of action to a joint. In this position the stresses in all the members for each plate truss can be found. The final stresses in each member of the truss will be the sums of the stress at each joint; for example,

Member $HC = -1.76 - 1.76 = -3.52$-k compression

The final stresses are noted on the sketch of the frame in Fig. 12–23.

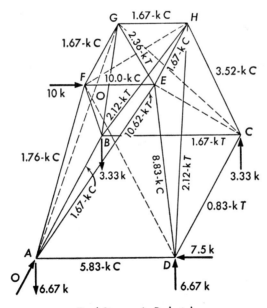

Final Stresses in Pedestal

Fig. 12–23.

The advantages of the solution are evident in its comparative time savings. For a general loading condition on such a pedestal, a solution by the method of joints would entail the solution of 8 joints $\times 3 = 24$ simultaneous equations. The solutions by the method of plates demands a solution of only 5 plates $\times 3 = 15$ equations at the most. Due to the limited loading condition, the illustrated solution required only six equations.

12–16. Extension of Plate Analogy. Several other structures are shown here to illustrate the plate analogy further. Fig. 12–24a shows a

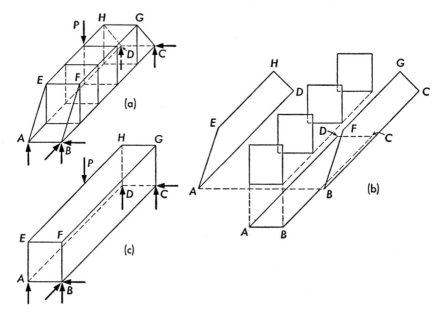

Fig. 12–24.

bridge structure supported upon two piers AB and CD. There are four vertical reactions and three reactions in the horizontal base plane. The diagonal and interior members are not shown in each panel of the truss so as not to complicate the drawing. The truss may be broken down for the plate analogy into n cross-plates: two longitudinal plates, $AEHD$ and $BFGC$, and the wind-bracing truss plate $ABCD$, as shown in the exploded view in Fig. 12–24b. The relationship of plates, reactions, and plate forces satisfies Eq. 12–45 as follows:

$3n$ cross-plates $+ 3 \times 3$ longitudinal plates

$$= (3n + 2) \text{ edge forces} + 7 \text{ reactions}   (12\text{–}50)$$

The structure is determinate for any number of cross-plates.

In Fig. 12–24c a bridge is supported similarly to that in Fig. 12–24a but this has two end plates, a top and bottom plate, and two side plates as well as seven external reactions. The application of Eq. 12–45, as follows, indicates that the structure is statically indeterminate to the first degree:

$$6 \text{ plates} \times 3 \neq 12 \text{ plate forces} + 7 \text{ reactions} \qquad (12\text{–}51)$$

Fig. 12–25 shows a framed hip roof. Again, for simplicity, the interior members of each of the plates are not shown. In this case the structure

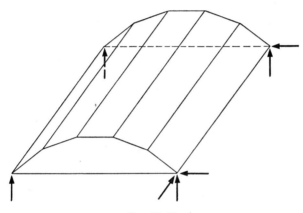

Fɪɢ. 12–25.

is made up of five roof plates and two end plates. Eq. 12–45 is satisfied for statical determinacy as follows:

$$7 \text{ plates} \times 3 = 14 \text{ edge forces} + 7 \text{ reactions} \qquad (12\text{–}52)$$

Note that the structure can carry loads which are applied at the folds and which may be resolved into each of the two adjacent planes. Loads applied along the eaves of the structure must be carried by additional posts which support the edge.

12–17. Solution by Simultaneous Equations; Tension Coefficients. When none of the more rapid short cuts are applicable to a complex structure, one must resort to the simultaneous solution of equations. There are three such equations for each joint in the structure, and therefore the number of equations will multiply rapidly as the extent of the structure increases. Nevertheless certain choices of equations and the introduction of tension coefficients sometimes simplify the solution. The tension coefficient x is defined by the equation

$$x = \frac{S}{l} \qquad (12\text{–}53)$$

where S is the stress in the member and l is the length of the member. It is a term that repeatedly arises in the equations of statics, and this substitution makes possible the simplification of the equations.

The method of solution is illustrated by the solution for the Zimmermann cupola * in Fig. 12–26. This type of structure is statically determinate if the upper closed ring consists of only half as many members as the lower ring. The structure illustrated could be attached to another with

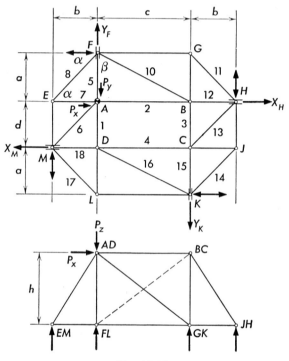

Fig. 12–26.

an eight-member top ring, and in this fashion multi-story structures could be constructed. The example structure is shown with arbitrary dimensions, and the solution is shown in general terms for a load P at point A. The load P is resolved into x, y, and z components, as shown in Fig. 12–26.

In the case of a directed reaction at F, H, K, and M, experience has shown that a proper choice of equations would be that $Y_F = X_H = Y_K = X_M = 0$. This will limit the number of equations that it will be necessary to write at the base plane joints. In the following equations, the number subscripts refer to the numbered members in Fig. 12–26.

* After Rudolf Kirchhoff, *Die Statik der Bauwerke* (Berlin: Wilhelm Ernst und Sohn, 1950).

Starting at joint F,

$$\Sigma F_y = S_8 \cos \alpha + S_5 \cos \delta + S_{10} \cos \beta = 0$$

$$= S_8 \frac{a}{l_8} + S_5 \frac{a}{l_5} + S_{10} \frac{a}{l_{10}} = 0$$

(12–54)

In the latter form of the equation the quantities S/l are involved, which have been defined as the tension coefficients x. Letting $S_8/l_8 = x_8$, $S_5/l_5 = x_5$, etc., Eqs. 12–54 becomes

$$a(x_5 + x_8 + x_{10}) = 0$$

(12–55)

Likewise, at H, K, and M, the following are found:

At H: $\quad \Sigma F_x = b(x_{11} + x_{12} + x_{13}) = 0$

At K: $\quad \Sigma F_y = a(x_{14} + x_{15} + x_{16}) = 0$ (12–56)

At M: $\quad \Sigma F_x = b(x_6 + x_{17} + x_{18}) = 0$

Taking joint A as a free body yields

$$\Sigma M_{EM} = x_5 hb + P_z b + (S_2 + P_x) h = 0$$

$$x_5 = -\left(\frac{P_z}{h} + \frac{S_2 + P_x}{b}\right)$$

(12–57)

Note that the component of stress of a member in a particular direction is the product of the tension coefficient and the projection of the member length in the direction of the stress component.

$$\Sigma M_{EH} = x_6 hd + S_1 h - x_5 ha + P_y h = 0$$

(12–58)

By substitution of Eq. 12–57,

$$x_6 = \frac{x_5 a}{d} - \frac{S_1 + P_y}{d} = -\left(\frac{P_z}{h} + \frac{S_2 + P_x}{b}\right)\frac{a}{d} - \frac{S_1 + P_y}{d}$$

(12–59)

By summation of forces at A,

$$\Sigma F_z = x_7 h + x_5 h + x_6 h + P_z = 0$$

$$x_7 = -\left(\frac{P_z}{h} + x_5 + x_6\right)$$

(12–60)

$$= \frac{S_2 + P_x}{b}\left(1 + \frac{a}{d}\right) + \frac{1}{d}\left(S_1 + P_y + \frac{P_z}{h}a\right)$$

At joint E, summing forces perpendicular to EM in the base plane yields

$$x_8 b + x_7 b = 0$$

$$x_8 = x_7$$

(12–61)

Equations similar to 12–57, 12–58, and 12–60 can be written for other joints in the structure by comparison. For example, the section $AFEM$ is similar to $BHGF$, and consequently the equations will be similar even if the proportions of the sections are dissimilar. Thus, by the interchange of x_6 to x_{10}, x_8 to x_{11}, x_5 to x_{12}, b to a, a to b, S_1 to S_2, and $(P_x + S_2)$ to S_3 in the equations mentioned, the new equations are

$$x_{10} = -\frac{1}{c}\left(\frac{S_3 b}{a} + S_2\right)$$

$$x_{11} = -\left[\frac{S_3}{a}\left(1 + \frac{b}{c}\right) + \frac{S_3}{c}\right] \tag{12-62}$$

$$x_{12} = -\frac{S_3}{a}$$

Likewise, comparing $AFEM$ with $CKJH$ yields

$$x_{13} = -\frac{1}{d}\left(\frac{S_4 a}{b} - S_3\right)$$

$$x_{14} = -\left[\frac{S_4}{b}\left(1 + \frac{a}{b}\right) + \frac{S_3}{d}\right) \tag{12-63}$$

$$x_{15} = -\frac{S_4}{b}$$

Comparison of $AFEM$ with $DMLK$ yields

$$x_{16} = -\frac{1}{c}\left(\frac{S_1 b}{a} - S_4\right)$$

$$x_{17} = -\left[\frac{S_1}{a}\left(1 + \frac{b}{c}\right) + \frac{S_4}{c}\right] \tag{12-64}$$

$$x_{18} = -\frac{S_1}{a}$$

Substitution of the various values of x into Eqs. 12–54 and 12–56, yields the final four simultaneous equations, as follows:

$$-a\left\{-\left(\frac{P_z}{h} + \frac{S_2 + P_x}{b}\right) - \left[\frac{S_2}{b}\left(1 + \frac{a}{b}\right)\right.\right.$$
$$\left.\left. + \frac{1}{d}\left(S_1 + P_y + \frac{P_z a}{h}\right)\right] - \frac{1}{c}[S_3 b - S_2]\right\} = 0$$

$$-b\left[\frac{S_3}{a}\left(1 + \frac{b}{c}\right) + \frac{S_2}{c} - \frac{S_3}{a} - \frac{1}{d}\left(\frac{S_4 a}{b} - S_3\right)\right] = 0$$

$$-a\left\{-\left[\frac{S_4}{b}\left(1 + \frac{a}{d}\right) + \frac{S_3}{d}\right] - \frac{S_4}{b} - \frac{1}{c}\left[\frac{S_1 b}{a} - S_4\right]\right\} = 0 \tag{12-65}$$

$$-b\left\{-\left(\frac{P_z}{h} + \frac{S_2 + P_x}{b}\right)\frac{a}{d} - \left(\frac{S_1 + P_y}{d}\right)\right.$$
$$\left. - \left[\frac{S_1}{a}\left(1 + \frac{b}{c}\right) + \frac{1}{c}\left(S_4 + \frac{Pb}{h}\right)\right] - \frac{S_1}{a}\right\} = 0$$

Values for S_1, S_2, S_3, and S_4, the stresses in the top ring, can be obtained directly from the simultaneous solution of these four equations. This is not carried out in general terms, since the final equations would be extremely complicated. However, numerical values substituted at this point would simplify the process. Next the solution for stresses in other members can be found, for example; thus:

$$x_5 = \frac{S_5}{l_5} = -\left(\frac{P_z}{h} + \frac{S_2 + P_x}{b}\right)$$

$$S_5 = -l_5\left(\frac{P_z}{h} + \frac{S_2 + P_x}{b}\right)$$

(12–66)

The Zimmermann cupola can also be solved by the substitute member method described in Art. 12–13; the four top ring members would be taken out and lateral reactions substituted to give rigidity at joints F, H, K, and M.

12–18. Domes. Framed domes are complex envelope structures, and they ordinarily need no special methods of analysis other than those already presented. They have come into recent prominence again because of their economy and their ability to span large areas without obstructing columns. On this basis they probably deserve a special article and will serve as further examples of the solution of complex frames. Several different types of domes exist, but most of them are statically indeterminate. The simple rib dome and the Schwedler dome will serve as representative cases which are statically determinate.

The rib dome consists of one-piece ribs supported at the top by a compression ring and at the bottom by a tension or foot ring or foundation supports. Fig. 12–27 illustrates a pleasing roof structure for an arena, using this structural system. Fig. 12–28a illustrates a schematic diagram of the structure. Circumferential rings have been introduced to support the roof structure but are not considered in the analysis. A section through the dome on a diametrical plane is shown in Fig. 12–28b. The analysis of a particular rib is identical with that of a three-hinged arch. The compression rings are assumed to exert only thrust on the upper connections. Refer to Chapter 11 for other details of the solution. The top compression ring is under the greatest compression when the entire roof surface is loaded. Note that when the ring has unsymmetrical loads, the solution is more difficult, since then the roof is actually a statically indeterminate structure. In this solution it is assumed to be only a compression ring.

Fig. 12–29 illustrates a dome for an auditorium structure of the Schwedler type. The illustration is complicated by the multitude of bracing members and extra ribs but can be reduced to the type of structure dis-

Fig. 12-27. A rib-type dome under construction for the arena at the Georgia Institute of Technology, Atlanta, Georgia. (Courtesy, Bethlehem Steel Company.)

cussed herein by removing these superfluous members. Fig. 12-30 illustrates a three-tiered hexagon-shaped Schwedler dome. It is loaded at a single joint on the second ring, and the foot ring is supported at all points by a vertical reaction and a force in the horizontal plane perpendicular to the radius to the joint. The structure is statically determinate, since 24 joints $\times$ 3 = 60 members + 12 reactions.

The rules of Art. 12-4 can be used to tremendous advantage in obtaining a solution. Starting at joint A, it is found that AB is the only noncoplanar member at an unloaded joint, and consequently it has zero stress. The same may be said for BC at B and the remainder of the top ring members. From the zero stress in the ring members, it can be concluded that the diagonals and ribs of the top tier are also zero, since each joint then consists of two bars intersecting with no external load. By the same reasoning, one may eliminate JK, KC, and LM of the second ring and the diagonals and ribs at joints L and K; and thus, also, the member QR of the third ring. Apparently all other members shown by heavy lines in Fig. 12–30 are stressed, including all members of the foot ring.

The solution may now proceed by the method of joints, starting with G, since there are only three stressed bars at that point. The solution then proceeds to H, S, N, O, P, in that order, repeatedly applying the three equations of statics. The stresses in all bars except those in the foot ring are now known.

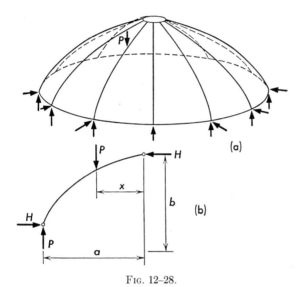

Fig. 12–28.

The foot ring poses a special problem. Fig. 12–31 shows a loaded condition in the foot ring. Only forces in the horizontal plane are shown. The vertical reactions at each foot joint can be found directly by summing forces vertically at each joint. A direct solution is not possible for the stresses in the foot ring bars.

In order to get a solution, first assume that one of the bar stresses is known, say, S_{TU}. With this assumption at U, the stress can be found in UV in terms of S_{TU}. Likewise at V, S_{VW} is found in terms of S_{TU} through S_{UV}. The procedure continues around the ring until T is reached. The closure statics equation will yield the actual stress S_{TU}, and immediately all other foot bars stresses are known.

A foot ring for any dome or space structure is unstable under certain conditions; i.e., directions of the reactions. This will be described in Art. 12–19.

Consider next the condition of stress in the dome when every joint is loaded, such as would be encountered under a snow load or roof dead load

Fig. 12–29. Steel-framed dome for auditorium. (Courtesy, Vierling Steel Works.)

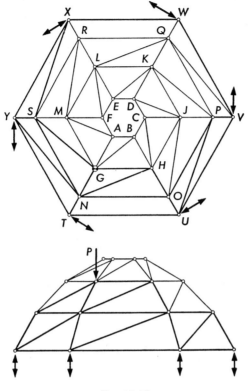

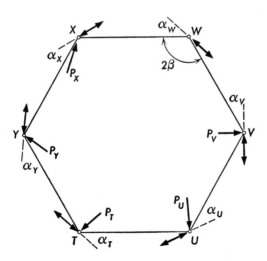

Fig. 12–30.

Fig. 12–31.

on the structure. Fig. 12–32a illustrates a rib under a symmetrical load. The same arguments apply to the dome rib as apply to the symmetrically loaded pedestal of Art. 12–11. Since the forces H must be in the plane of

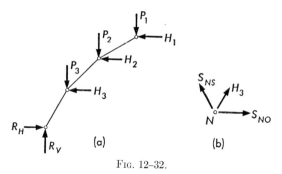

Fig. 12–32.

the rib to maintain equilibrium, the diagonal members must have zero stress. The conformation of the rib forms an equilibrium polygon for the vertical loads P and horizontal loads H, and consequently the stresses can be found directly. The stresses can be found in the ring members also by symmetry, as shown in Fig. 12–32b, since the forces in the plane of the rib are resisted by the ring.

The Schwedler dome has been treated extensively in other works for various conditions of load and stability.*

12–19. Critical Forms. If a structure could be shown to be a simple space truss or a compound space truss, then the analyst would be assured that a unique solution exists for the stresses in the bars. In the case of the complex structure, it is possible to join bars in arrangements such that results are inconsistent or that instability exists.

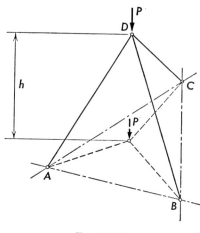

Fig. 12–33.

The simple tripod shown in Fig. 12–33 will be used to illustrate this condition. The tripod is, of course, a simple space truss which has a unique solution. If the height of the truss is decreased so that the height h

* For example, C. M. Spofford, *Theory of Structures*, 4th ed. (New York: McGraw-Hill Book Co., Inc., 1938), p. 492, and El-Sayed, El-Schasly, *Berechnung der Biegungsspannungen und Stabkräfte in Schwedlerkuppeln nach Theorie und Modelversuch* (Zürich, 1942).

approaches zero, the stability of the truss changes. This is the critical form. Physically it indicates that large lateral movements are possible in the z-direction with very little change in load. This condition can be expressed mathematically by writing the three equations of statics for the joint in terms of the tension coefficients.

$$\Sigma F_z = hx_1 + hx_2 + hx_3 + P_z = 0$$

$$\Sigma F_x = ax_1 + bx_2 + cx_3 + P_x = 0 \qquad (12\text{--}67)$$

$$\Sigma F_y = dx_1 + fx_2 + ex_3 + P_y = 0$$

$$x_1 = \frac{\begin{vmatrix} P_z & h & h \\ P_x & b & c \\ P_y & f & e \end{vmatrix}}{\begin{vmatrix} h & h & h \\ a & b & c \\ d & f & e \end{vmatrix}} \qquad (12\text{--}68)$$

In the determinant of the equation, the denominator vanishes if $h = 0$; then x_1 in Eq. 12–68 will approach infinity, which is an impossibility. If $P = 0$, then the equation yields $0/0$, an indeterminate form indicating no unique solution. One may conclude that any joint in a truss formed by three coplanar members is a critical form. Fortunately, these can be identified by visual inspection in most cases. For more complicated structures, however, it is impractical to evaluate the determinate of $3j$ equations to find if a critical form exists, so that more practical methods must be developed for identifying the condition. Note in the example of Fig. 12–33 that when $h = 0$, there are an infinite number of combinations of stresses in the members, which will yield equilibrium. That is, no unique solution exists even under zero load. Such an inconsistency is always an indication of a critical form.

Consider another example shown in Fig. 12–34a, a four-sided pedestal, or star cupola. Owing to symmetry, both members in the horizontal plane joining at a joint must have equal stress, and it may be deduced that $S_1 = -S_2 = S_3 = -S_4$, or $S_1 = -S_4$. This equality could be satisfied for many combinations of internal stresses that are not dependent on external load or that can exist under zero load. However, this condition indicates a vanishing indeterminate and a critical form.

Consider next the star cupola, or pedestal, in Fig. 12–34b. Examination of the top ring shows that

$$S_1 = -S_2 = S_3 = -S_4 = S_5 \qquad \text{or} \qquad S_1 = S_5 \qquad (12\text{--}69)$$

a condition that can exist only under a finite load and not under a zero load. Apparently this structure has a noncritical form, since no inconsistencies exist. Further considerations of such pedestals indicate that all even-sided star pedestals are critical forms but that all odd-sided pedestals are noncritical.

The foot ring or lower ring of a dome or pedestal truss, such as a Schwedler dome, offers a slightly different problem. Fig. 12–31 illustrates a regular polygonal ring of a typical type, loaded with the loads P_n provided by the dome superstructure. The arbitrary directions of the reac-

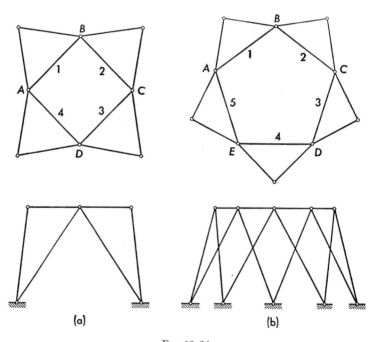

Fɪɢ. 12–34.

tions are specified at each point by the angles α_n and the internal angles of the polygon by 2β. Spofford * studied this type of structure by writing the equations of statics. He found that the determinate of the six equations vanishes (1) for an even-sided polygon when each reaction is normal to the radius of the circumscribing circle at the joint, or (2) for both odd- and even-sided polygons when the reactions at two adjacent joints are parallel to the nonmutual member at each joint; i.e., $\alpha_n = 0$ and $\alpha_{n+1} = 180 - 2\beta$.

---

* Spofford, *op. cit.*, p. 484. The author gives a detailed analysis of the foot rings of Schwedler domes and the critical reaction directions.

PROBLEMS

12–1. Find the stresses in the struts of the aircraft landing gear shown in the sketch, due to the vertical 20-k load applied through the wheel.

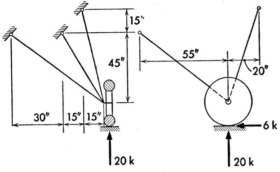

Prob. 12–1.

12–2. Find the stresses in the members of the wall bracket illustrated by (a) force summations and (b) moment equations.

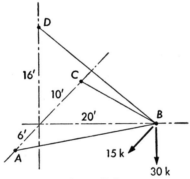

Prob. 12–2.

12–3. Find the stresses in the derrick shown.

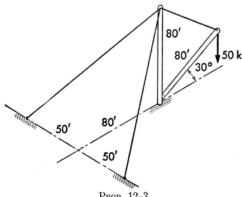

Prob. 12–3.

12–4. Find the stresses in the derrick shown, and draw the moment diagram for the vertical pole.

12–5. Find the stresses in the self-contained space frame in the accompanying illustration, which is in equilibrium due to the two couples applied as shown.

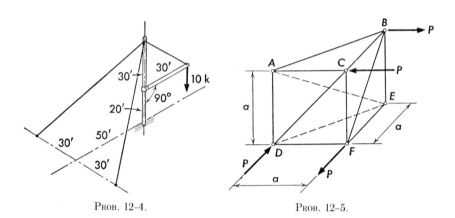

PROB. 12–4.   PROB. 12–5.

12–6. Find the stresses in the wall bracket structure shown due to the vertical load P.

12–7. The tower shown here in planview is 40 ft high. The radius of the circumscribing circle for the top ring is 15 ft, and that for the supports is 27 ft. Find the stresses due to a vertical load of 50 k applied at (a) A, (b) B.

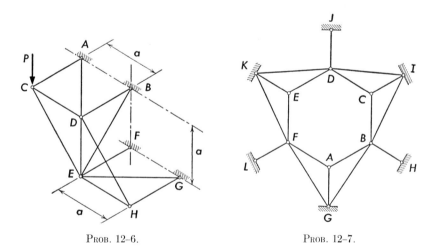

PROB. 12–6.   PROB. 12–7.

12–8. Find the stresses in the tower of Problem 12–7 if each top ring joint has a vertical load of 10 k.

12–9. The tetrahedron in the illustration is restrained by six external forces, one vertical reaction at each of the joints *A*, *B*, and *C*, and three additional reactions in the plane *ABC*. Find the stresses in the members if a vertical load of 20 k is applied at *D*.

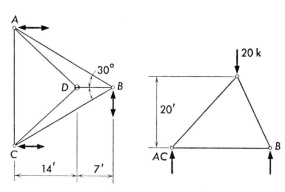

PROB. 12–9.

12–10. A monorail crane is supported by a series of struts, as shown in the figure. During operation the crane may induce longitudinal forces in the rail by impact against the end stop or by braking. Find the stresses in the members in terms of *P*.

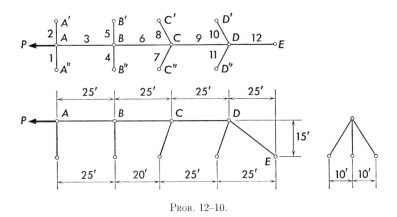

PROB. 12–10.

12–11. Find the stresses in the members of the triangular tower shown for (a) a vertical load of 10 k applied at *G*, (b) a horizontal force of 10 k, as shown, in a direction bisecting the angle *ACB*, and (c) a 10-k load at *F* in the direction *DF*.

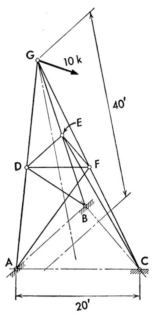

Prob. 12–11.

12–12. Find the stresses in the supporting members of the tank shown for the horizontal load *P* applied at the upper corner of the tank.

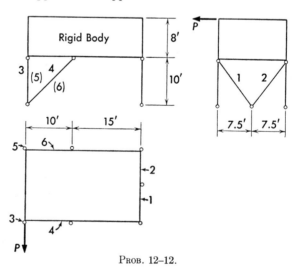

Prob. 12–12.

12–13. If the tank of Problem 12–12 weighs 200 tons when filled, what will be the stresses in the supporting members of the tank?

12-14. An aircraft engine mount is shown schematically in the accompanying illustration. The frame must resist torque, pull, and vertical weight of the engine. What are the stresses in the supporting members? The mounting ring is considered to be rigid.

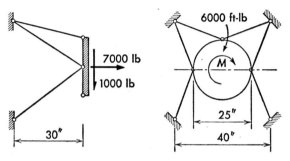

Prob. 12–14.

12-15. The triangles ABE and CDF of the frame shown here are equilateral, and $BCDE$ is a square. Find the stresses in the members due to the vertical load of 10 k at F.

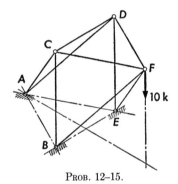

Prob. 12–15.

12-16. $ABCD$, $BFDE$, and $AFCE$ are squares in the frame shown. Find the stresses in the members due to the collinear loads of 10 k applied at A and C.

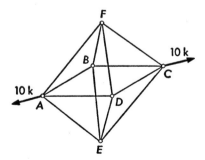

Prob. 12–16.

12–17. Each of the pyramids shown has a regular polygonal base 20 ft on a side. The height of all the pyramids is 30 ft. Determine the reactions and stresses due to the horizontal load of 10 k at the point P, as shown.

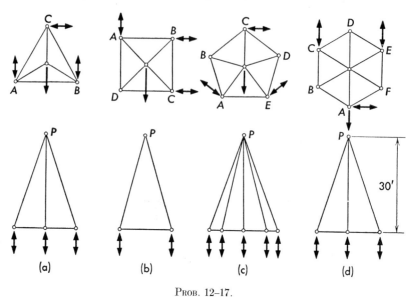

Prob. 12–17.

12–18. The frame shown is to be mounted on a roof of a power plant to support transmission wires. Determine the reactions and the stresses in the members due to the load of 5 k applied at A in the horizontal plane at an angle of $45°$ to AB.

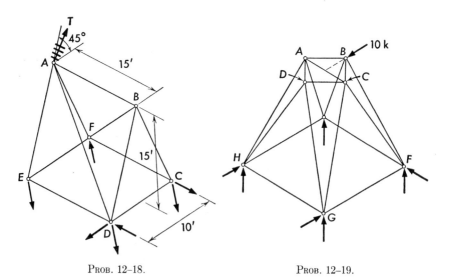

Prob. 12–18.   Prob. 12–19.

12–19. The pedestal shown is to be used to support a large bin in a chemical plant. The base square is 20 ft on a side, and the top ring is 10 ft on a side. The height is 30 ft. Find the reactions and stresses due to the 10-k wind load directed along the diagonal *BD*.

12–20. Find the stresses in the pedestal of Problem 12–19 due to a vertical load of 10 k at each joint in the upper ring.

12–21. Find the stresses in the triangular pedestal due to the 10-k load applied collinearly with member *GH*.

12–22. Find the stresses in the pedestal of Problem 12–21 due to vertical 10-k loads at each of points *G*, *H*, and *J*.

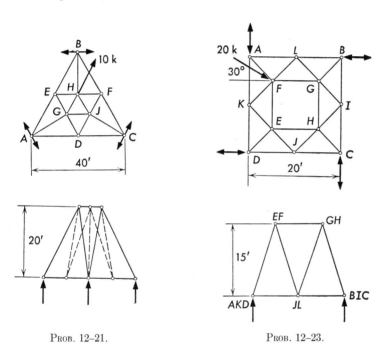

PROB. 12–21. PROB. 12–23.

12–23. Find the stresses in the pedestal shown due to the 20-k load in the horizontal plane, applied at F.

12–24. Find the stresses in the pedestal of Problem 12–23 due to four, vertical 30-k loads applied at *E*, *F*, *G*, and *H*.

12–25. The Schwedler dome shown is to support the roof of a large tank. The direction of the reactions in the plane of the base are shown. (a) Find the stresses due to a snow load of 30 psf of horizontal projected area; (b) find the stresses due to a single vertical load of 10 k applied at point *G*; (c) find the stresses due to a 10-k load applied at each joint in the middle ring.

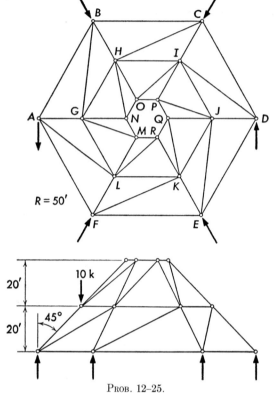

Prob. 12–25.

12–26. Find the stresses in the two-panel bridge shown, by using the plate analogy. There are four vertical reactions at *A*, *B*, *D*, and *E*, and three other reactions in the horizontal plane, as shown.

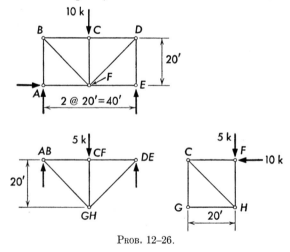

Prob. 12–26.

12–27. Find the stresses in the hipped roof due to the vertical load of 5 k at E. Use the plate analogy.

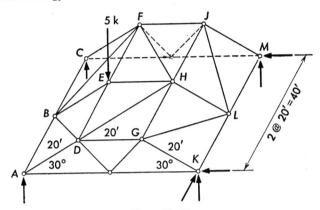

PROB. 12–27.

12–28. In Problem 12–27, what additional complication would result if there were a vertical load at B? What could be done to correct this condition?

12–29. The frame illustrated in Fig. 12–15 is square and has dimensions as follows: top ring, 20 ft on a side; intermediate ring, 40 ft on a side; and vertical height between rings, 20 ft. Find the stresses in the members due to a vertical load of 15 k applied at C.

12–30. A star pedestal similar to that illustrated in Fig. 12–14 is to be constructed with the following dimensions: top ring, 15 ft on a side; bottom ring, 25 ft on a side; and total height, 25 ft. What will be the stresses in the structure due to a vertical load of 10 k applied at D?

12–31. The frame illustrated in Fig. 12–26 has the following dimensions: $a = b = c = d = h = 20$ ft. What will be the stresses in the members due to a vertical load of 10 k at joint A? Use either the substitute member method or the simultaneous solution of the equations of statics.

12–32. Discuss the stability of the Schwedler dome of Problem 12–25 with reference to the direction of its horizontal reactions.

CHAPTER 13

STATICALLY INDETERMINATE STRUCTURES:
APPROXIMATE METHODS

Nearly all structures that are built today are statically indeterminate structures. That is, they cannot be solved by the use of the three equations of statics, $\Sigma F_x = 0$, $\Sigma F_y = 0$, and $\Sigma M_0 = 0$, alone. Other equations, usually involving the deflections or internal work of the structure, must be utilized. In order to calculate the deflections or energy, the sizes and exact characteristics of the members must usually be known. In the preliminary stages of a design these sizes are not known, and it would be foolish to perform an exact analysis which involved much more labor and time on preliminary guesses. In such cases the approximate methods have great value when choosing the members prior to the final exact analysis.

In other cases the exact analysis is not warranted because the joint conditions and conditions of loading are so variable or difficult to judge. This would be the case for structures usually loaded with lateral forces due to wind, vibration, earthquake, sway of vehicles, etc. Likewise, in situations where walls, floor systems, and architectural details disguise the actual structural action to a great degree, the approximate methods are probably as accurate as any other method. Remember—the length of time involved and the complexity of theory and mathematical computations are not necessarily measures of the exactness of the solution.

Even in structures which could be solved in a straightforward manner by the methods used on statically indeterminate structures, such as mill building bents and bridge portals, the analysis would involve an economically prohibitive length of time. The use of approximate solutions may result in the use of slightly more material in the actual design at times, and engineering judgment must be developed to indicate which methods should be used.

In order to solve such problems, one must make certain simplifying assumptions, based on experience and the "exact analysis." For example, in the analysis of a bridge with riveted joints, in order to get a solution, one makes assumption that the members are pinned. Nevertheless such trusses do have bending in the members to a certain degree, due to the partial restraint of the joint. Likewise, in the solution of continuous structures, the location of the points of zero moment (points of contraflexure)

and the joint conditions will be assumed, based on experience and knowledge of the exact analysis. Keep in mind that the problems presented in
this chapter can also be solved by the so-called exact method, but such
analysis is beyond the scope of this book.*

13–1. Frames or Portals with Pinned Ends. Fig. 13–1 shows a simple, rigid frame portal with pinned ends which is subjected to the lateral
load P at the joint B. It is assumed that the top member does not shorten
as a result of this load and that both members AB and CD deflect equal

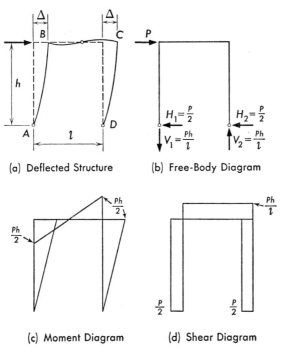

(a) Deflected Structure   (b) Free-Body Diagram

(c) Moment Diagram   (d) Shear Diagram

Fig. 13–1.

distances Δ. The elastic curves are identical on both sides of the frame,
as shown in Fig. 13–1a, and there is necessarily a point of contraflexure
in the top (the members at each rigid joint remain at right angles to
each other).

At the pinned ends, each reaction can be resolved into two components,
one vertical and one horizontal, so that there are four unknown forces,
two at each support. Since there are only three equations of statics for
coplanar force systems, this structure is statically indeterminate to the
first degree. An assumption of some sort must take the place of the

* For methods of exact solution, see, for example: Paul Andersen, *Statically Indeterminate Structures* (New York: The Ronald Press Co., 1953).

needed equation. The assumption is that shears are equal at the pins; i.e., $H = P/2$. This is correct only if the vertical members have the same relative stiffness, I/L. On this assumption the moment diagrams can be completed, and the moment at each corner of the frame will be

$$M_B = M_C = \frac{Ph}{2} \tag{13-1}$$

and the moment will be zero at the point of contraflexure of the girder. The moment and shear diagrams are shown in Figs. 13–1c and d.

13–2. Frames or Portals with Fixed Ends. Fig. 13–2 shows the same portal described in Art. 13–1, in which the ends of the vertical members are restrained from rotation (fixed). At each support is found a vertical force, horizontal shear and a moment, and a total of six unknowns for the

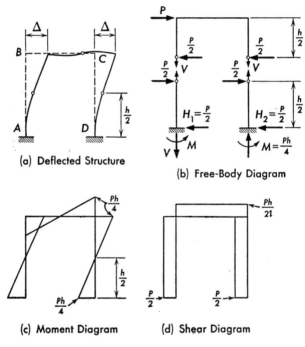

(a) Deflected Structure

(b) Free-Body Diagram

(c) Moment Diagram

(d) Shear Diagram

Fig. 13–2.

frame. Again, since the equations of statics will define only three of these unknowns, three assumptions must be made. These assumptions are: first, the horizontal shears are assumed equal; and, secondly, the points of contraflexure are assumed to be midway in the vertical legs. The frame may be broken into three free-body diagrams (Fig. 13–2b) for purposes of analysis. The lower half of the leg has only a horizontal shear of $P/2$

at the top and a vertical reaction collinear with the leg. Consequently it may be treated as a cantilever in order to find the moment at the base.

$$M_A = M_D = \frac{P}{2} \cdot \frac{h}{2} = \frac{Ph}{4} \qquad (13\text{–}2)$$

From the free body of the section above the points of contraflexure, the moment at the corners B and C are found to be

$$M_B = M_C = \frac{P}{2} \cdot \frac{h}{2} = \frac{Ph}{4} \qquad (13\text{–}3)$$

The complete shear diagram and moment diagrams are also shown in Figs. 13–2c and d.

13–3. Location of Points of Contraflexure—Degree of Fixity. Fig. 13–3 shows several conditions that could be encountered in structures relative to the point of contraflexure.

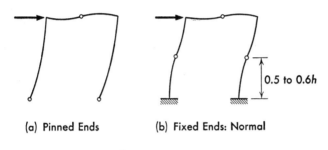

(a) Pinned Ends   (b) Fixed Ends: Normal

0.5 to 0.6h

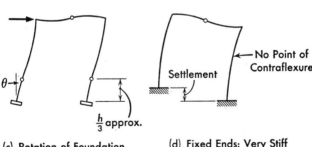

(c) Rotation of Foundation   (d) Fixed Ends: Very Stiff Columns

Settlement — No Point of Contraflexure

$\frac{h}{3}$ approx.

Fig. 13–3.

PINNED ENDS. When the frame has pinned ends, there are no points of contraflexure in the vertical legs. This condition will probably never occur ideally, since even a flat end on a column lends some restraint to the structure, but it is assumed, however, in many cases where the restraint of the end approaches the pin connection or cannot be predicted. It is the most conservative condition to select in case of doubt.

FIXED END. Three points of contraflexure will be evident for the elastic curve shown, one in each leg and one at the centerline of the cross-girder. Total fixity is difficult to obtain; however, if the columns are to be bolted solidly to the foundation with bolts collinear or adjacent to the flange, and tightened well, or in concrete structures are cast monolithically, the joint may be considered as fixed. The points of contraflexure in the legs will vary with the relative stiffnesses of the columns and cross-girders. For most structures the point will be between 0.5 and 0.6 of the height, with $0.5h$ being an average value to use in most cases. There need be no point of contraflexure in the column; the deflected structure may look like Fig. 13–3d. Such structures are unusual and will not ordinarily be encountered in the types of structures discussed herein. For such structures more exact methods must be used.

PARTIAL FIXITY. Even though the columns are securely fastened to the foundations, as previously described, there may not be complete fixity. If the footings are not extremely heavy or on the best foundation, they may rotate slightly, as indicated in Fig. 13–3c. Such rotations may also be due to slack and "take-up" in the column-foundation joint. The effect of such rotation will be to lower the point of contraflexure. Consequently some engineers prefer to use $h/3$ as the location of the point under most conditions. In case of doubt as to the degree of fixity, the column should be assumed pinned at the lower end, since this gives the most critical condition.

13–4. Trussed Portals. In many cases the horizontal member of the frame will be a truss structure. Some of the more common types are shown in Fig. 13–4; however, almost any type of truss could be used. Such structures are used at the entrance to bridges and also to provide sway bracing along the length of the bridge; thus, the name *portals*. Portal-type framing is also used in buildings. On the lower floors of buildings, trusses may be used to support the superstructure above large auditoriums and ballrooms, as in Fig. 13–4d, and as such must act as part of the wind bracing of the building. Mill buildings use the transverse bent of Fig. 13–4g to resist winds and lateral forces. Some of the trusses used in these structures may be internally statically indeterminate as well as being externally indeterminate, as previously discussed.

To illustrate the method of solution, the stresses will be found in the Warren truss portal of Fig. 13–5, due to a 10-k lateral load at the upper corner. The column extends through from the foundation to the top, and the joints at L_1 and L_3 do not affect the continuity of the column through the joint. Each column will be assumed to take one-half of the total shear and to have points of contraflexure at the mid-length of the column from the bottom of the truss. A free-body diagram is shown for the left column in Fig. 13–5b. The three unknown forces of the truss members which

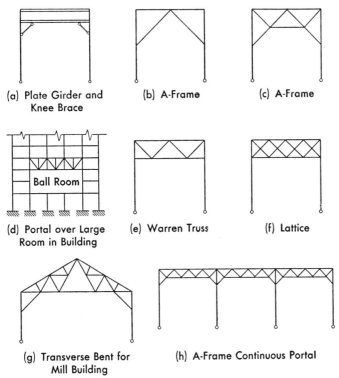

(a) Plate Girder and Knee Brace

(b) A-Frame

(c) A-Frame

(d) Portal over Large Room in Building

(e) Warren Truss

(f) Lattice

(g) Transverse Bent for Mill Building

(h) A-Frame Continuous Portal

Fig. 13–4.

frame into the column can be found by taking moments about U_1 and summing the forces in the vertical and horizontal directions. The necessary calculations are given in Eqs. 13–4 and 13–5.

REACTIONS:

$$V_1 = V_2 = \frac{18 \times 10}{20} = 9.0 \text{ k} \qquad (13\text{–}4)$$

STRESSES IN MEMBERS:

$$\Sigma M_{U_1} = 0; \qquad U_1 U_2 = \frac{5}{8} \times 10 = 6.25\text{-k tension}$$

$$\Sigma M_{U_2} = 0; \qquad (5 \times 18) - (9 \times 5) - 8 L_1 L_2 = 0;$$
$$L_1 L_2 = 5.63\text{-k compression} \qquad (13\text{–}5)$$

$$\Sigma F_V = 0; \qquad L_1 U_2 = 9.0 \times \frac{\sqrt{89}}{8} = 10.62\text{-k tension}$$

The remainder of the stresses can be found by ordinary methods, once stresses in the members framing into the columns have been found. The answers are found listed on the sketch of the portal, Fig. 13–5a. The moment diagram will have the moments $M_A = M_B = 5 \times 10 = 50$ ft-k, and $M = 0$ at U_1. The moment and shear diagrams are shown in Figs. 13–5c and 13–5d.

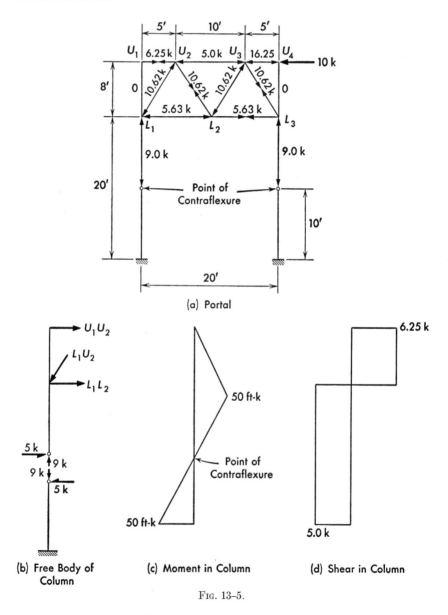

(a) Portal

(b) Free Body of Column

(c) Moment in Column

(d) Shear in Column

Fig. 13–5.

The stress diagram can also be adapted for use in finding the stresses in the truss members (review Chapter 5). In constructing the stress diagram, a problem immediately arises: the columns have moments and shears, whereas the stress diagram can be used where the truss members take axial load only. One may circumvent this problem by using a substitute truss for the column.

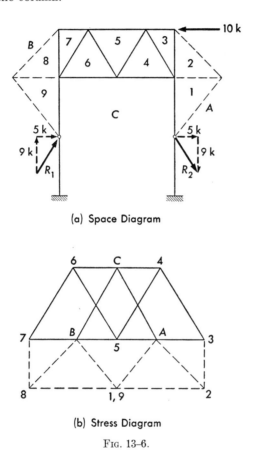

(a) Space Diagram

(b) Stress Diagram

Fig. 13–6.

Fig. 13–6 shows the stress diagram solution for the portal of Fig. 13–5. Here a substitute truss (dotted panels *1, 2, 8,* and *9*) is substituted for the column portions above the assumed points of contraflexure. The stress diagram is then drawn in the ordinary sequence, as shown. In the resulting diagram, only the stresses in the original truss members are correct. Thus the stresses *2–3* and *7–8* are "false" stresses. In order to get the stresses in the column, algebraic methods as described in Chapter 5 must be used.

13–5. **The Transverse Bent.** A transverse bent is a frame which is made up of a roof truss and its supporting columns, as shown in Fig. 13–7. It is necessary for this bent to resist the lateral loads placed on the building, due principally to wind loads but also due to impact and lateral thrust of crane loads. In order to resist these loads, the truss and columns must

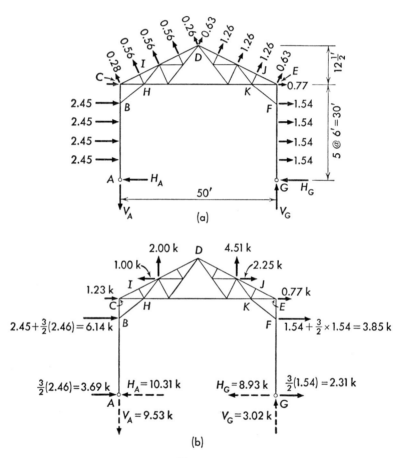

FIG. 13–7.

form a rigid frame. In the case of flat trusses (see Problem 13–10) the pins of the connections between the lower and upper cords and the column provide the necessary rigid conditions of continuity. For the mill building structure shown in Fig. 13–7, extra members must be provided to give continuity. These members are known as *knee braces* and extend diagonally from a panel point of the truss to the column at a point about 0.2 to 0.3 of the column length below the top joint.

If a lateral load is applied at or above the knee brace, the solution is similar to that used for the trussed portal. The same assumptions can be used to obtain a solution, i.e., (1) the horizontal shears will be distributed equally between the legs of the bent, and (2) in the case of the fixed base,

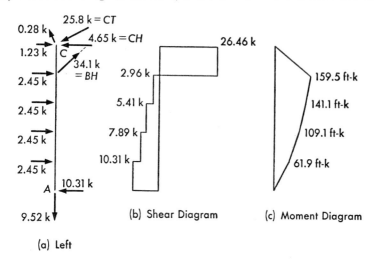

(a) Left   (b) Shear Diagram   (c) Moment Diagram

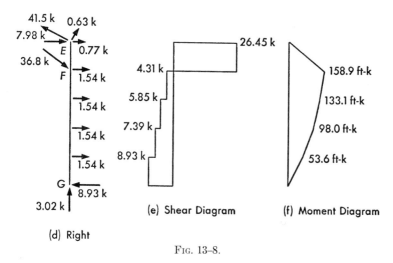

(d) Right   (e) Shear Diagram   (f) Moment Diagram

FIG. 13–8.

the point of contraflexure will be taken midway between the knee brace connection and the base (or, in cases of partial fixity, at some intermediate point).

In bents subjected to wind forces on the side (along the column), as indicated in Fig. 13–7, an additional assumption is needed to distribute the shears between the columns. These forces are transmitted to the bent from the wall sheathing by members called *girts*, which run between the bents and are spaced along the columns at intervals dependent upon the allowable span for the sheathing. Forces are also sometimes transmitted as uniform loads on the columns, as shown in Fig. 13–9. Since the loading is heavier on one side of the bent, it is evident that a greater proportion than one-half the shear must be in the windward column.

One method, which may be used to distribute the shears between the columns, is as follows: All the loads between the knee brace and the column base will be divided between the two as though a simple beam existed between them (*A* and *B* of Fig. 13–7a). The portal is then loaded with these substitute loads, applied at the knee brace and column base. The loads at or above the knee are distributed equally between the left- and right-column bases. Once the horizontal shears are established, one reverts to the original loading condition, and the moment and shear diagrams are completed in the ordinary manner.

The method is illustrated by the solution for the column moments and stresses in the truss members of the Fink mill building bent illustrated in Fig. 13–7. The bent has a span of 50 ft and is loaded with wind loading in accordance with the ASCE recommendations previously discussed, due to a 100-mph wind velocity. This results in positive pressure on the windward side and suction across the roof and the leeward side. The bents are 20 ft apart. The wind results in a series of concentrated loads on the girt-column joint and the panel points of the truss as shown. The substitute loads are shown in Fig. 13–7b, together with the horizontal and vertical resultants of the roof load. For column A the distribution of the load between A and B, as though AB were a simple beam, gives a substitute load of $3/2 \times 2.46 = 3.69$ k at the base. At the knee brace B, the total load is $2.45 + 3/2(2.46) = 6.14$ k. A similar process is carried out at the leeward column. Shears above the knee frame are then distributed equally between columns so that

$$H_A = 3.69 + \tfrac{1}{2}(6.14 + 1.23 - 1.0 + 2.25 + 0.77 + 3.85) = 10.31 \text{ k}$$
$$H_G = 2.31 + \tfrac{1}{2}(6.14 + 1.23 - 1.0 + 2.25 + 0.77 + 3.85) = 8.93 \text{ k} \tag{13-6}$$

The vertical reactions can be established by taking moment about the column bases:

$$\Sigma M_G = (6.14 + 3.85)24 + (1.23 + 0.77)30 + (2.25 - 1.00)36.25$$
$$+ 2.00(37.5) + 4.51(12.5) - 50V_A = 0$$
$$V_A = 9.53 \text{ k} \quad \downarrow \tag{13-7}$$

$$\Sigma F_V = 9.53 - 2.00 - 4.51 - V_G = 0$$
$$V_G = 3.02 \text{ k} \quad \downarrow$$

Once the external reactions are found, the free-body diagram of the left column is drawn as shown in Fig. 13–8a. By taking moments and summing forces, the stresses in the members connecting to the truss can be found:

$$\Sigma M_C = (10.31 \times 30) + 2.45(6 + 12 + 18 + 24)$$
$$- \left(\frac{7.81}{9.85} \times 6BH\right) = 0$$

$$BH = 34.10\text{-k tension}$$

$$\Sigma F_V = \left(34.10 \times \frac{6}{9.85}\right) - 9.52 - \frac{12.5}{27.94} CI = 0 \tag{13–8}$$

$$CI = 25.1\text{-k compression}$$

$$\Sigma F_H = \left(34.10 \times \frac{7.81}{9.85}\right) - \left(25.1 \times \frac{25}{27.94}\right) - CH = 0$$

$$CH = 4.65\text{-k compression}$$

The moment and shear diagrams can now be completed. The shear diagram (Fig. 13–8b) can be completed by starting at the bottom with the horizontal shear of 10.31 k and successively subtracting the girt loads. The moment diagram can be easily found by computing the area of the shear diagram. The moment and shear diagrams for the right column can be found by treating the free-body diagram in Fig. 13–8d.

The stresses in the other members can be determined by continuing the calculations according to the method of joints or sections in the ordinary manner or according to a stress diagram similar to that illustrated in Fig. 13–6, using a "false" truss on the column. The results of this wind analysis will be combined with the analysis due to dead loads and snow loads to obtain the maximum stress conditions for design. The stresses for snow loads can be found by treating the truss (Fig. 13–7) as though it were supported at B and F without knee braces. Although the columns provide some restraint, their effect is slight on the stresses in the truss for dead- and snow-load analyses. The moments induced in the columns due to snow and dead loads are also small when compared with the more critical moments due to wind. Several combinations of loads are usually superimposed in order to obtain the maximum design stresses. They are: (1) snow load plus dead load; (2) wind from right or left, plus dead load; and (3) wind from right or left, plus dead load, plus one-half snow load.

In the case of fixed column ends, the distribution of shears at the support can be found in the same manner as for the pinned ends.

13–6. Bents with Columns of Different Lengths and Different Moments of Inertia. Rarely do bents occur in which the columns are not identical. However, when they do occur, the previously described methods

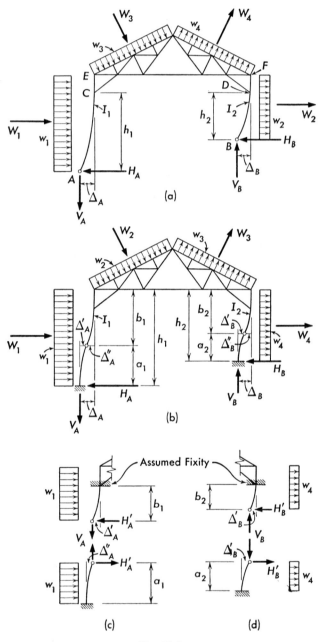

Fig. 13–9.

of making assumptions to establish statical determinacy are inadequate. The problem is to determine the distribution of the horizontal shears, which in turn depend upon the column length differential and the difference in the moments of inertias. Fig. 13–9a illustrates the general case in which the left column has a height h_1 and moment of inertia I_1, while h_2 and I_2 are associated with the right column. The bent is shown in the deflected position. The truss may be considered as a rigid member of constant length so that the deflections Δ_A and Δ_B are equal. The columns will be considered as fixed at the top due to the double connection, CE or DF, to the truss. These pins will allow some rotation, but because the joint is usually riveted, the rotation will not be so great as that provided by an ideal pin connection. Therefore the assumption of fixity at the truss is a proper one, providing that the distance CE and DF are about $0.25h$ or less. If any rotation should occur at this joint, it will affect both columns, and the errors induced by rotation will tend to counteract each other for the horizontal shear determination.

Consider the cantilever column AC. The deflection due to the unknown horizontal shear at the base A and the known uniform wind load on the column will be

$$\Delta_A = \frac{H_A h_1{}^3}{3EI_1} - \frac{w_1 h_1{}^4}{8EI_1} \tag{13–9}$$

and the comparable deflection for the right column will be

$$\Delta_B = \frac{H_B h_2{}^3}{3EI_2} - \frac{w_2 h_2{}^4}{8EI_2} \tag{13–10}$$

Since the deflections must be equal,

$$\frac{H_A h_1{}^3}{3EI_1} - \frac{w_1 h_1{}^4}{8EI_1} = \frac{H_B h_2{}^3}{3EI_2} - \frac{w_2 h_2{}^4}{8EI_2} \tag{13–11}$$

An additional equation can be obtained from the summation of horizontal forces:

$$H_A + H_B = \Sigma W_{\text{horizontal}} \tag{13–12}$$

The horizontal shears H_A and H_B can be found by the simultaneous solution of Eqs. 13–11 and 13–12. The vertical reactions can then be determined by summing moments about each column base.

The case where the column bases are fixed, illustrated in Fig. 13–9b, is more difficult. Again it is assumed that the truss is stiff and that the deflection of the columns AC and BD are equal. The columns are considered to be composed of two cantilever beams, one fixed at the column base and the other fixed at the truss, but the two are joined at the location of the point of contraflexure. Deflection equations are written, using the wind loads on the columns and the unknown shear at the point of contraflexure. Free-body diagrams of the columns are shown in Figs. 13–9c and 13–9d. The necessary equations are

$$\Delta_A = \Delta'_A + \Delta''_A$$

$$= \frac{H'_A a_1{}^3}{3EI_1} - \frac{w_1 a_1{}^4}{8EI_1} + \frac{H'_A b_1{}^3}{3EI_1} - \frac{w_1 b_1{}^4}{8EI_1} \tag{13–13}$$

$$\Delta_B = \Delta'_B + \Delta''_B$$

$$= \frac{H'_B a_2{}^3}{3EI_2} - \frac{w_2 a_2{}^4}{8EI_2} + \frac{H'_B b_2{}^3}{3EI_2} - \frac{w_2 b_2{}^4}{8EI_2} \tag{13–14}$$

in which

$$\Delta_A = \Delta_B$$

$$H'_A + H'_B = \Sigma W_{\text{horizontal}} \quad \begin{array}{l}\text{(for all forces above the} \\ \text{point of contraflexure)}\end{array} \tag{13–15}$$

$$H_A = H'_A + w_1 a_1 \qquad H_B = H'_B + w_2 a_2$$

H'_A and H'_B are obtainable by the simultaneous solution of Eqs. 13–15. However, in order to do this, the location of the points of contraflexure must be selected; i.e., a_1 and a_2 must be chosen. These points are usually taken at the mid-length or at the third points, as discussed in connection with portals, Art. 13–2. After computing the shears at the points of contraflexure, the vertical reactions, column bending moments and shears, and stresses in the truss can be computed by the methods of statics.

Similar equations are developed in a like manner for many other cases of mill bent column situations involving concentrated girt loads on the columns, stepped columns with crane rails, and other end conditions.*

13–7. Continuous Portals. Portals are sometimes made continuous; i.e., joined to provide roof cover for large areas or to provide lateral bracing for multi-lane bridges, etc. The analysis for vertical loads is made either by exact methods or by considering each truss as simply supported on the columns. The stresses due to lateral loads can be analyzed quickly by making certain assumptions. The portal system with three bays and four columns, Fig. 13–10, will be used for explanation. This structure is statically indeterminate to the fifth degree and thus necessitates five simplifying assumptions. The shear distribution in the horizontal direction will be one of these assumptions. If the lateral deflection of all the columns is identical, due to the nonshortening of the truss, the following deflection equation can be written:

$$\frac{H_A h_A{}^3}{3EI_A} = \frac{H_B h_B{}^3}{3EI_B} = \frac{H_C h_C{}^3}{3EI_C} = \frac{H_D h_D{}^3}{3EI_D} \tag{13–16}$$

* Extensive coverage is given to this subject by A. Jakkula and H. Stephenson, *Fundamentals of Structural Analysis* (Princeton, N. J.: D. Van Nostrand & Co., Inc., 1953).

The summation of horizontal forces yields

$$H_A + H_B + H_C + H_D = P_1 + P_2 \qquad (13\text{--}17)$$

Simultaneous solution of Eqs. 13–16 and 13–17 gives the values of H at each column. If the lengths and moments of inertia of the columns are identical, it is found that all shears are equal, or

$$H = \frac{P_1 + P_2}{4} \qquad (13\text{--}18)$$

The remaining four necessary assumptions will be supplied by specifying the vertical reactions in each of the legs. It will be assumed that the portals act like a cantilever beam projecting from its foundations. The

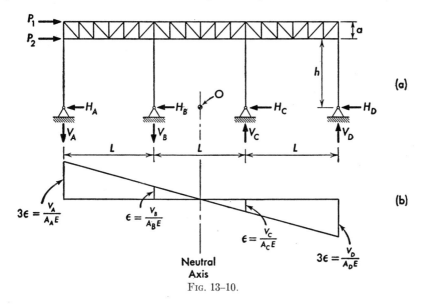

Fig. 13–10.

strain in the columns B and C will be designated ϵ, and assuming that a plane remains a plane after bending, the exterior columns A and D will have a strain of 3ϵ, as shown in Fig. 13–10b. By applying Hook's law to the strains, the following relationship is found to exist:

$$\frac{V_A}{A_A} = \frac{3V_B}{A_B} = \frac{3V_C}{A_C} = \frac{V_D}{A_D} \qquad (13\text{--}19)$$

or, if the areas of the columns are equal,

$$V_A = 3V_B = 3V_C = V_D \qquad (13\text{--}20)$$

By taking moments about point O,

$$\frac{3}{2}V_A L + V_B \frac{L}{2} + V_C \frac{L}{2} + \frac{3}{2}V_D L = P_2 h + P_1(h + a) \qquad (13\text{--}21)$$

The simultaneous solution of Eqs. 13–19, 13–20, and 13–21 yields the values of V needed, and the problem may be continued with the three equations of statics.

If the columns were fixed at the base, the points of contraflexure at the mid-length or at the third points of the column would be established to supply the needed extra four assumptions. Point O would be taken on a horizontal line through the points of contraflexure of the columns and an analysis of deflections by Eq. 13–16 would be carried out on this line to find the horizontal shears at the points of contraflexure (the h distances would extend from the truss to the point of contraflexure in this case).

13–8. Lateral Forces on Buildings. One of the most difficult problems facing the structural engineer is the analysis of buildings under lateral loads due to wind and earthquake. Since these forces are highly indeterminant themselves, it is even more difficult to make justifiable assumptions with regard to the approximate solution of such structures.

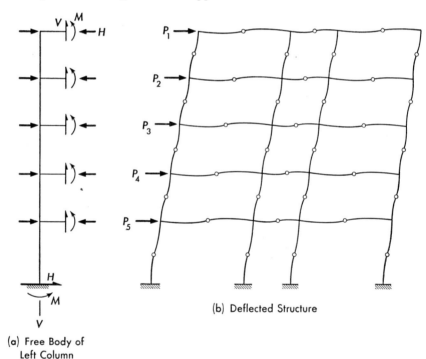

(a) Free Body of
Left Column

(b) Deflected Structure

Fig. 13–11.

Consider the building in Fig. 13–11b, loaded with a set of lateral loads. It takes on the shape of a series of portals, one tier upon another. By intuition it can be seen that there must be a point of contraflexure in each of the columns and girders. The degree of indeterminacy of the structure can be obtained by examination of the free-body diagram of a column from the building shown in Fig. 13–11a. To make the structure statically determinate, it would be necessary to cut the frame into columns similar to this. On the face of each of the cut girders, there is an unknown moment, thrust, and shear. Besides these unknowns, there are the unknown reactions at the base of the isolated column, consisting of a moment, thrust, and shear. Only three of these unknowns can be found from the equations of statics; this would eliminate, say, the base reactions, and leave the girder unknowns undetermined. Isolation of each of the other columns would yield three more unknowns for each girder and three more for the support. One may conclude that there are three unknowns for each girder and three unknowns for each support in excess of one; i.e., the degree of indeterminacy is equal to $3n + 3(s - 1)$, where n is the number of girders and s is the number of fixed supports.

This result would indicate that the building under consideration was $(15 \times 3) + (4 - 1)3 = 54$ times statically indeterminate. In accordance with analysis used previously on ordinary portals, this would entail 54 different assumptions to make possible a solution by statics. This will be done by assuming (1) positions for the points of contraflexure in the columns and girders, and (2) a distribution of either the shear forces or axial forces in each of the columns. Several reasonable assumptions can be made, depending upon the relationship between the sizes of interior and exterior columns. Two methods are in common use: (1) the portal method, and (2) the cantilever method. A description and a typical problem solution by each method follows.

13–9. The Portal Method of Lateral Analysis. The portal method is based upon the assumption that each of the bays of a building acts as a continuous portal, as shown in Fig. 13–12. Each of the separate portals

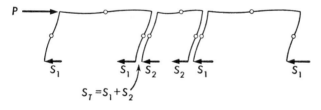

Fig. 13–12.

has one or two columns common to an adjacent portal. All the columns have the same deflection, since the girders are assumed not to shorten. The shear forces at the points of contraflexure need not be equal but will be dependent upon the relative stiffnesses of the columns and girders with respect to one another.

The following assumptions are usually made:

1. Points of contraflexure exist at the mid-length of all girders.
2. Points of contraflexure exist at the mid-height of all columns.
3. The total shear taken by each portal will be proportional to its span.

With regard to the last assumption, the shear in each column is due to its resistance to bending. Such bending is directly dependent upon the restraint provided by the girders. Since the girders are designed for dead and live load, they will vary as the square of the span, L^2; i.e., the moment of inertia of the girder varies as L^2. The restraint provided by the girder

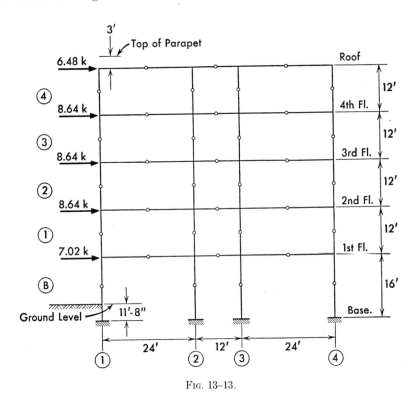

Fig. 13–13.

is dependent upon its relative stiffness, which is defined as the moment of inertia divided by the length, I/L. Therefore the restraint is $I/L = KL^2/L = KL$ or is dependent directly upon L. This rule is valid only when the columns are equal in size. In cases where the columns also vary, the shears may be distributed in each portal in proportion to the moments of inertia of the columns. When there is considerable variation in span and column size, especially when there is no symmetry, exact methods should be used.

Fig. 13–13 illustrates a five-story building for which the moments to be found are due to a lateral wind exerting 30 psf on the walls. The moment frames are spaced 24 ft apart. A parapet wall extends 3 ft above the centerline of the roof, and the ground level protects the bottom 4 ft of the lower story.

The wind forces to be applied at the floor levels are:

At roofline:

$$9 \times 24 \times 0.030 = 6.48 \text{ k}$$

At second, third, and fourth floors:

$$12 \times 24 \times 0.030 = 8.64 \text{ k}$$

At first floor:

$$\left(6 \times 24 + 4.33 \times 24 \times \frac{13.83}{16} \right) 0.030 = 7.02 \text{ k}$$

The shears in the roof columns are determined according to the third assumption. The first number of the subscripts in Eqs. 13–22 refers to the

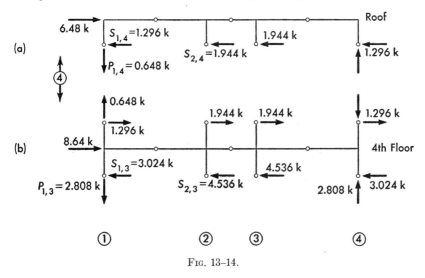

Fɪɢ. 13–14.

column (No. 1 for exterior and No. 2 for interior column), and the second number refers to the floor which is the origin of the column. Referring to Fig. 13–14a,

$$S_{1,4} = \frac{1}{2} \times \frac{24}{24 + 12 + 24} \times 6.48 = \frac{12}{60} \times 6.48 = 1.296 \text{ k}$$

$$S'_4 = \frac{6}{60} \times 6.48 = 0.648 \text{ k} \qquad\qquad (13\text{–}22)$$

$$S_{2,4} = S_{1,4} + S'_4 = 1.296 + 0.648 = 1.944 \text{ k}$$

Likewise the shears can be found in the columns supporting the fourth floor; referring to Fig. 13–14b,

$$S_{1,3} = \frac{12}{60}(6.48 + 8.64) = 3.024 \text{ k}$$

$$S'_3 = \frac{6}{60}(6.48 + 8.64) = 1.512 \text{ k} \tag{13–23}$$

$$S_{2,3} = 3.024 + 1.512 = 4.536 \text{ k}$$

The remainder of the shears at each floor can be found in the same manner. The results are recorded in Fig. 13–15.

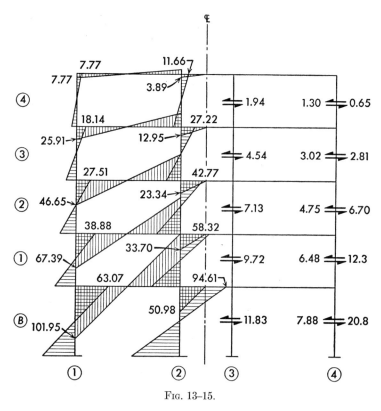

Fig. 13–15.

No additional information other than the shears is needed to draw the moment diagram. The moments at the top and base of column 1,4 will be $6 \times 1.296 = 7.77$ ft-k, and the moment in column 1,3 will be $6 \times 3.024 = 18.14$ ft-k. The moments in all the columns can be found in a similar fashion, dependent only on the shears previously found. The moment in the exterior girder joint at the fourth floor will be

$$18.14 + 7.77 = 25.91 \text{ ft-k} \tag{13–24}$$

Likewise, since the moments are identical at each end of the girder, the moment at the joint of the interior girder of the fourth floor can be found by summing moments about the joint. Thus:

$$6 \times 1.94 + 6 \times 4.54 - 25.91 - M_{2,4} = 0$$
$$M_{2,4} = 12.95 \text{ ft-k} \tag{13-25}$$

Thus one may proceed from joint to joint in a methodical manner, computing shears and moments with very few recorded calculations. This illustrates the greatest advantage of the portal method—its simplicity.

The axial load in the exterior column $P_{1,4}$ will be found by taking moments about the point of contraflexure of the exterior roof girder in Fig. 13–14a.

$$12P_{1,4} - 6 \times 1.296 = 0; \qquad P_{1,4} = 0.648 \text{ k} \tag{13-26}$$

By taking moments about the interior point of contraflexure, the axial force in the interior column is found to be

$$0.648 \times 30 - 1.296 \times 6 - 1.944 \times 6 + 6P_{2,4} = 0$$
$$P_{2,4} = 0 \tag{13-27}$$

The axial force in the interior column is zero.* This will always be true for the interior columns, and the calculations may consequently be simplified. The moment of the wind forces about a section through the points of contraflexure at any floor level is resisted by a couple composed of the axial forces in the exterior columns. Therefore the axial forces in the basement exterior columns can be found; thus:

$$6.48 \times 56 + 8.64 (20 + 32 + 44)$$
$$+ 7.02 \times 8 - 60P_{1,B} = 0$$
$$P_{1,B} = 20.8 \text{-k tension} \tag{13-28}$$

in left exterior column; compression in right exterior column.

The other axial forces are shown in Fig. 13–15 along the line of the right exterior column.

13–10. The Cantilever Method of Lateral Analysis. In the cantilever method the building is treated as a cantilever projecting vertically from its fixed foundation line. It is an extension of the continuous portal method which was applied to single-story buildings in Art. 13–7. Three

---

* Oftentimes, rather than using the third assumption for the distribution of shears in the columns, it is assumed that the interior columns have zero axial load. Both assumptions are identical.

assumptions are made, similar to those made for the portal method. They are:

1. Points of contraflexure exist at the mid-length of all girders.
2. Points of contraflexure exist at the mid-length of all columns.
3. The axial unit stress in each of the columns is proportional to the distance from the neutral axis of the bent.

The three foregoing assumptions are sufficient to reduce the problem to one in which the equations of statics will completely determine the stresses and moments. The method is applied to the same problem solved by the

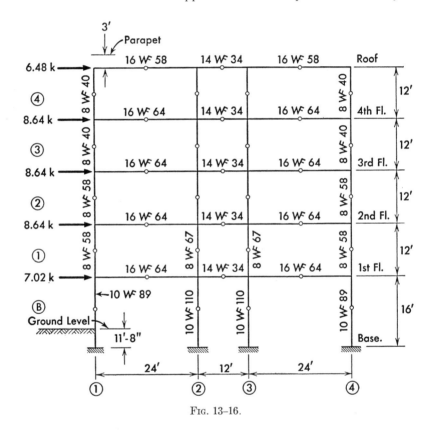

FIG. 13–16.

portal method, with the exception that specific column and girder sections have been chosen, as indicated in Fig. 13–16. The areas of the columns are also indicated in the diagram. The cantilever method is easily adapted to such column size variations.

First the axial loads in the vertical members will be evaluated. If $P_{1,4}$ denotes the load in the outside column on the fourth floor, and $P_{2,4}$ the load in the interior column, the strain at $P_{1,4}$ will be five times that

of the interior column, due to the preservation of plane sections as prescribed by the beam action assumed and illustrated in Fig. 13–17a.
Application of Hooke's law to these strains, yields

$$\frac{P_{1,4}}{11.76} = \frac{5P_{2,4}}{14.11} \quad \text{or} \quad P_{1,4} = 4.17\,P_{2,4} \tag{13–29}$$

in which 11.76 and 14.11 are the cross-sectional areas of the columns.

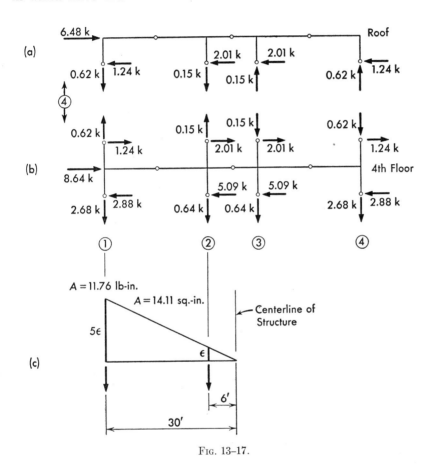

Fig. 13–17.

Also, $P_{1,3} = 4.17P_{2,4}$ since the same columns are continuous for two
stories. Fig. 13–17b shows a free-body diagram of a horizontal section
through the points of contraflexure of the fourth floor. Taking moments
about a point on the neutral axis in line with the points of contraflexure
yields

$$2(30P_1 + 6P_2) = 6.48 \times 6 \tag{13–30}$$

From Eqs. 13–29 and 13–30,

$$P_{1,4} = 0.62 \text{ k} \qquad \text{and} \qquad P_{2,4} = 0.15 \text{ k}$$

The shearing forces in the columns of the fourth floor can now be found by taking moments about the point of contraflexure of the outside girder in the roofline:

$$6S_{1,4} = 0.62 \times 12$$
$$S_{1,4} = 1.24 \text{ k} \tag{13–31}$$

and by taking moments about the point of contraflexure of the interior girder, $S_{2,4}$ can be found:

$$6(S_{1,4} + S_{2,4}) = (0.62 \times 30) + (0.15 \times 6)$$
$$S_{2,4} = 2.01 \text{ k} \tag{13–32}$$

In order to find the similar values for the third floor, moments are balanced about a point on the neutral axis of the entire section above the points of contraflexure in the third floor; thus:

$$2(30P_{1,3} + 6P_{2,3}) = (6 \times 8.64) + (18 \times 6.48)$$
$$P_{1,3} = 2.68 \text{ k} \tag{13–33}$$
$$P_{2,3} = 0.64 \text{ k}$$

A section is passed through the lines of the points of contraflexure in the third and fourth floor levels to isolate the section in Fig. 13–17b. Then the sum of moments about the outside point of contraflexure yields

$$6S_{1,3} + (1.24 \times 6) - (2.68 - 0.62)12 = 0$$
$$S_{1,3} = 2.88 \text{ k} \tag{13–34}$$

and the sum of moments about the interior point of contraflexure yields

$$S_{2,3} = \tfrac{1}{2}(6.48 + 8.64) - 2.88 = 4.68 \text{ k}$$

Likewise, the axial and shearing forces can be found for the rest of the columns

SECOND AND FIRST FLOORS

Axial Force Relationship:

$$\frac{P_{1,2}}{17.06} = \frac{5P_{2,2}}{19.70} ; \qquad P_{1,2} = 4.33P_{2,2} \tag{13–35}$$

Axial Forces:

$$2(30P_{1,2} + 6P_{2,2}) = (30 \times 6.48) + (6 + 18)8.64$$
$$P_{1,2} = 6.40 \text{ k}$$
$$P_{2,2} = 1.48 \text{ k}$$
$$2(30P_{1,1} + 6P_{2,1}) = (42 \times 6.48) + (6 + 18 + 30)8.64$$
$$P_{1,1} = 11.77 \text{ k}$$
$$P_{2,1} = 2.72 \text{ k}$$

$$(13\text{--}36)$$

Shear Forces:

$$6S_{1,2} - (6.40 - 2.68)12 + (2.88 \times 6) = 0$$
$$S_{1,2} = 4.56 \text{ k}$$
$$S_{2,2} = \tfrac{1}{2}(6.48 + 8.64 + 8.64) - 4.56$$
$$S_{2,2} = 7.32 \text{ k}$$
$$6S_{1,1} - (11.77 - 6.40)12 + (4.56 \times 6) = 0$$
$$S_{1,1} = 6.17 \text{ k}$$
$$S_{2,1} = \tfrac{1}{2}(6.48 + 25.92) - 6.17$$
$$S_{2,1} = 10.03 \text{ k}$$

$$(13\text{--}37)$$

BASEMENT

Axial Force Relationship:

$$\frac{P_{1,\text{B}}}{22.67} = \frac{5P_{2,\text{B}}}{29.43}$$
$$P_{1,\text{B}} = 3.85P_{2,\text{B}}$$

$$(13\text{--}38)$$

Axial Forces:

$$2(30P_{1,\text{B}} + 6P_{2,\text{B}}) = (56 \times 6.48) + (20 + 32 + 44)8.64$$
$$+ (8 \times 7.02)$$
$$P_{1,\text{B}} = 19.78 \text{ k}$$
$$P_{2,\text{B}} = 5.14 \text{ k}$$

$$(13\text{--}39)$$

Shear Forces:

$$8S_{1,\text{B}} - (19.78 - 11.77)12 + (6.17 \times 6) = 0$$
$$S_{1,\text{B}} = 7.39 \text{ k}$$
$$S_{2,\text{B}} = \tfrac{1}{2}[6.48 + (3 \times 8.64) + 7.02] - 7.39$$
$$S_{2,\text{B}} = 12.32 \text{ k}$$

$$(13\text{--}40)$$

The moments at the tops and bottoms of all columns can be found by multiplying the respective shears in the columns by one-half the column heights. Thus the moment at the top and bottom of column 1,4 will be $M_{1,4} = 2.007 \times 6 = 12.042$ ft-k. The shears in the horizontal members can be found from statics, and multiplying them by one-half the girder length will yield the end girder moments. As a final check, the sum of the

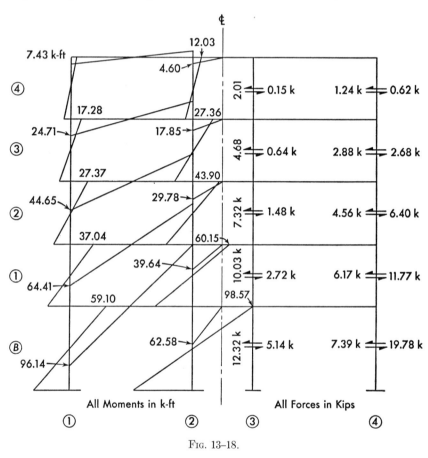

FIG. 13–18.

moments about any joint must be equal to zero. The final moment diagram is shown in Fig. 13–18. On the right side of the diagram are shown the column shears and axial forces.

13–11. Choice of Wind Analysis Methods: Tall Buildings. Exact analysis of building frames by the methods of statically indeterminate structures shows that the point of contraflexure is not generally at the mid-point of the columns, as assumed in both the approximate methods illustrated. The point actually varies according to the location of the column in the building. In the lower portion of the building (for the floors above the second floor but in the lower third of the building) the point is about 0.6 the story height above the girder centerline. In the upper third of the building the point is lower, being at 0.4 of the column length above the girder centerline. In the center portion of the building the point is near the mid-height of the column, as assumed. The assumption of the mid-height is satisfactory in all cases, however, with one exception. Serious error may result in the lower story if it has extra height. In this case the point of contraflexure will be much higher than the mid-height.*

A number of other factors also affect the analysis. First, the effect of partitions, masonry, and architectural details obscure the true action of the building to a large degree. The assumption that the frames only are instrumental in resisting the wind loads is necessary, since the effect of the rest of the building has not or probably will not be accurately evaluated. Masonry may increase the stiffness of the building three or four times that of the frames acting alone. In addition, although the joints are assumed rigid, there may be some rivet slip or partial fixity at the joints which will modify the actual calculated moments by partial release of the moments.

The literature on the subject of wind and wind analysis of buildings is quite extensive. Of the immense amount of published data, one of the most comprehensive studies was made by the Sub-committee No. 31 of the Committee on Steel of the Structural Division, ASCE. Six progress reports and a final report † were issued between 1930 and 1940. The following recommendations were made with respect to approximate methods: The portal method may be used for buildings up to 25 stories in height and with moderate height-width ratios. Its main advantage is its simplicity of application. The cantilever method is more desirable for high narrow buildings and is generally suitable for buildings not exceeding 25 to 30 stories. This method is more easily applied to variations in column size than the portal method, but nevertheless it is not as widely used. Several other methods of a more exact nature are described in these reports, including those of Spurr, Grinter, Goldberg, and Cross. These methods generally consider in detail the geometry of deformation, properties of materials, and variation in member size in arriving at a solution.

One of the most important problems in tall buildings is to keep the deflections within certain bounds, based upon the reaction of the occupants of the building and other considerations. This feature frequently

---

* G. M. Jones. *Wind Stresses in Tall Buildings* (Ann Arbor, Michigan: University of Michigan, 1934).

† "Wind Bracing in Steel Structures," *Trans. ASCE*, 105, 1713–1739 (1940).

controls the type of wind bracing used. Further treatment of this problem can be found in other sources*

13–12. Maximum Design Moments. The analysis of the building frame under vertical loads also involves a statically indeterminate analysis. Fig. 13–19a illustrates the interior girder span of a building loaded with a uniform load w, and Fig. 13–19b shows the approximate deflected shape of a girder. There are two points of contraflexure which would have to be chosen before an approximate analysis could be completed

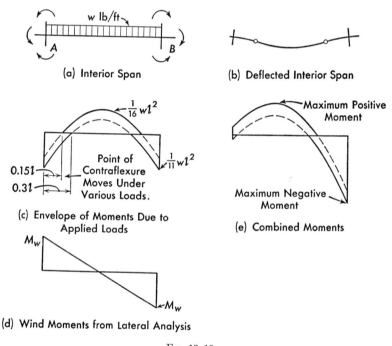

(a) Interior Span

(b) Deflected Interior Span

(c) Envelope of Moments Due to Applied Loads

(d) Wind Moments from Lateral Analysis

(e) Combined Moments

Fig. 13–19.

in accordance with previously discussed methods. Fig. 13–19c illustrates the envelope of moment diagrams that would be found from the exact analysis of a continuous structure of several spans. Various conditions of loadings would have to be considered to obtain these curves, such as (1) every span loaded, (2) alternate spans loaded, and (3) adjacent spans loaded, together with alternate spans loaded on the remainder of the building, and other combinations. Consideration of these loads would result in the approximate moment coefficients as written in Fig. 13–19c

* For example: L. E. Grinter. *Theory of Modern Steel Structures,* vol. 1. (New York: The Macmillan Co., 1936.)

for an interior span.* Note that for the envelope of moments, the point of contraflexure also varies in a zone, which would make a direct choice of this variable more difficult. Other moment coefficients are specified for the end spans of the building and for variations in the continuity. In reality the loads are most likely not uniform loads, since the beams framing into the girders supply concentrated loads rather than uniform loads, or the building may be subjected to a variety of concentrated loads and distributed loads. In general it is impossible to give general rules for the moments due to vertical loads; each case must be considered individually. Reference may be made to the various codes for the allowable approximate moment coefficients for other cases. Probably some modified exact analysis rather than these coefficients should be used.†

These moments can be combined with the moments due to lateral analysis to obtain the maximum moments. This is illustrated in Fig. 13–19e, which is obtained by direct addition of the diagrams in Fig. 13–19c and d. In addition, the wind from the other direction would have to be considered, resulting in the inversion of Fig. 13–19d and turning of the final diagram, Fig. 13–19e, end for end. The discussion here is intended merely to indicate some of the problems inherent to building analysis. Before attempting a design, further study must be made of continuous structures by the exact methods.

13–13. Statically Indeterminate Trusses. A truss may be statically indeterminate for two reasons: (1) It may have more than three external reactions, in which case it is called *externally indeterminate;* or (2) it may have extra or redundant members in the truss work, and it is then referred to as *internally indeterminate.* It is the latter case which this article discusses.

The equation representing the condition of determinacy as discussed in Art. 5–2 is $m = 2j - 3$. If the number of members is less than that specified by the equation, the truss will be unstable, and if the number of members exceeds $2j - 3$, the truss is statically indeterminate to that degree. Thus the truss illustrated in Fig. 13–20 is $21 - (20 - 3) = 4$ times indeterminate. This necessitates making four simplifying assumptions to make the truss statically determinate and solvable by the method of sections or joints.

The truss shown in Fig. 13–20 is the most common type of statically indeterminate truss encountered in practice. It is used for lateral bracing in the top or bottom chords of trusses and also for lateral bracing in

* The coefficients shown are for reinforced concrete, continuous structures specified by *Building Code Requirements for Reinforced Concrete,* American Concrete Institute.

† See, for example, *Continuity in Concrete Building Frames,* Portland Cement Association.

buildings. It is generally considered as a secondary element, and approximate methods are usually used. Two different assumptions may be made.

FIRST ASSUMPTION. It may be assumed that the diagonal members can
resist only tension. This could be the case where the members are relatively slender and will buckle under small compression loads.

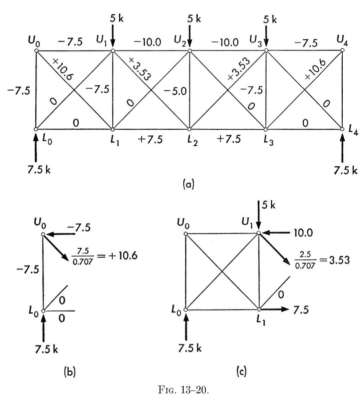

FIG. 13–20.

SECOND ASSUMPTION. It may be assumed that the diagonal members
are equally capable of resisting compression and tension. This could be
the case where the diagonals are made from rolled sections, angles, etc.
In this event the shears in the truss are taken or divided equally between
the diagonals.

Figs. 13–20b and c illustrate the computation for the first assumption.
Summation of forces in the vertical direction yields:

$$0.707 U_0 L_1 - 7.5 = 0, \qquad U_0 L_1 = 10.6\text{-k tension}$$
$$0.707 U_1 L_2 - 7.5 + 5.0 = 0, \qquad U_1 L_2 = 3.53\text{-k tension} \tag{13–41}$$

The remainder of the stress can be found by standard methods. The results are written on the truss in Fig. 13–20a.

In the second assumption, one diagonal will be in tension and one will be in compression, as shown in Figs. 13–21a, b, and c. Summation of forces in the vertical direction yields:

$$2 \times 0.707 U_0 L_1 - 7.5 = 0, \quad U_0 L_1 = 5.3\text{-k tension}$$

$$L_0 U_1 = 5.3\text{-k compression}$$

$$(2 \times 0.707 U_1 L_2) - (7.5 - 5.0) = 0, \quad U_1 L_2 = 1.76\text{-k tension} \tag{13–42}$$

$$L_1 U_2 = 1.76\text{-k compression}$$

The remainder of the stresses can be found by ordinary methods, and the results are written on the truss in Fig. 13–21a.

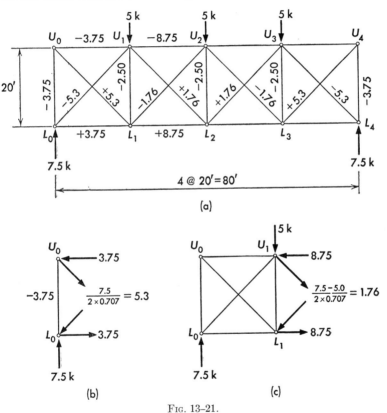

Fig. 13–21.

13–14. Deep Bracing for Buildings. When the lateral bracing of a building is accomplished by a truss built integrally with the columns and girders, it is referred to as deep bracing. It is used in place of moment (knuckle) connections between the girders and the columns. The advantage of this type of bracing is that it provides a stiffer structure which will not vibrate or deflect with as great an amplitude as the moment frame, an important asset in extremely tall buildings. On the other hand, diagonal bracing in the panels restricts the placement of windows and access openings. Moment frames also have a decided advantage when earthquake is a design consideration, since it has been observed that flexibility reduces damage under shocks, and the stiffer,

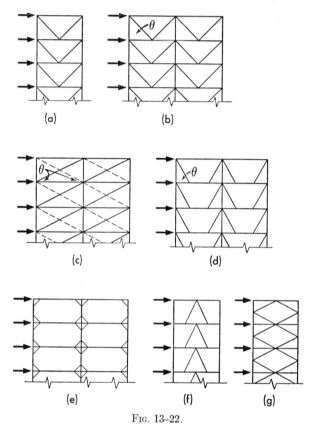

Fig. 13–22.

deep bracing does not have this flexibility. In many cases combinations of the two types are used, and Fig. 13–22 illustrates several types. The systems in Figs. 13–22a, b, d, e, and g also have the advantage of giving partial support to the girder, making it continuous over shorter spans and thus accomplishing a rather substantial economy.

Figs. 13–22a and b illustrate the K-type truss, which has the advantage of not inducing high stresses in the diagonals under column deformation. Any of the bracing systems shown may also have the struts inverted to form different types. The truss in Fig. 13–22a is statically determinate, but when bays are joined as in Fig. 13–22b it is indeterminate one degree for each column common to two bays. It may be solved by assuming that pin connections exist at the joints and that the horizontal shear is taken equally by the diagonals. This method is similar to the solution of the truss in Fig. 13–21.

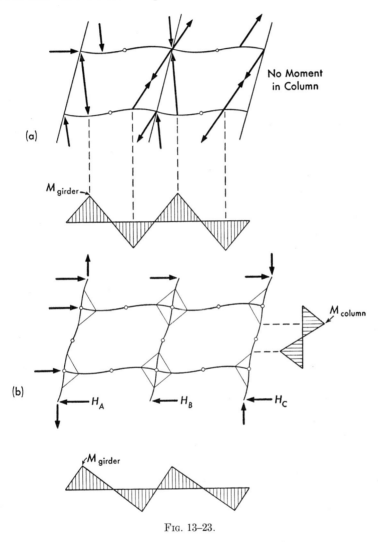

Fig. 13–23.

The truss of Fig. 13–22c can be made with the diagonals running in just one direction or with counters (dashed lines). In either case the diagonals are assumed to take equal amounts of shear. If the counters are inactive because they are capable of resisting tension, only the truss of Fig. 13–22c can be solved like the truss of Fig. 13–20. On the other hand the diagonals may have a pre-tension induced in them by turnbuckles; then the tension will be partially released under wind loads, giving the effect of a regular compression member. The bracing of Fig. 13–22d uses partial diagonals. The diagonals are still assumed to take all the shear, and the columns are assumed to take no shear. The distortion of the panels under load are shown in Fig. 13–23a. The vertical component of the diagonal stress will load the girder and induce a bending moment into it, as illustrated. The stress in the diagonals of the bracing in Figs. 13–22a, b, c, or d will be

$$S = \frac{\pm H}{n \cos \theta} \tag{13–43}$$

where H is the total horizontal thrust above the panels being analyzed, and n is the number of diagonals across the section. The vertical load on the girder by the diagonal will be

$$V = \frac{\pm H \tan \theta}{n} \tag{13–44}$$

and the moment in the girder due to this tension or thrust will be a maximum at the diagonal connection equal to

$$M = \frac{Vba}{L} \tag{13–45}$$

The knee-brace system of Fig. 13–22e merely provides a slightly modified rigid joint, and the structure can be analyzed by the portal or cantilever methods, but the portal method would be the more adaptable. Points of contraflexure will occur at the mid-height of the column and at the column girder connection, as shown in Fig. 13–23b.

13–15. Trusses with Multiple Web Systems. Some types of trusses appear to have web systems of two different trusses superimposed on each other. The lattice type shown in Fig. 13–24 is such a truss. Although used in the past as a timber truss for covered bridges and also for steel trusses of various types, it is now used primarily for its ornamental value rather than its economy. In the analysis an approximate solution for the stresses can be found by assuming that such structures are indeed trusses superimposed upon each other and which have common upper and lower chords. It is found that the truss is statically indeterminate to the third degree. The truss may be decomposed into the four trusses shown in Fig. 13–24b, c, d, and e, each of which is statically determinate. The stresses in the original truss chords are then found by adding the stresses from each of the separate component trusses.

The procedure is illustrated by the double Warren truss, also called a *lattice* truss, shown in Fig. 13–25a. The truss is a common type used for wind bracing and for tower structures. Obviously the truss may be decomposed into the two single Warren trusses shown in Figs. 13–25b and c.

The stresses for each of the trusses, acting independently, are shown in the diagrams. The stresses in the web members are as shown in the component solutions, but those in the chords must be found by adding the chord stresses of the two components. Thus, for example, the stress in $U_1U_2 = -6 - 3 = -9$-k compression. The final calculations are indicated in the figure.

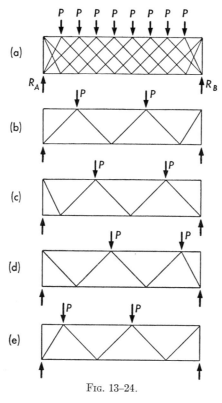

Fig. 13–24.

A certain fallacy exists in the indiscriminate use of the previously described procedure. For example, if alternate panel points were loaded only, no stress would be indicated in one of the web systems. This is known to be contrary to the facts. The analysis must be limited to uniform symmetrical types of loads for which good results are obtained. This is the case, ordinarily, for wind loads and dead loads. Other cases would be treated with care, and exact methods of analysis would have to be used.

When panel points of the truss are too far apart, the double Warren truss of Fig. 13–25 may be subdivided as shown in Fig. 13–26, in this case making it statically indeterminate to the seventh degree. The truss is divided into the single Warren trusses shown in Figs. 13–25b and c, and the auxiliary trusses shown in Fig. 13–26b, which may be analyzed separately. Each of the six auxiliary trusses has the same solution and has the effect of transmitting the panel loads at the points of subdivision to the panel points at either side. The final stresses can be found by combining the solutions of the eight trusses.

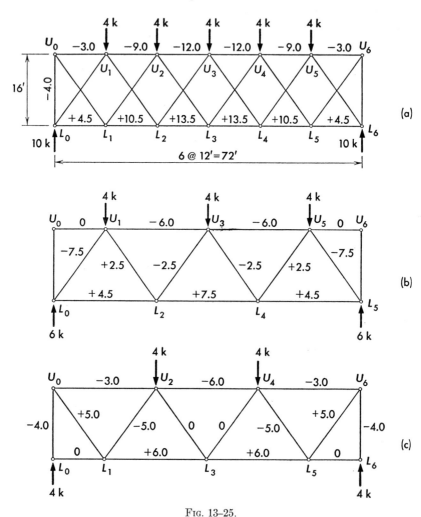

FIG. 13–25.

As previously discussed, a modified analysis must be used when the loads do not occur at every panel point. In Fig. 13–27, for example, a lattice truss is subjected to a concentrated load. Ordinarily, the lattices could be decomposed into four trusses, as shown in Fig. 13–24. This would result in an analysis giving stress in every fourth web member. In this case the truss can be treated as a beam in which the web members take only shear. The web member stresses are found by cutting a vertical section between the reaction and load, Fig. 13–27b. If the members are capable of resisting compression and tension, there are six members to share the 12-k vertical shear. The stress in each will be $12 \times (1.414/6)$

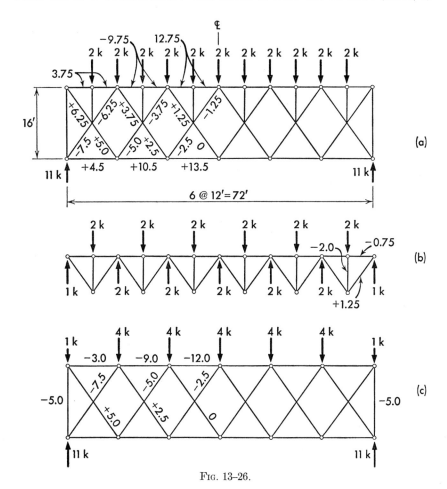

Fig. 13–26.

$= 2.83$ k. The stress in the top chord first panel will be $2.83 \times 0.707 = 2.0$-k compression, and the lower chord first panel will have stress of 2.0-k tension. Since all the web members to one side of the load have the same stress, a generalization can be made for the chord stresses. A typical lower chord joint is shown in Fig. 13–27c. The web members always join in the same manner, resulting in a change in chord tension of

$$T_{(n+1)} - T_n = 2 \times 2.83 \times 0.707 = 4.0 \text{ k} \qquad (13\text{–}46)$$

The chord stress can be found by adding 4 k to the stress in the end panel for each panel toward the load at C, to obtain the chord stresses written on the truss in Fig. 13–27a. A similar system can be deduced for the right end.

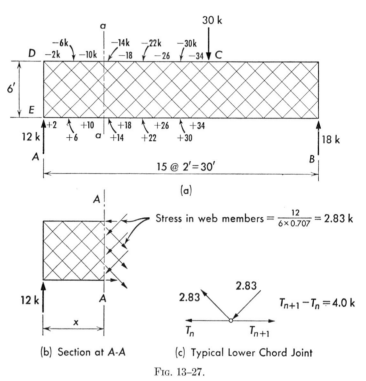

Stress in web members $= \dfrac{12}{6 \times 0.707} = 2.83$ k

$T_{n+1} - T_n = 4.0$ k

(b) Section at A-A   (c) Typical Lower Chord Joint

Fig. 13–27.

PROBLEMS

13–1. Draw the moment and shear diagrams for the frame shown.

13–2. Find the stress in the knee braces, and draw the moment and shear diagrams for the members of the portal shown.

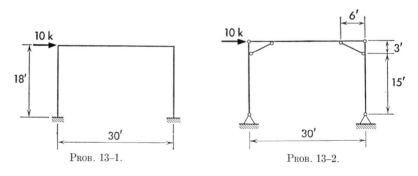

PROB. 13–1.   PROB. 13–2.

13–3. The top lateral wind-bracing truss of a bridge frames into the portal shown, loading it with an estimated 12-k load. Find (a) the shear and moment diagram for the columns, assuming the points of contraflexure to be at the third points; and (b) the stresses in the portal truss by the use of the stress diagram.

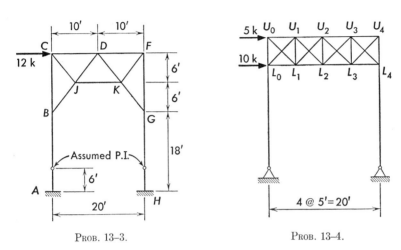

PROB. 13–3.   PROB. 13–4.

13–4, 13–5, 13–6, 13–7. Draw the shear and moment diagrams for the portals shown, and obtain the stresses in the members which frame into the columns.

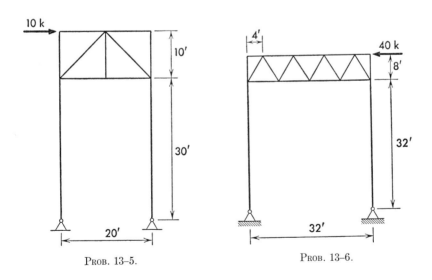

PROB. 13–5.   PROB. 13–6.

13–8. Draw moment and shear diagrams for the portal of Fig. 13–5a if the columns have pinned ends. Find the stresses in the members by use of the stress diagram.

13–9. Find the wind loads according to the Duchemin formula for a 100-mph wind, and draw the shear and moment diagrams and obtain the stresses in the members of the transverse bent.

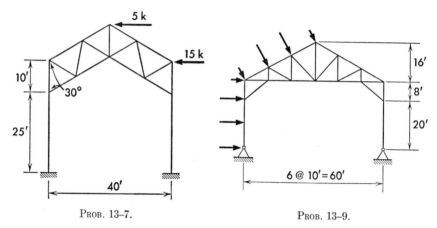

PROB. 13–7.   PROB. 13–9.

13–10. Compute the stresses in the members which frame into the columns, and draw shear and moment diagrams for the transverse bent loaded by a uniformly distributed load on the left column as shown.

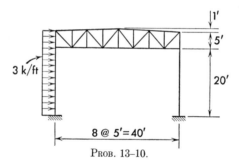

PROB. 13–10.

13–11. Find the loads on the transverse bent for a 100-mph wind by one of the methods of determining wind pressures, as assigned by the instructor, find the stresses in the members, and draw the shear and moment diagrams for the columns. The columns have a step for a crane rail. The girts, which transmit

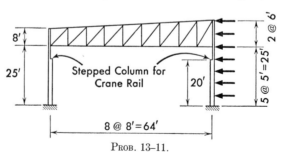

PROB. 13–11.

the load to the columns, are spaced as shown in the sketch. *Hint:* The points of contraflexure are usually taken at the change in section for columns with steps.

13–12. Assume that the transverse bent of Fig. 13–7a has fixed ends, find the stresses in the members framing into the columns, and draw shear and moment diagrams for the columns.

13–13. What would be the distribution of horizontal shears in the transverse bent of Fig. 13–7a if the column sections were identical in cross-section but the right column was only 18 ft long, being supported on a concrete pier?

13–14. Draw shear and moment diagrams for the continuous portal shown.

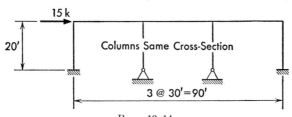

PROB. 13–14.

13–15. Draw shear and moment diagrams for the columns, and find the stresses in the members framing into the trusses for the saw-tooth continuous transverse bent shown. All the columns have the same cross-section.

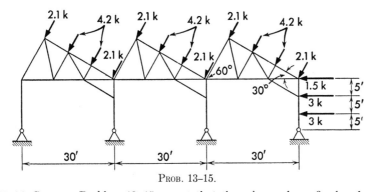

PROB. 13–15.

13–16. Same as Problem 13–15 except that the columns have fixed ends.

13–17. Draw the shear and moment diagrams for the columns of the continuous portal shown in the illustration.

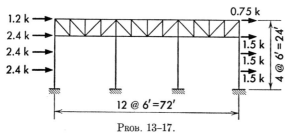

PROB. 13–17.

13–18. Draw the shear and moment diagrams for the columns of the double-story bent. Columns have the same cross-sections and are continuous through to the roof.

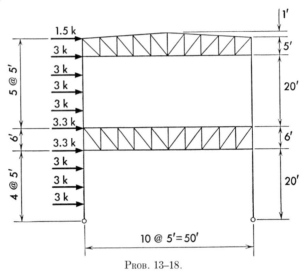

PROB. 13–18.

13–19. Draw the moment diagrams for the columns and girders for the building shown, using the portal method. Frames are spaced at 20 ft and the wind pressure is 20 psf.

13–20. Same as Problem 13–19 but use the cantilever method. Columns may be assumed to have the same cross-section on each floor.

13–21. Draw the moment diagrams for the building shown, using the portal method. The wind pressure is 30 psf and the frames are spaced 20 ft apart.

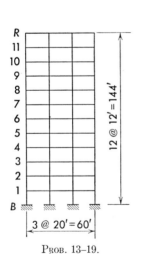

PROB. 13–19.

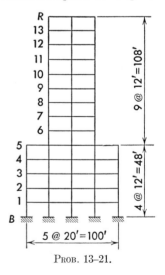

PROB. 13–21.

13–22. Use the cantilever method to draw the moment diagrams for the basement and first floor columns and girders in the building of Problem 13–21. All the girders are 21 *WF* 59, the exterior columns are 14 *WF* 95, and the interior columns are 14 *WF* 136.

13–23. A five-story building, 15 ft between girder centerlines, and 25 ft wide (one bay), is subjected to a 5-k load at each column-girder joint on one side of the frame only. Find the stresses and moment diagrams of the members if:

(a) The K-type bracing of Fig. 13–22a is used.
(b) The X-bracing of Fig. 13–22c is used (members can take compression and tension).
(c) The bracing of type shown in Fig. 13–22d is used, with the connection between the knee and girder at the girder quarter-points.
(d) The bracing of Fig. 13–22e is used, with the knee-brace connections 4 ft from the joint along both the girder and column.
(e) The bracing of Fig. 13–22f is used, with the girder-brace connection at the mid-length of the girder at the top and at the girder quarter-points at the bottom.
(f) The bracing of Fig. 13–22g is used.
(g) The cantilever method is used with knuckle connections.
(h) The portal method is used with knuckle connections.

13–24. A ten-story building, 12 ft between floor centerlines and composed of two bays 24 ft wide, with frames spaced at 24 ft in the other direction, is subjected to a wind load of 30 psf. Analyze the stresses in the members for one of the bracing systems designated in Problem 13–23.

13–25. Analyze the top three stories of the structure in Fig. 13–22g if the building is 26 ft wide, 14 ft between floor centerlines, and the lateral load at each floor level, including the roofline, is 5 k. Make a sketch of the deflected structure.

13–26. The sketch shows a Wipple truss, used from about 1850 to 1890 but no longer constructed. Many of these bridges are still in existence. It was used to introduce a greater number of panel points for support purposes and yet keep an economical diagonal slope. Analyze the truss by dividing it into two trusses, as shown by the dotted-line and solid-line web systems.

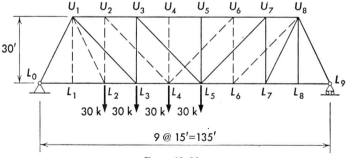

PROB. 13–26.

13–27. Draw influence lines for the members U_2L_3 and U_3L_3 of the Wipple truss of Problem 13–26.

13–28. Analyze the tower structure in the illustration assuming that the members can take both compression and tension.

13–29. Analyze the tower structure shown here, by decomposing it into two truss systems.

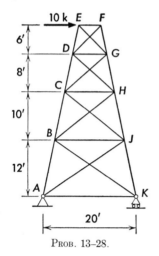

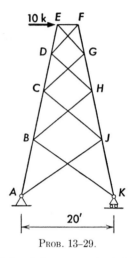

PROB. 13–28.   PROB. 13–29.

13–30. Analyze the lattice truss in Fig. 13–27 for (a) a concentrated load of 3 k at each panel point, and (b) a concentrated load of 30 k at the center of the span.

13–31. Find the stresses in the truss of Fig. 13–21, assuming that the loading consists of a 10-k load at U_2 and a 15-k load at U_3. Members are assumed to take tension and compression.

13–32. Find the stresses in the members of the truss and the moment and shear diagrams of the columns for the lattice portal shown in the illustration.

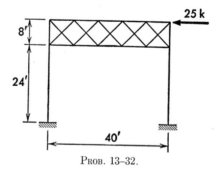

PROB. 13–32.

13–33. Draw a deflected portion of the building of Fig. 13–22g similar to Figs. 13–23a and 13–23b.

13–34. In general terms, write an equation describing the maximum moment in the girders and columns of Fig. 13–23b.

INDEX

LIBRARY
JUNIOR COLLEGE DISTRICT
ST. LOUIS, MO.

INVENTORY 74

INVENTORY 1983